A Tropical
RAINFOREST

Editor	: Aileen Lau
Associate Editor	: Catriona Prebble
Design & DTP	: Karen Leong
Production	: Brian Wyreweden
Editorial Assistance	: Irene Khng
	Emma Wilcox Tan
DTP Assistance	: Sares Kanapathy
Maps/Diagrams	: Charles Ban

The invaluable assistance, cooperation and unstinting support of the Earl of Cranbrook, Dr David Edwards and Mr Nigel de Winser towards the production of this book are gratefully acknowledged.

A TROPICAL RAINFOREST

© 1994 A co-publication between:

The Royal Geographical Society   &   **Sun Tree Publishing**
1 Kensington Gore   205 Henderson Road
London SW7 2AR   03-01, Henderson Industrial Park
United Kingdom   Singapore 0315
Tel: (44) 71 589 5466   Tel: (65) 276 4700
Fax: (44) 71 823 7200   Fax: (65) 276 4727

First Edition

ISBN: 981 00 5531 5
Printed in Singapore

Corporate Patrons of the Universiti Brunei Darussalam / Royal Geographical Society Brunei Rainforest Project 1991-92:
- *Royal Brunei Airlines*
- *The Baring Foundation*
- *Daiwa-Dicam*
- *GreenCard Trust*
- *Hongkong Bank*
- *Morgan Grenfell*
- *Nomura-NIMCO*

A Tropical
RAINFOREST

The nature of biodiversity in Borneo at Belalong, Brunei

by

Earl of Cranbrook
David S Edwards

"There is a mask of theory over the whole face of Nature."

William Whewell

Chapter 3 by Alan P Dykes
Chapter 4 by Sheila M Ross

With other contributions by

George Argent
Martin Barker
Roger A Beaver
Peter F Becker
Peter S Bellwood
Elizabeth L Bennett
Webber E Booth
Philip E Bragg
Dietrich Burkhardt
Joe K Charles
Satish C Choy
Mark A Cook
Indraneil Das
Martin Drake
John Dransfield
Soejatmi Dransfield
Alan P Dykes
Peter P Eaton

Charles M Francis
Freddy Gathorne-Hardy
David T Jones
Kamariah Abu Salim
Chris J Kofron
Ruth Levy
A Q Malik
Clive F Mann
Nick Mawdsley
Jason, Lord Medway
Tom C Mitchell
Jonathan Moran
D Neil Morgan
Ingrid de la Motte
Mark Mulligan
Nico Nieser
Albert G Orr
Colin A Pendry

Penroose Saleha
Axel Dalberg Poulsen
Klaus Riede
Gaden S Robinson
Sheila M Ross
David Roubik
Samhan Nyawa
Martin Sands
Haji Serudin Tinggal
Gavin C Smith
Rowland Snazell
Brian M Spooner
Mary C Stockdale
Peter Wilkie
Yanina Willcox
John T Wills
Yong Nget Yung

"In the end,

we will conserve only what we love,
we will love only what we understand,
we will understand only what we are taught."

Baba Dioum

**UNIVERSITI
BRUNEI DARUSSALAM**

His Majesty
Paduka Seri Baginda Sultan Haji Hassanal Bolkiah Mu'izzaddin Waddaulah
Ibni Al-Marhum Sultan Haji Omar 'Ali Saifuddien Sa'adul Khairi Waddien,
Sultan and Yang di-Pertuan of Brunei Darussalam,
Chancellor of Universiti Brunei Darussalam.

CONTENTS

Foreword
by His Royal Highness The Prince of Wales

Message
by Her Royal Highness Princess Maha Chakri Sirindhom of Thailand

CHAPTER 1	▶	Belalong: the Place	5
CHAPTER 2	▶	The Tropical Climate	17
CHAPTER 3	▶	Landform Processes	31
CHAPTER 4	▶	Soils and Hydrology	51
CHAPTER 5	▶	Biodiversity	67
CHAPTER 6	▶	Tropical Rainforest Formations	91
CHAPTER 7	▶	Trees and Woody Shrubs	115
CHAPTER 8	▶	Other Plant Life	147
CHAPTER 9	▶	Fungi	179
CHAPTER 10	▶	The Forest Environment	193
CHAPTER 11	▶	Invertebrate Biodiversity	223
CHAPTER 12	▶	Vertebrate Animals of the Forest	277
CHAPTER 13	▶	Freshwaters	309
CHAPTER 14	▶	The Forest and Man	333
CHAPTER 15	▶	Belalong: the Future	353
	▶	Glossary	358
		General Index	363
		Species & Genus Index	372
		Acknowledgements	377
		Text Credits	381
		Photo Credits	385

ST. JAMES'S PALACE

With so many global environmental problems competing for our
attention, and our resources, it is perhaps more important than
ever for us to decide where our priorities lie. It seems to me
that the world's tropical rainforests represent one of the most
fragile, most diverse, and least understood of all natural
ecosystems. They are also currently perhaps the most threatened.

I am therefore delighted that the University of Brunei Darussalam
and the Royal Geographical Society have joined forces to study
together at a magnificent site in the pristine rainforest of
Temburong District. This exciting project has been made possible
by a major commitment of resources from within Brunei in support
of the University, of which His Majesty the Sultan and Yang Di-
Pertuan is Chancellor.

The enterprise of the Royal Geographical Society, and a number
of associated institutions in the United Kingdom (including the
Royal Society, the Royal Botanic Gardens, Kew, the Natural
History Museum and the Natural Environment Research Council), has
received most welcome financial backing from corporate sponsors,
other benefactors and generous well-wishers.

The scientific work carried out during the term of the Project
in 1991 and 1992 created a splendid opportunity for collaboration
between students, research workers and senior professionals from
Brunei, the United Kingdom and other nations, working together
with the common aim of improving our understanding of aspects of
the intricate ecology of the tropical rainforest. Their efforts
have also set the course for continuing programmes of school
visits, undergraduate training and research at the new Field
Studies Centre, from which many benefits will flow.

I congratulate everyone involved for their determination in
completing this most worthwhile project, and I welcome this
marvellous book as a valuable product of their work.

From 10 - 14 September 1991, as a guest of His Majesty, Sultan Haji Hassanal Bolkiah Mu'izzaddin Waddaulah, the Sultan and Yang di-Pertuan of Brunei Darussalam, I had the pleasure of visiting the Kuala Belalong Field Studies Centre and seeing the members of the Universiti Brunei Darussalam/Royal Geographical Society Brunei Rainforest Project 1991-92 at work. I have told the story in my book : ป่าสูงน้ำใส (Mountainous Green, Crystalline Creek).

At Belalong, I was thrilled to see the glories of the pristine rainforest covering the steep hillsides and valleys. I enjoyed my forays into the forest where I saw the rich wildlife : insects, frogs, snakes, birds and mammals. I braved the rapids of the rushing Belalong River. I was sometimes hot, sometimes drenched with rain and, like everyone else, tired at the end of each day. I was thankful to come back to the sturdy wooden buildings of the Field Centre. Here I could relax and sleep in comfort, surrounded by friends, and forever lullabied by the rich noises of the jungle life which seemed never to sleep!

Through ASEAN, our countries are linked in friendship. I congratulate the government of Brunei Darussalam, Brunei Shell and the University, with the Royal Geographical Society, on their initiative in establishing this marvellous field studies centre. In the Belalong forest, the young people of Brunei can discover the full richness of their natural environment. I hope students, scientists and other visitors from ASEAN countries will always be welcome to come to learn, to study and to research the wealth of biodiversity that flourishes here in these green valleys.

Through this book, I am delighted that many others throughout the world will also be able to share in the beauty, the richness and the scientific interest of the Belalong rainforest.

Sirindhorn

The Field Studies Centre stands on the banks of Sungai Belalong.

CHAPTER 1

BELALONG: THE PLACE

Tropical rainforests grow in those parts of the tropics where the rainfall generally exceeds 2,000 mm per year, and where there is little or no seasonal water shortage. These forests are ever- green (although some member trees may be periodically deciduous) and, except at high altitude or on very poor soils, they are often more than 30 m tall. They are rich in climbers and in

5

Lying at the heart of the islands of South East Asia, Brunei Darussalam is surrounded on its landward borders by the Malaysian states of Sarawak and Sabah.
The Indonesian province of Kalimantan forms the remaining part of the island of Borneo.
[Reproduced with permission from the Curriculum Development Department,
Ministry of Education, Brunei Darussalam].

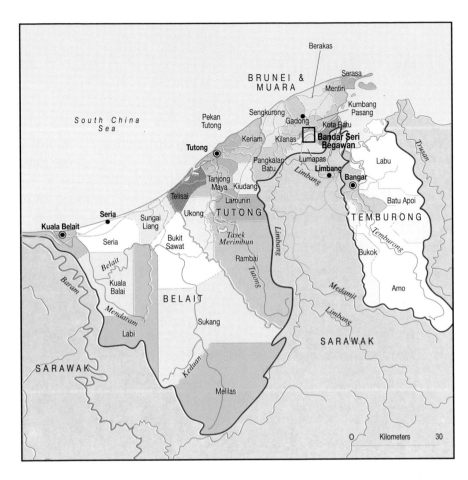

Brunei Darussalam's administrative districts.
Brunei Darussalam: showing the four administrative districts and their subdivisions (Mukim).
(Reproduced with permission from the Curriculum Development Department, Ministry of Education, Brunei Darussalam).

woody and herbaceous epiphytes.

The three main continental blocks of tropical evergreen rainforests lie in the equatorial zones of South America, Africa and South East Asia. Although separated by great distances, composed of different plant communities and populated by animals of disparate origins, these forests share many structural and functional similarities.

This study is focused on an area of pristine forest in the heart of South East Asia, on the northwest coast of Borneo, some 500 km ($4^1/_2°$ latitude) north of the equator, in the State of Brunei Darussalam.

Brunei is divided administratively into four districts: Brunei-Muara (563 sq km), where the capital Bandar Seri Begawan is situated, Belait (2,696 sq km), Tutong (1,152 sq km) and the separated, eastern enclave of

Temburong (1,288 sq km) with which this book is mostly concerned.

The country is ruled by His Majesty, Sultan Haji Hassanal Bolkiah Mu'izzaddin Waddaulah, the Sultan and Yang di-Pertuan, 29th ascendant of one of the world's oldest continuous royal lines, tracing back its history to the 15th century. The state religion is Islam.

The country is prosperous and developed. The population is a little over 260,000 persons (1991), a quarter of whom reside in Bandar Seri Begawan. Other settlements are concentrated in the coastal strip, including the principal towns of Kuala Belait and Seria.

The economy is heavily dependent on oil and gas, and on associated exploration, extractive and refining activities. Local agriculture (including tree crop plantation) has dwindled in recent years to a low level and most foodstuffs are imported.

FOREST RESERVES

The Brunei State Forest Department regulates forestry and controls access to designated permanent Forest Reserves. Since 1991 lumber extraction from Brunei forests has been limited to 100,000 cu m annually, restricted to local use only. Further needs have to be met by imported timber.

The country's largest Forest Reserve is Batu Apoi Forest Reserve, in Temburong District. It was gazetted many years ago and covers 48,857 ha, extending from the lowlands southwards to the highest peaks on the Brunei/Sarawak border. Research programmes have been carried out in this reserve from the 1960s. In the 1980s contractors carried out a complete inventory of the timber resources. In 1991, the Brunei Government declared its intention to designate the whole area as a National Park.

THE RAINFOREST PROJECT

In the Batu Apoi Forest Reserve, the University of Brunei Darussalam Kuala Belalong Field Studies Centre (KBFSC) is situated on the Sungai Belalong just upstream of its junction with the Sungai Temburong.

The study of the Belalong forest, as told in the following pages, began as the Brunei Rainforest Project 1991/92, a joint enterprise of the University of Brunei Darussalam and the Royal Geographical Society of London.

GETTING THERE

Access to this pristine reserve at Belalong is not swift or direct, but for those who make a visit, the journey itself is full of interest.

Lacking a road connection through the Limbang District of Sarawak in Malaysia, the journey from Brunei-Muara to Temburong relies very

7

GEOGRAPHICAL INFORMATION SYSTEM

The use of the GIS (Geographical Information System) in tropical rainforest research is quite new. By recording data in this way, the long term survival and use of the project results are ensured. The GIS allows for revisiting the sites (through accurate locational records), frequent update and expansion in the scope and use of the system. It can be used as an educational tool for students and members of the public to illustrate the research work which has been conducted.

The first stage in establishing an effective GIS is to create and maintain an accurate topographical record. Maps of the project area were digitised and stored in the system, with separate coverages for contours, streams and rivers and the grid

reference system (Rectified Skew Orthographic). To improve accuracy a Trimble Transpack Global Positioning System (GPS) was used to fix the position of permanent scientific plots and streams not recorded on the Ordnance Survey maps.

It was found that in locations unobscured by the forest canopy, three or more satellites could be tracked and the GPS used in two dimensional or three dimensional mode. Under closed canopy, it was necessary to use two dimensional mode permanently as the physical obstruction of the trees limited the number of satellites 'visible' and hence caused considerable position drift. By taking several readings and giving an accurate height value it was found to be still possible to

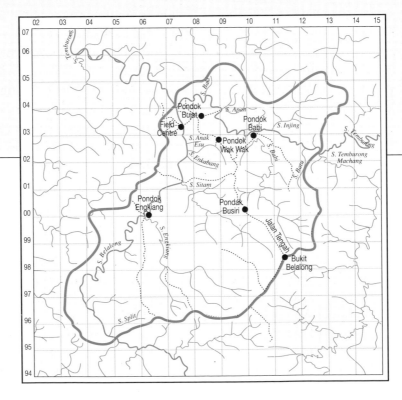

GIS base map, showing the bounds of the Belalong study area, principal watercourses and paths.

obtain a good position cluster, of which the centre could be taken as the theoretical optimum location.

After completing the topographic coverages, existing data relating to the project area were taken from *Brunei Forest Resources & Strategic Planning Study 1988* (by Anderson and Marsden Forestry Consultants, for the Government of Brunei Darussalam). Relevant maps were digitised and exist as a separate coverage. Other coverages were created with the scientific data pertaining to the research conducted by project members. Data were entered into specific subject database files which were modified and updated as required.

These files contain both attribute and spatial data, some from individual scientists and some from two or more scientists working in the same field. Each specific subject database file is stored in a different layer to allow clear viewing of the results and to avoid confusion.

Twenty-four such coverages containing scientific results were created. With another six relating to the topology, this series of coverages accurately reflects the complexity of the real world in a clear, intelligible way. Sample maps in this book show the product of the GIS.

much on the public launch service. The route follows channels in the mangrove running eastward from the mouth of the Brunei river, through Sungai Bulir to the frontier post. Entering Sarawak territory, the launch crosses the mouth of the Sungai Limbang, where rainforest logs may be seen stacked for export, and ultimately emerges into open water. Across the southern arm of Brunei Bay lies the mouth of the Sungai Temburong which snakes its way through mangrove forests inland to Bangar town.

Bangar is the administrative and trading centre of Temburong District. There have been some local agricultural developments, but the main industry is gravel extraction from the alluvial riverine deposits. This material is carried by a relay of flat-bottomed barges down the lower Temburong and across Brunei Bay, in order to meet the nation's continual needs for ballast and hardcore.

From Bangar, metalled roads serve the coastal strip and run some 16 km inland to Kampong Batang Duri. Here, the traveller transfers to the river and the open longboat. The duration of the onward journey varies with the state of the river. When the water level is high, the skills of the boat driver and prowman are tested in the rapids. In low water, after spells of dry weather, it becomes impossible to push a loaded boat, in which case passengers simply take a walk!

BELALONG FOREST

The Sungai Temburong drainage basin occupies 1,100 sq km and is the third largest catchment in Brunei, amounting to almost a fifth of the total national land area. Most of Batu Apoi Forest Reserve lies within the Temburong basin, except for a narrow strip on the western margin which is within the catchment of the border

9

The ferry launch speeds through tidal channels in the mangrove forest.

After prolonged spells of dry weather, river levels drop to an extreme low. It can be a long trudge for boat passengers up the cobbled bed of Sungai Temburong.

The skills of the Iban boatmen are invaluable when negotiating the turbulent Sungai Temburong.

A loaded longboat approaches KBFSC.

river, the Sungai Pendaruan.

The Belalong forest section of reserve allocated to the University for the Brunei Rainforest Project extends over approximately 5,000 ha, from the Sungai Belalong - Temburong junction in the north to the summit of Bukit Belalong (913 m) in the south. It includes both banks of the Sungai Temburong as far east as Kuala Temburong Macang and, in the west, both banks of the Sungai Belalong and the entire Engkiang system (See maps).

A PROTECTED RESERVE

Since it was formally gazetted under Brunei law the entire forest reserve has been protected. It has been saved from

Walkways connect the KBFSC housing units.

slash and burn by shifting cultivators, although there are farm clearings along the river bank almost to its boundary. Fish have customarily been taken from the rivers by members of local communities. Since historic times no Bruneians have lived in any part of the forest reserve and there are no local people holding rights to the land, waters, forest products or wild creatures.

With the help of photographs and the reports of colleagues and scientists who took part in the 1991/92 Project, we shall explore the rich wildlife of the tropical evergreen rainforest. The project examined the natural processes which sustain forest diversity. In this book we examine these, and the wider issues involved in understanding the background for long term sustainability of this magnificent natural resource, the tropical rainforest.

Much of the information has been incorporated into a Geographical Information System (GIS), linked with the map of Belalong forest prepared for this purpose. The base map exists in digital form, on computer. It can be extended, up-dated and modified, and (as shown by the examples in this book) can be printed out on many scales and in varied forms, to provide users with any number of different plots, according to their need.

The Kuala Belalong Field Studies Centre lies at the bottom of the valley, enveloped by the forest.

THE FIELD STUDIES CENTRE

The Kuala Belalong Field Studies Centre (KBFSC) was built in 1990. It comprises four housing units (to accommodate up to 26 visitors), a well-equipped laboratory and a dining unit. The KBFSC is provided with a filtered water supply, electricity and a sewage system. Communication links are through two-way radio and cellular telephone. Following the completion of the 1991/92 Project, the Universiti Brunei Darussalam has made the Centre available to research scientists and other visitors. Short courses for secondary schoolchildren are held regularly throughout the year.

Returning to the Field Studies Centre after a trip up Sungai Belalong.

A bamboo clump rides out the rain in the Belalong valley.

CHAPTER 2

THE TROPICAL CLIMATE

Tropical rainforests depend on a continuously warm, wet climate. The tropical zone of the world is defined by the geometry of the globe in its orbit. The earth is a roughly spherical planet circling the sun in an elliptical orbit. It receives energy radiated from the sun over a wide spectrum, some of which we perceive as light. Some (mostly short wavelength radiation) is absorbed by the earth's surface, which is warmed and in turn emits long-wave radiation thus heating the lower atmosphere and initiating **convection**. During convection, warmed air of the lower atmosphere rises while cooler air moves in to replace it. The effects of convection, directed by rotational forces of the

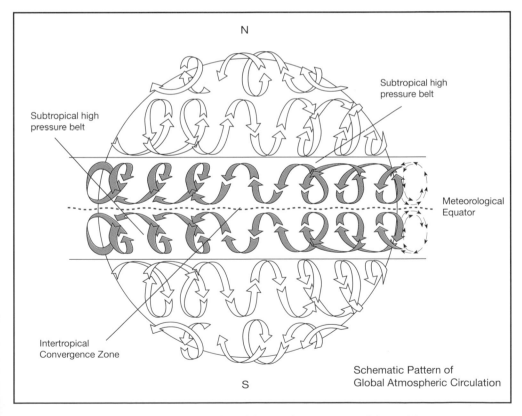

N

Subtropical high
pressure belt

Subtropical high
pressure belt

Meteorological
Equator

Intertropical
Convergence Zone

Schematic Pattern of
Global Atmospheric Circulation

S

A simplified representation of the weather processes of the world.
[Adapted with permission from *New Scientist*]

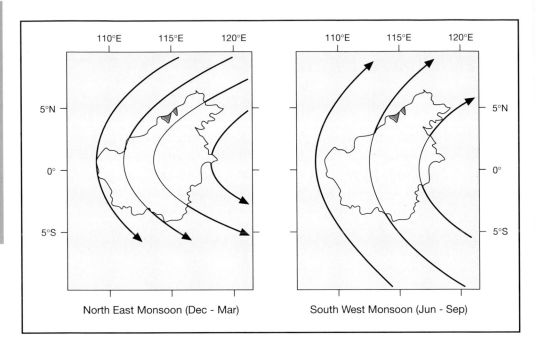

| 110°E | 115°E | 120°E | | 110°E | 115°E | 120°E |

North East Monsoon (Dec - Mar)   South West Monsoon (Jun - Sep)

The winds blow across Borneo in opposite directions during successive seasons.

spinning globe, drive the weather systems of the world.

SOLAR POSITION

Incident solar radiation is greatest where the sun is overhead at noon (the meteorological equator). Because the earth is tilted at $23\frac{1}{2}°$ to the perpendicular in its orbit, the latitude of the overhead sun progresses during the year from the Tropic of Cancer ($23\frac{1}{2}°$ North) on the solstice in June to the Tropic of Capricorn ($23\frac{1}{2}°$ South) in December. The tropical region, where the sun passes overhead twice a year, lies between these extremes and has a

largely internal weather system.

THE TROPICAL WEATHER SYSTEM

Warm air rises by convection around the meteorological equator, creating a low pressure zone. As it rises, the air cools and hence loses carrying capacity for water vapour, which condenses and falls as rain. Rotational forces divide the rising air flow, which moves pole-wards at high altitudes before descending again at sub-tropical latitudes, north and south, creating surface high pressure zones. Since air flows from high to low pressure areas, low-level

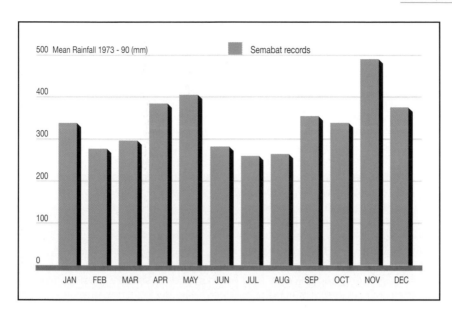

Average monthly rainfall over 18 years (1973-90) at Semabat Agricultural Station,
9 km west-northwest of Kuala Belalong.

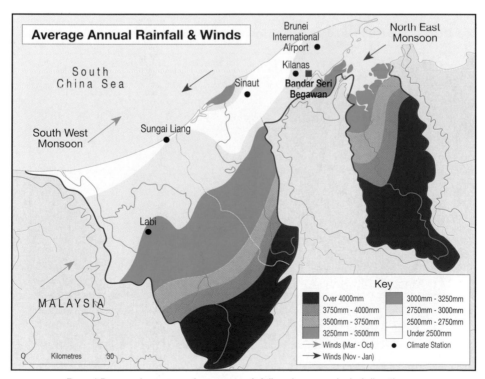

Brunei Darussalam: map of average rainfall and seasonal wind directions.
[Reproduced with permission from the Curriculum Development Department, Ministry of Education,
Brunei Darussalam]

AUTOMATIC WEATHER STATIONS

Large clearings are needed for climate and meteorology measurements because nearby obstructions, e.g. stands of trees, might disrupt wind flows or cast shade on the recorder when the sun is low. As a result, two automatic weather stations were installed. Both measured solar and net radiation, wind speed and direction, wet and dry bulb temperatures, all averaged for each hour, and total rainfall per hour.

The low altitude station, known as AWS1, was about 60 m above sea-level and 14 m above the river level at Kuala Belalong. A large area of 30-year old secondary forest covering a small knoll was clear-felled and the weather station was erected in the centre of the clearing, on the summit. At this location, the valley sides rise to about 100 m above river level and their ridgetops are about 1 km apart. This valley bottom location probably had minimal effect on the recorded data, except for the unusual feature of winds being channelled by the valley alignment. Hourly measurements were made at this station from 18 June 1991 to 24 April 1992, when the station was dismantled.

AWS2 was installed on the summit of Bukit Belalong at an altitude of 913 m. The summit comprises a narrow ridge about 20 m long and 4-5 m wide, with a flat top and slopes of 45-90° down each side. The entire summit area was cleared in the 1960s, and provided an ideal exposed site on the highest ground for at least 14 km in any direction. The station was therefore exposed to weather from all around and even below. Full measurements began on 18 May 1991 through 24 April 1992.

Data of these stations are believed to be unique for the simultaneous high and low altitude records of a tropical rainforest environment.

An Automatic Weather Station (AWS2) on the summit of Bukit Belalong, looking southeast to the interior hills of Temburong district.

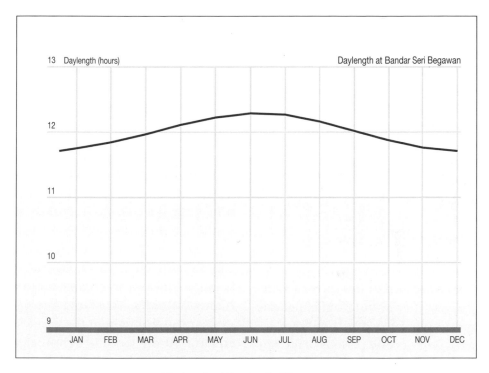

Daylength at Bandar Seri Begawan.

winds return towards the equator. Their convergence defines the **Inter-Tropical Convergence Zone** (ITCZ).

Seasonal climatic events in the tropics are dominated by the annual progression of the Inter-Tropical Convergence Zone, which moves north and south, following the sun. The ITCZ moves southwards across Borneo and the equator during November, and from December to March lies at around 5-10° South. During this season, Brunei experiences winds veering from northeast to northwest as they curve into the ITCZ. The ITCZ moves northwards across Borneo again during May, so that from June to September a reverse airflow curves across the Equator

to become broadly southeast winds over northern Borneo, extending to the ITCZ at around 15° North.

Typically, the movements of the ITCZ produce two wet seasons each year. In Brunei the cycle is modified to some extent by monsoons, the seasonal winds driven by the alternation of winter high pressures and summer low pressures over the continental landmass of central Asia. Rainfall in April/May is associated with the northward passing of the ITCZ, but there is usually a more prolonged wet season centred on November which coincides with the southward movement. These wet seasons are separated by drier periods which are usually most pronounced during the months of February/March and July/August. However, the climate is extremely unpredictable, and any month can be as wet or as dry as any other. For example, at Semabat Agricultural Station (9 km west-northwest of Kuala Belalong, in the Pandaruan valley), 21 mm of rain fell in August 1978 but 721 mm in August 1988.

THE CLIMATE OF BRUNEI DARUSSALAM

In the dry season of the early months of the year in lowland Brunei, periods of two or more weeks without rain are not uncommon and periods of moderate rainfall averaging less than 200

Sunshine after rain at Bukit Belalong.

mm per month can last up to five months. In the last months of the year, wet seasons can be extreme: 1,500 mm of rain within three months is not unusual, and this much rain within two months has been known twice since 1984 at Semabat.

Topography has a strong local influence on rainfall so that mean annual rainfall rises from around 2,300 mm along the coast to over 4,000 mm in the interior hills.

In other aspects of the climate, the environment of the equatorial zone is fairly constant in comparison with higher latitudes. Day-length remains unchanged throughout the year at the equator. At the latitude of Brunei, the longest days in June provide 36 minutes more daylight than the shortest in December.

Daily mean temperatures at sea level vary little from 27°C in any month, but tend to be slightly lower during wet months when increased cloud cover reduces the number of sunshine hours. The diurnal range is about 10°C throughout the year, between around 22°C just before dawn to around 32°C in the early afternoon.

Onshore wind speeds are generally lower than 8 m/s and vary little throughout the year, with many observed wind speeds being less than 0.2 m/s (calm). Many lowland wind patterns in the coastal areas are controlled by land and sea breezes. During localised squalls associated with intense convection and thunderstorms, wind speeds can exceed 30 m/s for a few minutes or more at a time.

THE CLIMATE OF BELALONG

The climate at Belalong was monitored over a nine-month period (July 1991-March 1992) by the two automatic weather stations. This period was notable for being fairly dry compared with long-term averages. The dry weather began during December 1991, earlier than usual, and continued until the end of April 1992.

During the other half of the year, almost half of the September 1991 rain fell in two afternoons at Kuala Belalong, and within a single 60-hour period at Bukit Belalong, leaving November 1991 as the only truly wet month.

At Kuala Belalong the driest month was March 1992, with 19 days in which less than 1 mm of rain fell (in November there were 6 mm). Not only were there more storms in November, but the rainfall which accompanied them was often much greater than in the drier months. As expected, in all months except February 1992, more rain fell at the station on Bukit Belalong than at Kuala Belalong. Despite individual variations in storms, the overall monthly rainfall pattern was similar at both stations.

AIR TEMPERATURE

At Kuala Belalong the highest air temperature was 37.1°C, on 27 March 1992; yet in the slightly cloudier month of January even 33°C was reached only twice. The monthly mean maximum temperature fell slightly around the turn of the year, but rose in March, probably to an unusual extent as a consequence of the prolonged dry, cloudless conditions. Monthly mean air temperatures remained consistently

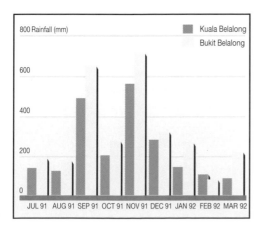

Monthly rainfall at Kuala Belalong and Bukit Belalong.

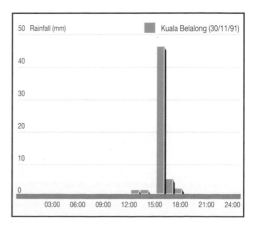

Hourly rainfall intensity profile of the storm of 30 November 1991 at Kuala Belalong.

about 26°C in all months. Very clear skies in early 1992 did allow night-time temperatures to fall as low as 19.2°C on 23 February 1992. These instances were rare and did not alter the monthly mean because, on most nights, overnight clouds formed in the valleys, thus preventing the loss of heat by radiation.

On the summit of Bukit Belalong, the temperature regime was about 4°C cooler. The highest temperature recorded here was 33.4°C on 21 August 1991; in January 1992 it was 27.8°C. The clear skies in February allowed temperatures to fall at night to as low as 15.8°C (on 22 February 1992). The monthly trend in the monthly mean maximum temperature was similar to that at Kuala Belalong, but the monthly mean minimum dropped around the turn of the year as the skies here remained clear at night.

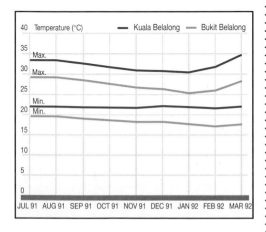

The monthly mean maximum and minimum temperatures at Kuala Belalong were always around 4°C higher than at Bukit Belalong.

RAINSTORM PATTERNS

Most rain was observed to fall during thunderstorms. These originate as convection cells over warm land, most often in the afternoon. The rising moist air produces towers of dense cloud, often over 10 km tall; several such cells may develop together. Condensation produces heavy rain which creates strong down draughts while falling. The opposing air movements in the clouds generate electrical charges, producing lightning and thunder. The passage of storms is usually accompanied by gusts of wind, often violent.

Raindrops on birah (*Alocasia*) by night reflect a thousand sparkles from the flash.

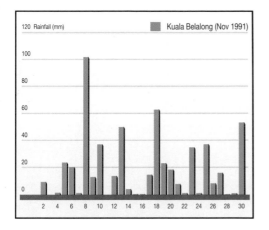
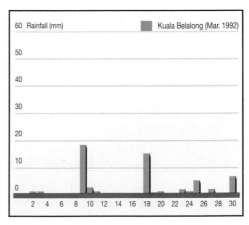

Daily rainfall at Kuala Belalong in November 1991 and March 1992.

Such storms form almost daily during the wet season, although not always producing rain. Some were very local, resulting in much rainfall at one place and none nearby. For example, on 18 November 1991, 63.5 mm of rain fell at Kuala Belalong, and only 19.0 mm at Bukit Belalong; but on 26 November 1991, while Bukit Belalong received 60.0 mm of rain, a mere 8.5 mm fell at Kuala Belalong. Storms during the dry season are probably even smaller in area: for example, more rain fell on Bukit Belalong during the first three days of March 1992 than in the whole of March at Kuala Belalong, where on those three days almost no rain fell.

The intensity profile of a storm at Kuala Belalong on 30 November 1991 is typical, with most of the rain falling within an hour. (See diagram on p. 23.) The most dramatic rainstorm recorded, occurred on 19 September 1991, when 116.5 mm of rain fell in 75 minutes, between 1730 and 1845 hours. This represents an average rainfall intensity of 93.2 mm per hour, the highest measured so far in this area. On this occasion, only 37 mm of rain was recorded on Bukit Belalong.

RELATIVE HUMIDITY

Relative humidity is a measure of the quantity of water vapour contained in the air, compared with the maximum possible at a given temperature. It therefore varies through the day in response to the temperature cycle. At Kuala Belalong the relative humidity at night was always 98-100%, indicating that the air was saturated. On a clear day, the relative humidity could fall as low as 60% as temperatures rose towards their peak.

At Bukit Belalong, night-time rela-

Automatic Weather Station 2 at work.

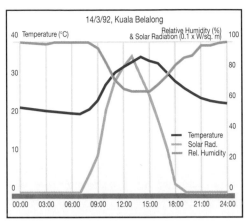

Hourly changes in solar radiation, temperature and relative humidity on a typical day in the dry season: 14 March 1992 at Kuala Belalong.

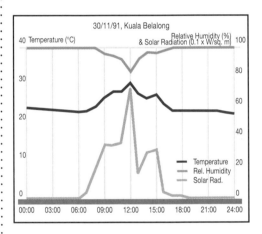

Hourly changes in solar radiation, temperature and relative humidity on a typical day in the wet season: 30 November 1991 at Kuala Belalong. A break in the clouds just before midday allowed the temperature to reach 30°C, and the relative humidity fell to 83% for a brief time.

tive humidities rarely reached 100% due to the greater availability of un-saturated air at the more exposed location, but daytime humidities were usually higher than at Kuala Belalong. This is because the cooler air at the higher altitude needs less water vapour to become saturated.

WINDS

Wind directions were fairly consistent throughout the nine months of monitoring, though different at the two recording sites. At Kuala Belalong, the air flow was generally from the south (down the Belalong valley) except during the hottest few hours of the day, during which the winds were broadly northerly to northeasterly. Cool air descending the valleys from the ridges probably controls the wind pattern at this site.

At Bukit Belalong the pattern was completely different, with a diurnal variation between broadly easterly to southeasterly winds through the night and early morning, and generally westerly winds between late morning and the early evening. Here, the effect of warm air rising up from the large Engkiang catchment below the western edge of Bukit Belalong's summit,

Sunset from Bukit Belalong.

may be responsible for the daytime wind flows.

The hourly mean wind speeds recorded were low: 4 m/s was exceeded only once, on the summit of Bukit Belalong between 1600 and 1700 hours on 27 March 1992 (4.2 m/s). Whilst representative of the general long-term conditions, the recorded values do not show how violent and destructive some of the short-term, localised winds can be during large thunderstorms.

Trees, with trunks sometimes a metre in diameter, were snapped several metres above the ground, and the combination of wind and rain during a storm in 1991 flattened an area of forest of around 1,000 sq m on a ridgetop above the Esu river.

EVAPOTRANSPIRATION

Water is lost by evaporation to the atmosphere directly from the soil surface, rivers and open water areas. Water is also lost to the atmosphere by transpiration from plants. Living plants take up water from the soil by their roots, and then subsequently release it into the atmosphere through their leaves.

Evapotranspiration is the combined effect of evaporation and transpiration. Evapotranspiration rates are high in the rainforest because of the large quantity of vegetation taking water from the soil, and the high air temperatures. Solar radiation provides the necessary energy.

The mean annual evapotranspiration from South East Asian tropical rainforests is around 1,350 mm (ranging between 100 and 120 mm in a month). At Belalong, similar values are expected. Thus at the end of February 1992, soil moisture deficits would have occurred around Bukit Belalong because more water was lost from the soil to the atmosphere than was received as rainfall.

Rain falling on the Sungai Belalong.

27

Hills of the interior of Temburong seen from Bukit Belalong.

CHAPTER 3

LANDFORM PROCESSES

by Alan P. Dykes

Seen from a high point on the reserve, clouds lying in the low ground emphasise the complex pattern of ridges and valleys of this forest. The visible shape of the land surface, the **landform**, is the result of erosion by water and gravity acting on the soil and underlying geology. The rate of erosion and the kind of landform produced, reflect the structural features of the underlying rock. The erosive processes have their greatest effects when the land itself has been raised by uplift due to folding, faulting, or both.

31

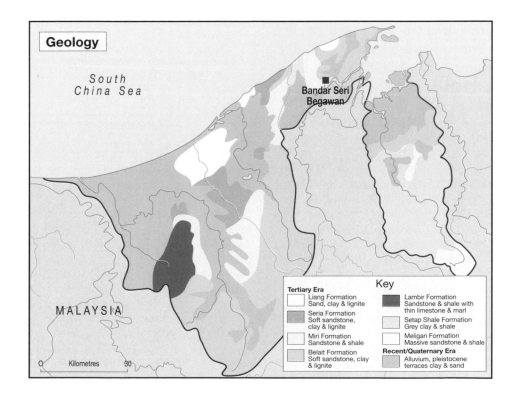

Geological map of Brunei Darussalam.
[Reproduced with permission from Curriculum Development Department,
Ministry of Education, Brunei Darussalam]

GEOLOGY OF TEMBURONG DISTRICT

Brunei lies on part of a geological province which also includes most of Sabah. This province represents a zone where eroded sediments from the older land mass to the south were deposited offshore from a coastline which was much further southeast than it is today.

The present coastline of Brunei and northwest Sabah is thought to represent the line of a former continental margin; in this case a subduction trench where the thin floor of the South China Sea was forced beneath the old Borneo which was then moving northwestwards. Blocks of the overriding rocks were forced upwards along

Bedrock of shale interbedded with a narrow band of sandstone, is exposed in a dry streambed. Note the steeply inclined angle produced by folding.

PLATE TECTONICS

The surface landforms of any region reflect the nature and origin of the underlying rocks and their resistance to erosion by water and gravitational processes, in the context of the geological and tectonic history. At Belalong, erosion processes act on a land that has been raised by uplift due to folding and faulting of the underlying rock.

The forces responsible for these geological processes derive from immensely slow but hugely powerful lateral movements of individual sections ("plates") of the earth's crust. Convection cells within the weak upper mantle of the earth, caused by heat from the decay of radioactive isotopes within the mantle, provide the driving force.

There are two types of crust material. Ocean floors are made of thin but dense rocks. The continental land masses are less dense but may be several tens of kilometres thick.

Where two continental plates move towards each other, their collision can buckle the rocks upwards and form mountain chains. This is taking place in the Himalayas today. Where the two different types of material meet, the oceanic plate is usually forced beneath the other. The overriding material becomes deformed due to the effect of subterranean friction.

The geological history of northwestern Borneo is complex. Although now stable, it is thought that, until geologically very recently, Brunei may have been situated on an active continental margin, that is, a zone where the edges of different plates of the earth's crust meet, and may be moving in different directions.

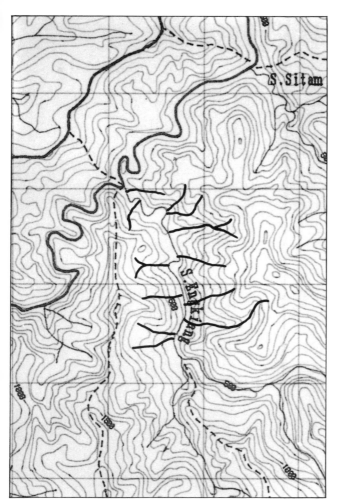

The topographic map of the Batu Apoi Reserve used for the GIS base shows the rugged nature of the topography. Permanent streams in the lower Engkiang valley, not shown on the original maps, are marked here to illustrate the high drainage density.

33

They have subsequently been uplifted and severely folded, with the size of the folds increasing towards the southeast.

Although these rocks are the oldest in Brunei, they are still young in geological terms. They consist predominantly of shales of the Setap (or Temburong) Formation. This formation comprises a great thickness of sandy, dark grey to black shales, with occasional thin beds of hard, quartzitic sandstone within. On ridgetops and summits in the extreme south, the shale is overlain by the Meligan Formation of the same age. This is a medium to coarse-grained sandstone, grey in colour, and generally occurs in hard, thick beds.

The folding of the rocks in this region is thought to have been progressive and it is likely that the process of the uplift also took place slowly but continuously. Currently the most reliable estimate of the rate of uplift for this region is almost 20 mm per cen-

the collision zone.

In the basins behind these up-lifted blocks, sandstone was deposited in river deltas along the shoreline, whilst the shales accumulated further out in the offshore basin, beyond the sandstone.

The geology of the Batu Apoi Forest Reserve consists entirely of sedimentary rocks laid down about 16-30 million years ago, as deltaic and marine deposits off the ancient shore line.

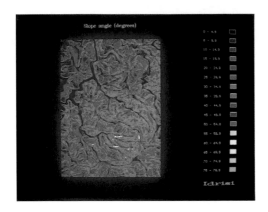

Map of slope angles (colours at 5° intervals) - Sungai Engkiang, Sungai Sitam and Sungai Esu, tributaries to Sungai Belalong.

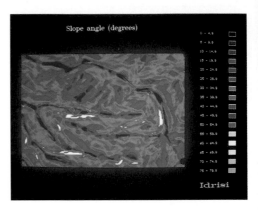

Close-up of northeast head of the Engkiang catchment and Bukit Belalong. The steepest slopes are coloured red to yellow/green.

tury for at least the last two million years. This uplift may be continuing today at a similar rate.

The erosion processes associated with this uplift has produced a sharp topography with high relief. In the extreme southeast of the Batu Apoi Reserve, the hard Meligan sandstone caps the ridges, while the valleys have been cut into the less resistant shales beneath. Elsewhere, the steeply dipping bedding-planes of the bedrock have influenced the shape and steepness of the sides of the ridges and valley slopes.

The drainage pattern of the southern Temburong area provides a good example of the effect of geological structure on resultant landform. The main rivers flow generally northwestwards, across the regional strike of the rocks, but the smaller rivers and streams are resisted by the hard shales and sandstones.

A trellis drainage pattern has

The depth of the weathered soil at Belalong can only be discovered by digging: Alan Dykes in a soil pit.

therefore developed. The main rivers follow long, roughly straight courses, with many short tributaries joining along from each side.

High waterfall at the head of Sungai Engkiang.

Large sediment in the lowest reach of Sungai Engkiang.

Sungai Sitam just above the point where it debouches into Sungai Belalong.

A small landslide scars the hillside.

Bedrock exposed in the stream headwaters.

The Sungai Sitam has cut back to bedrock exposed in a series of shallow falls.

Low flow in Sungai Engkiang is directed by gravel bars.

Surveying the Belalong channel sediment patterns.

Layered tree trunks across Sungai Engkiang.

Traditional pathways in the forest follow the narrow ridge-tops.

TOPOGRAPHY & DRAINAGE

The topography of the Batu Apoi Forest Reserve is steep and sharp. The landscape rises from about 30 m above sea level at Kuala Belalong, to 1,850 m at Gunung Pagon, the highest point in Brunei in the extreme southern part of the Reserve.

Apart from this and the other high peaks, Bukit Retak (1,618 m), Bukit Lesong (1,192 m) and Bukit Tudal (1,181 m), most of the area remains below 1,000 m. Bukit Belalong, 913 m, situated at the head of the Belalong forest, is the highest point for at least 14 km in any direction.

Within this 1,000 m of relief is a landscape entirely composed of deep, V-shaped valleys separated by sharp, often knife-edge ridges. The steep slopes rise directly from the edges of the rivers in the valley bottoms. The course of the valleys closely follow the course of the rivers, and incised or ingrown meanders are frequently included in the landscape. This is because the incising river has generally maintained its meandering course as it cuts down into the valley floor. There are no floodplains. The sides of the main valleys are further dissected by deep and steep tributary valleys. The sides of these valleys are usually short but extremely steep, often greater than 45°. The sides of the main valleys are also steep, most commonly between 25° and 35°, although in places they reach 60°. Almost all hillsides in the area bear the scars of landslides. It is in these scars that the steepest slopes occur.

As well as the small tributaries which flow continuously into larger streams and main rivers, there are many more small channels which are dry most of the time, but which swell into torrents during heavy rains.

The permanent channels are all steep and have cut deep into the bedrock, although some parts may be filled with coarse sediment. High waterfalls are common along smaller tributaries, and they drop steeply into the main valleys below.

Boulders of unweathered shale in Sungai Engkiang, too large to have been transported far by water, must have fallen in from a nearby landslide.

Two large tree trunks carried down Sungai Engkiang and deposited on different dates in 1991.

Early morning sunlight just reaches Sungai Engkiang through the trees which line the steep valley slopes.

LANDSLIDES

Hillslopes lie between the rivers and the ridges. Erosion occurs by downward movement of soil and other material due to gravity. The effect of erosion over thousands of years is to lower the altitude of the entire surface of the landscape.

In Belalong forest, as in many humid tropical regions, the rate of weathering and soil production is greater than the long-term transport capacity provided by water and gravity. Therefore soil and weathered debris accumulate on the slopes. The rainforest vegetation limits the surface loss of soil, but the deep layer of soil on the steep slopes then gives rise to a different kind of erosion.

Landslides are perhaps the most dramatic of all the erosion processes. They come in many shapes, sizes and forms: they may be imperceptibly slow or dangerously rapid events. In all cases they involve the downslope movement of a significant mass of soil, weathered debris or even bedrock. Landslides occur when the strength of the hillslope

LANDSLIDES AT BELALONG

Two types of landslides dominate:

Shallow landslides. These usually occur on steep, straight slopes alongside rivers in the bottom of valleys, where soil and weathered material simply slide off the underlying bedrock. They occur as a consequence of rainfall, heavy enough to saturate the soil at depth, thus reducing their effective strength. Collapse of the slope is rapid. These landslides are usually 20-100 m long and 5-50 m wide, rarely involving more than a few thousand cubic metres of hillslope material. Three large (up to 60 m long) and three smaller ones were found to have occurred during 1990 and 1991 within a few kilometres of Kuala Belalong. One such shallow landslide fell into the Sungai Engkiang in September 1991. The mean angle of this slope was around 50° before the surface layer of soil and weathered material slid off the bedrock. The resulting slope angle is similarly steep, demonstrating the parallel retreat of the hillslopes. Not more than 500 cu m of material was involved.

Deep-seated landslides. These involve an entire section of hillslope sliding along a curved plane of failure deep within the bedrock. The moving mass may remain intact as it slumps or it may disintegrate into a flow of debris. Water pressures within the rock are again the cause, but the event may not be due to any particular storm. These landslides vary in size from a few square metres to entire mountainsides. Very large sections of the upper slopes of Bukit Belalong have moved in this way and created a small pond where water trapped behind one moving block has been unable to drain away. Movements on this scale may last from a few minutes to many tens of years, and many years may pass by between successive landslides of this type. At Belalong all hillslopes apparently continue to decline due to huge, deep-seated landslides, but on a timescale far greater than can be observed. The scars of these landslides, though, are evident everywhere. The view southwest from Bukit Belalong shows an entire mountainside which has slumped downwards into the valley. The scale of these movements is clearly demonstrated by this example, which is a deep-seated landslide large enough to be identified from above the trees. A later, smaller landslide has also occurred on one side of the material which had earlier slumped downwards. This enormous landslide would have dammed the valley at its foot and created a temporary lake until either the stream eroded through the dam or the second landslide helped to destroy it.

Landslides such as this deposit soil and boulders into the river, which becomes turbid in spate.

Sungai Engkiang upriver reach.

In a riffle there is shallow flow over bedload deposit. Sungai Engkiang.

material is insufficient to resist the downslope force due to gravity. Hillslopes of any angle may be stable or unstable according to their internal conditions or their external characteristics at any time.

EFFECTS OF LANDSLIDES

Ecologically, landslides constitute an important feature at Belalong. They destroy areas of standing forest, and create new habitats for re-colonisation by plant and animal life. As we shall see, such gaps in the forest contribute to the maintenance of the biological diversity encountered at Belalong.

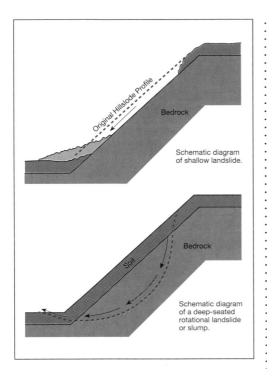

Two types of landslide are shown schematically for hillslopes with a thin soil cover. The curved sliding plane of the deep-seated landslide may not extend as far as the bottom of the slope, but it may extend upwards to include an entire ridgetop.

INTERPRETATION OF A HILLSLOPE PROFILE

The hillslope profile illustrated is a cross-section through the Engkiang valley approximately 1.8 km upstream from the Sungai Belalong, obtained by measuring the angle of each 5-10 m length of hillslope along a straight line compass bearing.

The characteristic steep, straight lower valley slopes are represented by the eastern side, where the mean slope angle for the section is almost 49°.

The shallow landslide that fell into Sungai Engkiang in September 1991.

Representative angles of slope segments steeper than 40° are shown. Here, slope retreat by shallow landslides is most likely to be responsible for the current form of the hillslope. On the west side of the river, a similar situation would be expected, but at this particular site the inclination of the hillslope has begun to be lowered due to a large deep-seated landslide. The actual shape and size of the failure plane of these landslides can only be postulated, but two possibilities for the extent of movement of this one are shown.

Further up the valley side, three stream-head gullies descend steeply towards the south (not illustrated). They join together about 50 m below the line of this profile then descend eastwards to the Sungai Engkiang in a deep and narrow valley almost parallel with the illustrated section.

The upper section of this valley side has a mean inclination of 27°, but is characterised by (at least) two large

Pebbles of shale and sandstone from upriver are mixed in the Belalong bedload.

deep-seated landslides, and is also complicated by three-dimensional factors not shown by the profile. As before, the curved failure planes are only hypothesised. The lower landslide may extend down to the western gully, whilst the upper one may actually extend back to the ridgetop. The upper landslide and the level section of land between the two landslides shown here, lie just to the north of a large ridge and somewhat below it. The level area is probably the upper surface of a block of hillside which is sliding northwards or northwestwards off the side of the large ridge. If so, the upper landslide indicated on the profile may in fact be part of the larger movement, with the lower failure oc-

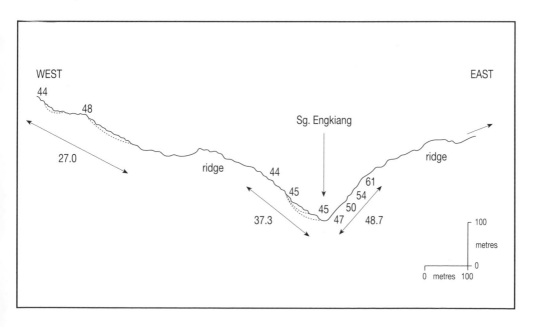

Engkiang valley profile.

The Sungai Belalong was gauged at a point opposite KBFSC and river height was routinely recorded during 1991/92.

curring subsequently.

LANDSCAPE INTERPRETATION

The difficulties of interpreting individual components of this landscape are considerable, especially when the sequence of landslide events or the geometrical configuration of subsurface features such as bedrock fractures, tension cracks, or the failure planes themselves are not known.

Interpreting the landscape as a whole is also very difficult. Although all hillslopes have been altered and scarred by landslides in the past, these events are highly infrequent, and may even be insignificant contributions to the erosion of the landscape surface. In the long term, the continuous removal of soil minerals in solution, dissolved by rainwater which entered the soil during storms, may be sufficient to control the general topographic form of the Belalong region. This is an example of large, catastrophic events possibly being much less important than insidious and sometimes invisible micro-scale landform processes.

STREAMS AND RIVERS

Water flows in streams and rivers from the upper hillslopes of a catchment to the sea. With uplift of the land, the rivers incise into the landmass headwards from the sea. The upstream progress of this incision is indicated by the presence of waterfalls.

At the present time, waterfalls occur on the smaller tributaries which have the least erosive capacity, such as along the Sungai Esu and many upper tributaries of the Sungai Engkiang. The Engkiang itself has been able to incise a long way back towards its headwaters, whilst the Esu has only adjusted its lower 200 m or so.

SUNGAI ENGKIANG

The channel profile, from the top of the Engkiang catchment to Bangar, begins with a steep upper headwater originating in a topographic hollow. These headwaters flow within deep and narrow valleys, often on exposed slabs of bedrock with small pools between each slab, rather like a staircase. Lower down, the channel becomes less steep within its own small valley, but with occasional waterfalls, and increases in size and discharge as other small headwaters join it. Further downstream, it develops into a major tributary. (See p.46)

Until about 1 km from Sungai Belalong, the Engkiang is a large mountain stream a few metres wide, entirely contained within a bedrock channel in the valley floor. It has varying arrangements of deep and rocky pools, straight sections infilled with sandy material, shallow rapids where larger gravel and pebbles have accumulated within the rocky channel, or combinations of all these features. This is characteristic of an incising channel with a regular supply of sediment, which the stream is only able to transport during its largest floods. Waves of sediment are therefore carried down the channel.

The gradient of the Sungai Engkiang lessens towards its lower end, but minor tributaries continue to join it by means of small waterfalls from higher levels up the side of the main valley.

Once the main Sungai Belalong is reached, a different situation is encountered. Here, the bedrock channel is mostly filled with fine and very coarse sediment, including large boulders, so that the actual bed of the channel is rarely seen. The tributary streams supply large quantities of sediment to the main river; in fact, more than those rivers can transport. Sediment has therefore accumulated, and the energy of the river is utilised in transporting the sediment which provides protection for the channel bed against downward incision.

SEDIMENT TRANSPORTATION

There are many types of sediment transported by these rivers. The most important for determining the shape of the channels is the coarse bedload, that is, the large boulders and pebbles which occupy the river bed in the main valleys. These rocks are mostly fresh (dark grey) or weathered (orange-pink) shale, but there is some quantity of grey-yellow sandstone which has been transported down from the most southerly headwaters. As the rocks are transported and further eroded, they become more rounded, and may break up into smaller pieces.

The sandstone river pebbles are almost all very rounded, indicating much transport, and there are large quantities of sand in the river, which result from eroded sandstone.

Sungai Belalong provides a typical example of a steep channel with a large load of coarse sediment. Exten-

SEDIMENT PATTERNS IN A CONFINED CHANNEL

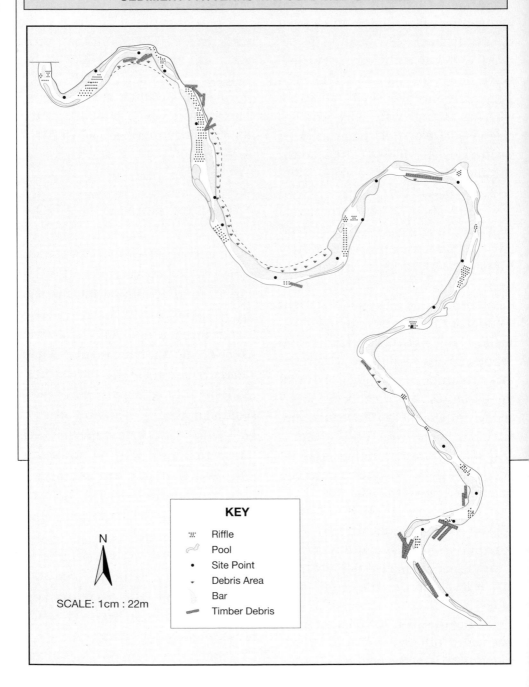

KEY

☼	Riffle
∿	Pool
•	Site Point
⌄	Debris Area
	Bar
▨	Timber Debris

N

SCALE: 1cm : 22m

Engkiang channel plan.

A 1.2 km stretch of the lower Engkiang was surveyed during low flow (dry season) conditions using a level and staff, and sediment deposits. Other channel features were also mapped. Downstream changes in width, depth, and slope of the channel, and spacing, size and form of riffle and pool sequences within the channel, were analysed to establish how the observed patterns in this steep, confined bedrock channel with lots of coarse bedload, compared with that in alluvial channels formed entirely by sediment deposition in the valley floor and floodplains.

Over the length of this survey, the width of the channel did not increase downstream although deposition of coarse bedload at riffle sites enabled wider sections to occur locally. Channel depth alternated between the shallow riffles and the deep pools which immediately followed riffles, due to channel bed scour and erosion by water flowing off the steep riffle sections. The exaggerated length of pool sections indicated prolonged downstream scour due to the restraining effects of the channel on lateral expansion. The mean depth did not increase significantly along the surveyed reach, and width-depth ratios showed no pattern. The channel slope varied little from 0.5% throughout this reach of the river, and this low gradient, with a high bedload dem-onstrated a channel regime dominated by sediment deposition and transport, which, with erosion, may be able to proceed in some places at high flows.

The spacing between riffles was 3-5 times the mean width of the channel. This spacing, smaller than expected, may be due to the inability of the channel to expand to the width required for the observed riffle spacing. In general, features of alluvial channels such as riffles, pools, gravel bars, and a degree of regularity in the overall arrangements of these features, show that this sediment-laden stretch of the Engkiang appears to behave like an alluvial channel.

In this rainforest environment, the accumulation of vegetation and debris in the channel may greatly influence the processes operating. Debris such as fallen tree trunks may reduce local flow velocities and cause deposition to occur, which may then alter the local channel gradient. Sediment bars may therefore form where they would not normally be expected, such as on the outsides of bends, and the rhythmic pattern of pools and riffles may be disrupted by sedimentation due to vegetation debris. Both the vegetation and the sediment bars are likely to move during floods and the size, form and pattern of sediment structures change with the river water level.

47

sive steep but shallow reaches over areas of bedload deposition (**riffles**) are common, interspersed with deep, low gradient, slow flowing stretches (pools) containing generally finer sediment. Other features of a high sediment regime are the deposition of coarse sediment on the inside of bends, with deep pools and slope-foot erosion on the outside of these bends.

Sediment is transported downstream during floods, when the river flows increase dramatically due to rainfall on the catchment. At these times the rivers can be seen to be transporting large quantities of very fine solid materials in suspension, such as sand grains or particles of soil. Dissolved solids do not affect the apparent colour of the water, but may also be transported in the shape of the entire river bed, by moving pebbles and even rocks downstream, but most of the time the bedload remains still.

Decomposition processes will recycle the organic matter of a fallen forest giant.

CHAPTER 4

SOILS AND HYDROLOGY

By Sheila M. Ross

The Belalong forest has provided an ideal testbed for studying the hydrochemistry of overland flow, infiltration and throughflow of tropical moist forest (rainforest) on steep terrain. The main processes which form soil are the weathering of parent rock and the decomposition of organic matter (the surface litter layer of dead leaves and twigs, fallen boughs and trunks). Throughout the humid tropics, these soil-forming processes are rapid in the prevailing warm temperatures and high rainfall.

SOIL FORMATION

Soluble constituents are removed in solution: this process is known as **leaching**. The resultant soils are usually deep and are predominantly composed of clay minerals, which are the insoluble end products of weathering. Many tropical soils, including those in the Belalong forest, are coloured yellow, orange or red, indicating the presence of iron oxides.

The parent shales in the Belalong valley have produced soils dominated by two minerals: coarse particles of quartz, a form of silica (silicon dioxide, SiO_2), and fine particles of kaolinite (a clay containing aluminium). Both minerals are highly unreactive and consequently, the soils have poor ability to retain nutrients and solutes by absorption or exchange, so that soluble compounds are easily leached.

SOIL CHARACTERISTICS AND CLASSIFICATION

Soils can be classified on the basis of the sizes of mineral particles. Particles of 0-0.002 mm diameter are **clay**, particles of 0.002-0.02 mm diameter are **silts** and particles >0.02 mm are **sands**. The soils of the Belalong forest are mainly silty clays. Such fine textured soils are relatively impermeable, allowing water to pass only slowly. However, penetrating this impermeable soil matrix are **macropores**, large cracks and channels caused by periodic dehydration, or by animal burrows, root channels, etc. In some places, this network of subsurface macropores allows water to flow through the soil very rapidly indeed.

A vertical section through the soil is described as the **soil profile**. Soil profile descriptions provide the basis for all the soil, hydrology and geomorphological studies. A soil pro-

51

Jason Medway examines the weathering zone, where parent shales break down to produce soil mineral material.

Weathered parent shale material at the base of the soil profile.

file description is useful for two main purposes: firstly, to understand how the soil has formed in relation to the hillslope geomorphological and hydrological processes; secondly, to discover how the soil provides water, nutrients and anchorage for the trees, shrubs and herbs that it supports.

The silty clay soils in the Belalong valley are deeper on lower slopes and shallower on upper slopes and ridgetops, but are rarely deeper than 2 m. Soil development has been due to a combination of *in situ* rock weathering and downslope mass movements, ranging from small scale soil creep to large scale landslides (See Chapter 3).

The soil profile development processes in Belalong soils are extremely well advanced, and can be divided into four steps:

Step 1. Decomposition in the leaf litter layer releases organic acids which percolate into the surface mineral soil.

Step 2. This speeds up the chemical weathering of rock minerals and the release of basic **cations** (potassium, sodium, calcium and magnesium) and silicon, which are leached.

Step 3. Iron and aluminium oxides accumulate in the soil.

Step 4. Kaolinite, the most resistant

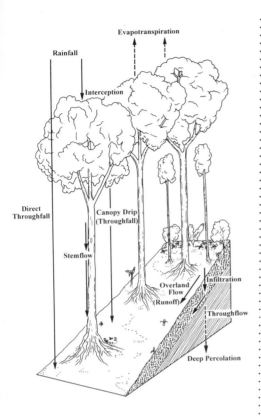

Forest hydrological cycle.

clay mineral, accumulates in the soil.

The resultant soil material is high in quartz, iron and aluminium oxides and kaolinite, but extremely low in plant nutrients (such as nitrogen and phosphorus which are rapidly recycled in the litter layers), and also low in the basic nutrients such as calcium and magnesium (which are present in only small quantities in the parent shale, and are rapidly leached from the soil after weathering). It is rare for organic matter to be found at depth in the soil since decomposition rates are so fast. A

further reason is that water percolation through the soil is slow and the fine and very tortuous pore spaces present in the clay soils matrix prevent the passage of even finely fragmented organic matter. Soil texture and structure combine to produce soil bulk densities in the range 0.7 g per cm^3 in surface horizons, to 1.2 g per cm^3 in the subsoil.

Soil scientists have not agreed on a common terminology for soil classification, and several nomenclatures exist. By the international soils classification devised by the FAO and UNESCO in 1974, soils in the Belalong valley can be described as **orthic acrisols** (= udult ultisols, by the US Department of Agriculture classification). This denotes highly weathered, iron-rich soils, relatively poor in basic chemicals, with an argillic (clay-enriched) B horizon (See p.55). The soils are acidic, with soil water pH values ranging from 5.5 to 6.5. Acrisols are commonly found developed on silicious rocks throughout the tropics, from South America to Africa and South East Asia.

SOIL HYDROLOGY

The slopes in the Belalong forest average 30-35°. These conditions are ideal for illustrating the tropical rainforest hydrological cycle.

Eight main hydrological processes can be seen: (i) interception, (ii)

53

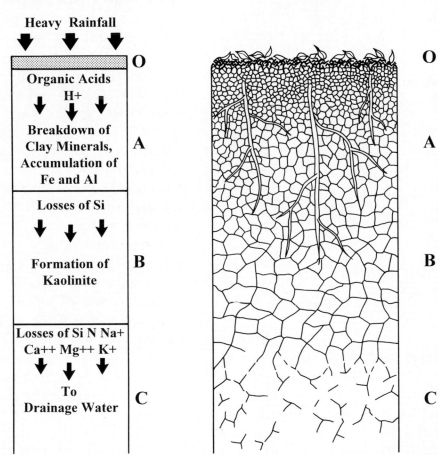

SOIL PROCESSES

Heavy Rainfall

O

Organic Acids
H+

Breakdown of
Clay Minerals,
Accumulation of
Fe and Al

A

Losses of Si

Formation of
Kaolinite

B

Losses of Si N Na+
Ca++ Mg++ K+

To
Drainage Water

C

SOIL PROFILE

O

A

B

C

54

Horizon	Depth (cm)	General description	Specific description
O	> 0	Superficial litter, fragmented organic matter and root mat.	100% cover of loose leaf litter, averaging 2-3 cm depth. Identifiable and unidentifiable fragments. Dense mesh of very fine roots (up to 1 mm diameter) ramifying through the litter. Sharp boundary to:
A	0-10	Surface soil mineral horizon	Very fine crumb structure with tiny fragments of leaf litter. Silty clay texture. Colour dark reddish brown. Friable and visibly porous. Very few tiny stones (<2 mm) at soil surface. Diffuse and regular boundary to:
B	10-30	Sub-surface mineral horizon	Medium angular blocky structure, around 5 cm diameter. Silty clay texture. Colour yellowish brown. Few visible pores with no cracks. Frequent medium sized roots (<4 mm diameter) to a depth of 17 cm but no roots below this. Diffuse and irregular boundary to:
C	> 30	Weathered and weathering parent	Stones and weathered shale fragments (10-15 cm diameter) very frequent, making up 40-60% of the horizon down to 70 cm. Below this, stones make up >70% of the horizon. Soil matrix yellowish red, with weathered shale of many colours, including yellows and reds, with white mottles. Unweathered, very dark grey. Stones and shale fragments show sloping orientation (40°) through the profile, due to geological dip of parent shales. No roots.

55

A wide range of bright red, orange and yellow colours are shown by weathering shales. These colours represent different chemical forms of iron oxides.

CHARACTERISTICS OF THE SOILS OF BELALONG FOREST

Soil samples were collected at different depths down the soil profile and analysed for a range of physical and chemical characteristics. The sizes of soil particles change with depth in the profile since percolating water has washed all the fine particles out of topsoils and deposited them lower down the profile (Fig. a). This is why the B horizon has a high content of clay-sized particles and is called an **argillic** horizon. These clayey conditions also indi-cate that the soil becomes more imperme-able at depth. Soil surface horizons thus have sandier textures and their organic matter contents are also higher due to leaf litter influx.

The higher organic matter content of the topsoil results in higher nitrogen and phosphorus concentrations, while the higher potassium in the lower horizons of the soil is due to release from the chemical weathering of the parent shales (Fig. b).

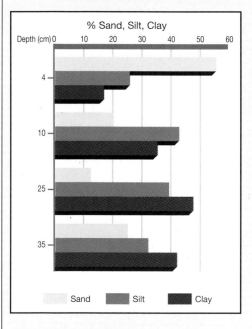

Fig a. Soil texture

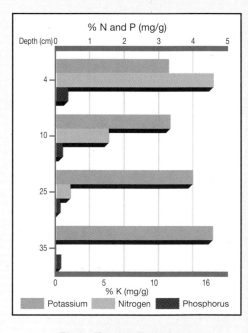

Fig b. Total soil nutrients

evapotranspiration, (iii) throughfall, (iv) stemflow, (v) infiltration, (vi) over-land flow (runoff), (vii) throughflow, and (viii) deep percolation.

Anything from 5% to 95% of rain-fall can be intercepted by the forest canopy, and 20-30% of this water may be re-evaporated immediately from the canopy by the high temperatures re-ceived there. Water arriving at the for-est floor comes predominantly from canopy drip throughfall, with ex-tremely small amounts (0.5-2%) flow-ing down the stems (stemflow).

Undisturbed forest soils are usually friable and show high rates of water infiltration. Infiltration rates slow down if the soil surface is compacted or crusted, or if the hillslope is steep. Under these conditions, water runs off as overland flow. High surface soil infiltration rates were measured in Belalong soils, ranging from 503-878 mm per hour. Comparing this rate to the highest observed rainfall intensities on the area between June 1991 and April 1992 (67 mm per hour), it is clear that almost all of the rainfall reaching the ground should enter the soil.

However, a runoff and erosion experiment set up on 30° slopes in the forest recorded significant water runoff volumes throughout the year, even on totally undisturbed forest sites. Runoff is generated during the more intensive rainstorms because the steepness of the slopes allows the force of gravity to overcome the suction forces which draw the water into the soil during dry conditions. Even more runoff can be generated when the soils are wet because the soil suction forces are much reduced.

SOIL EROSION

Any conditions which enhance water runoff on hillslopes will cause soil erosion. Tree canopies intercept raindrops while the tree roots stabilise the surface of the soil. Removal or alteration of the forest vegetation has immediate repercussions.

Soil erosion is affected by three main groups of factors: (i) those determining the quantity of water runoff - such as, rainfall amount and intensity, hillslope angle, infiltration rate; (ii) those controlling sediment supply, namely, disaggregation and disruption of soil particles, transportability of soil particles; (iii) type and amount of vegetation and litter layer at soil surface. The channelling of water by leaves, twigs and branches in the forest canopy produces throughfall water-drop sizes larger than the original raindrops. Drip impact directly onto a bare soil surface is one of the ways in which soil particles are disrupted and moved downslope, causing soil creep and the beginnings of soil erosion. This erosional process is inhibited by the presence of leaf litter and a root mat at the forest floor.

Soil erosion is a serious problem in the tropics. Studies elsewhere have concentrated on the effects of wholesale forest clearance, or of partial forest removal by commercial lumbering. Studies at Belalong show that a 20-fold increase in soil erosion can be caused by removal of the forest floor litter layers alone. From the bare soil experimental plots, soil erosion removed several centimetres of surface soil. Soil erosion carries with it the losses of organic matter and plant nutrients, thus causing soil degradation. At Belalong the beginnings of soil degradation are evident, even where the tree

57

On the steep hillsides a thin covering of leaf litter protects the soil surface.

Leaf litter is cleared off a bounded soil erosion experimental plot.

Red and white tapes were used to mark off soil study sites on the West Ridge above KBFSC.

A double-ring infiltrometer is used to measure the rate of water percolation into the soil surface.

Moisture conditions are measured at different depths in the soil, using tensiometers.

In the bare soil, plant roots originally 5-6 cm below the surface were exposed after only two months of erosion.

canopy itself remains intact.

SOIL MOISTURE CONDITIONS

The forces holding water in the soil are measured using tensiometers. When the soil is dry, suction forces in the soil are high and water is sucked out of the reservoir inside the tensiometer, causing a suction and a negative value of hydraulic head on the tensiometer

RUNOFF AND SOIL EROSION FROM THE DIPTEROCARP FOREST FLOOR

Quantities of water and sediments washed from the soil surface in erosion were measured in plots built into the 30° slope, bounded with timber to prevent soil washing into the plot from elsewhere. The downslope edge of the plot was fashioned into a trough, channelling all water and sediment into a collection tank. These waters and sediments were measured every two days. Three types of slopes were studied: (i) virgin forest, with intact canopy and forest floor, consisting of litter layer and root mat overlying the mineral soil, (ii) intact canopy with the litter layer removed but the root mat intact, and (iii) intact canopy with both litter layer and root mat removed, providing a bare soil surface. During both the wet season and the dry season in the Belalong valley, very big differences were seen between the intact forest floor and the areas cleared of litter and roots. In Fig.4.1 comparison is made between the runoff and sediment losses observed in the wet season (November, 1991) and in the dry season (March, 1992). Remembering that the Y-axis scales in the two graphs are different, both runoff and sediment losses in the wet season are around 10-11 times more than in the dry season.

Calculated over a 12-month period, six times more water runs off as overland flow and 20 times more sediments are eroded from bare soil surfaces under the forest canopy than from the intact forest floor. These results show that water can flow relatively freely over and through the litter and root mat of the forest floor. Sediments and organic matter particles are, however, trapped by the litter/root mat and not eroded in large quantities from the intact forest floor. In the most serious examples of soil erosion after rainforest removal, dissolved nutrients washed away from the soil surface collectively in overland flow and leaching, can amount to as much as 75% of all nutrient inputs to the forest floor in rainfall and litterfall. Quantities of nutrients washed away in eroded soil particles are being studied, and appear to account for as little as 5% to over 90% of all nutrient inputs to the forest floor.

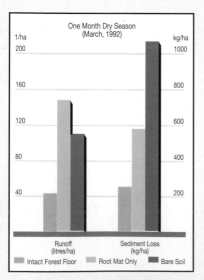

Fig 4.1a. Dry season runoff and sediment losses.

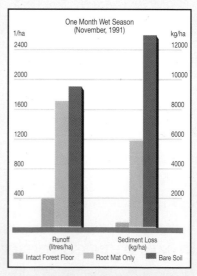

Fig 4.1b. Wet season runoff and sediment losses.

Leached nutrients entering the rivers are rapidly carried out of the forest ecosystem.

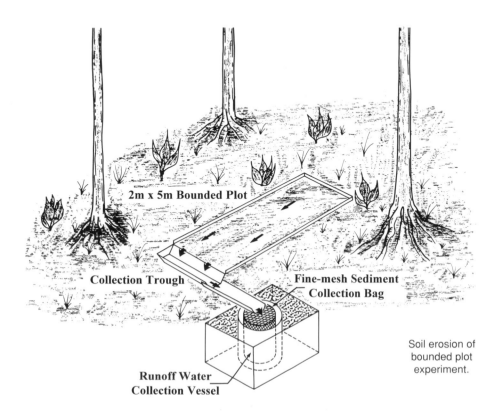

2m x 5m Bounded Plot

Collection Trough

Fine-mesh Sediment Collection Bag

Runoff Water Collection Vessel

Soil erosion of bounded plot experiment.

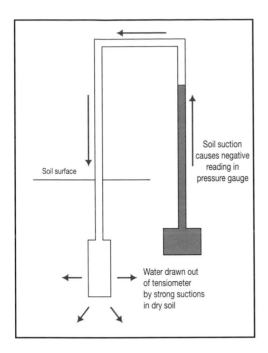

Fig 4.2. Dry soil conditions generating **negative suctions.**

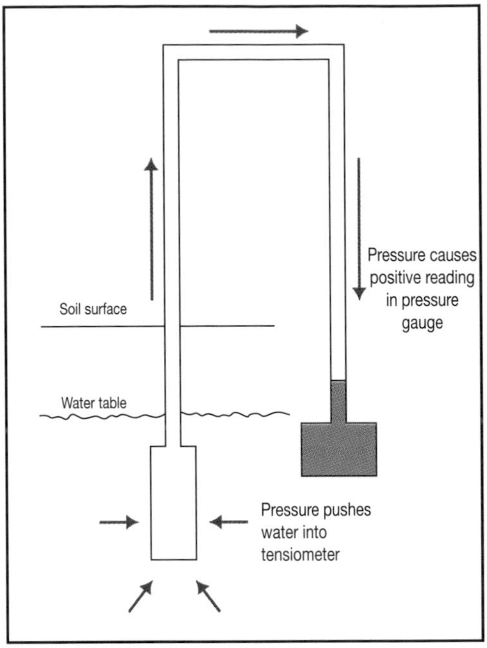

Fig 4.3. Saturated soil conditions generating **positive pressures.**

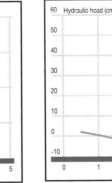
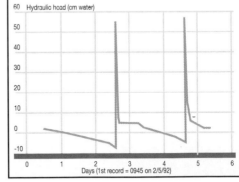

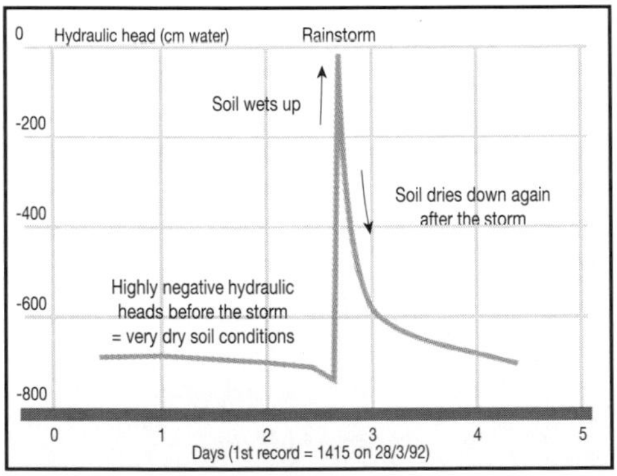

Fig 4.4.Tensiometer response to rainfall in the **dry season.**

Fig 4.5. Tensiometer response to rainfall in the **wet season.**

Bounded soil erosion experimental plot on 30° slope in the Belalong forest.

gauge (Fig 4.2).

When the soil is totally saturated, water is pushed back into the tensiometer. Instead of a suction being recorded, a pressure is observed and recorded as positive values of hydraulic head on the gauge (Fig.4.3).

Suction patterns for a 90 cm deep tensiometer on the Belalong hillslope are shown in Fig. 4.4 for a typical five-day period in the dry season. Fifteen mm of rain fell on 30 March, 1992. Prior to the storm, highly negative hydraulic heads indicate extremely dry conditions. On 30 March, the soil wets up very rapidly after rainfall, but not wet enough to cause a positive pressure. The rapid build-up of saturated conditions during two storms in May,

1992 (86.8 mm and 47.0 mm respectively) show a similar pattern for wet season soil moisture conditions (Fig. 4.5), with peak flushes of water through the soil being recorded as positive pressures on 4 and 6 May, indicating saturated soil conditions.

The Belalong subsoil has a high clay content. Normally such clayey soils have very slow hydraulic conductivities, or rates of soil water transport. At Belalong, however, the soil micro-aggregate structure and its stoniness, both encourage fast water transmission. It is thus surprising that forest plants and trees do not appear to root more deeply, both for stability in the steep Belalong terrain and for moisture uptake.

An elegant tree fern (*Cyathea*) in riparian forest at Belalong.

CHAPTER 5

BIODIVERSITY

The atmosphere and climate, the water falling as rain (and the substances dissolved in it), the geology and soils are constituent parts of the non-living environment. Dependent on this environment are the living components. Living things utilise substances derived from outside themselves for the purposes of growth, the repair of their own structure and the maintenance of their functional systems, and reproduction.

Fossil records show that there have been living things on earth for the past 3, 300 million years. During that time, an enormous variety of different forms has arisen.

We are not concerned, in this book, with extinct forms, but with the variety of wildlife of all kinds now occurring in the Belalong forest. This is the biological diversity, or **biodiversity**, and can be described in terms of the diversity within species (genetic diversity), the diversity of species or the diversity of ecosystems.

THE GENETIC CODE

A short section of a gene of the fruit fly as it is arranged along one of the strings of a DNA molecule, showing the sequence of bases: **c** = cytosine, **a** = adenine, **g** = guanine and **t** = thymine. Each triplet provides the code to trigger the production of one of a wide variety of molecules, indicated by the subscript capital letters.

cca	gcg	agc	aga	tct
S	E	O	I	Y
acg	gga	gcc	cct	cca
G	S	P	S	S
gca	gcc	cct	acg	aat
S	P	Y	E	C
gtc	tgc	gcc	agt	cat
L	R	Q	S	C
gct	cca	tcc	tca	tga
S	I	L	I	S
gca	cga	tga	aca	agt
T	M	N	K	L.
tgg	cca	cag	cca	tgc
A	T	A	M	Q
agg	aag	gcg	agt	atg
E	G	E	Y	D

BIODIVERSITY

The United Nations Convention on Biological Diversity defines the term as follows: *the variability among living organisms from all sources including, among others, terrestrial, marine and other aquatic ecosystems and the ecological complexes of which they are part; this includes diversity within species, between species and of ecosystems.*

GENETIC DIVERSITY

Genetic diversity takes account of the variety of forms of life in terms of information-carrying molecules, notably **DNA** (deoxyribonucleic acid). These molecules are the basic materials of genetic diversity. The new scientific technique known as 'DNA finger-printing' reminds us that each living individual is genetically unique at the molecular level.

The core of the DNA molecule is a double string composed of a mixture of four **nucleotides** (adenine, cytosine, guanine and thymine) which are arranged in varying linear order.

The unit of the genetic code is a triplet of three successive nucleotides on either string (each one is complementary to the other). Each triplet can signal the production (in the living cell) of a distinct molecule. The scientist in the laboratory can now decipher the genetic code of any living thing, and today pages of scientific journals are filled with diagrammatic representations of DNA.

DNA AND THE FOREST

The DNA in a rather simple organism,

Even a simple fungus such as *Omphalina* contains millions of nucleotides in its DNA.

TAXONOMY

Once it is recognised as distinct, a species needs to be named and described. It is exciting that several undescribed species have been discovered at Belalong. These will have to be given names. By agreed rules, the scientific name of a species must be a binomial (that is, consisting of two words). The first word is the genus and the second is the species name. Species names must be used together with the name of a genus (sometimes indicated by an initial), but the genus name can be used by itself to refer to all the different species in that particular genus. It is also a rule that all scientific names must be in Latin (or in Latinised classical Greek, or in a Latin-like form), and appear in italic typeface when printed.

As an example, the scientific name for mankind is *Homo sapiens,* but several other extinct species are known in the genus *Homo,* including *Homo erectus* and *Homo afarensis*. Familiar plants and animals (such as *H. sapiens* - man) also have vernacular names which can be in any language. In this book we use Malay and English vernacular names, together with the Latin names. The value of scientific names is that they are international and exact. Vernacular names vary from one language to another, and even between regional versions (dialects) of one language. Moreover, there is no formal way of settling the correct use of a vernacular name, which may be applied by different speakers to different plants or animals, or groups of plants or animals. Thus, the Straits rhododendron *(Melastoma malabathricum)* is known as senduduk in Malaysia and kodok-kodok in Brunei, both names referring to several other species of *Melastoma* (and all quite unrelated to the 'true' rhododendrons). In addition many plants and animals do not have vernacular names.

The scientific activity that involves the identification, description and naming of an organism, living or extinct, and determining its place in the overall classification of life forms, is termed taxonomy.

The taxonomic classification of organisms, both living and extinct, is called hierarchic because it is based on an arrangement of ranked grades of increasing inclusiveness denoting groups of species with recognisable affinity, which are presumed to represent common evolutionary origins.

69

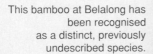
This bamboo at Belalong has been recognised as a distinct, previously undescribed species.

HIERARCHIC CLASSIFICATION

The principal grades of plants and animals in the hierarchic classification are listed below, with examples of Latin and vernacular names.

It is customary for genus and species names to be printed in italic typeface; genus names (but not species names) always have an initial capital letter. In this book, when used in a taxonomic sense, the terms Kingdom, Phylum or Division, Class, Order and Family are given capital initial letters.

Animals

KINGDOM : Animalia
(all animals)
PHYLUM : Arthropoda
(joint-legged invertebrates)
CLASS : Insecta
(insects)
ORDER : Lepidoptera
(moths and butterflies)
FAMILY : Papilionidae
(swallowtail butterflies)
GENUS : *Trogonoptera*
(birdwings)
SPECIES : *Trogonoptera brookiana*
(Rajah Brooke's birdwing)

Plants

KINGDOM : Plantae
(all plants)
DIVISION : Angiospermae
(flowering plants)
CLASS : Dicotyledonae
(dicotyledons)
ORDER : Guttiferales
(dipterocarps & others)
FAMILY : Dilleniaceae
(mempelas and simpur)
GENUS : *Dillenia*
(simpur)
SPECIES : *Dillenia reticulata*
(simpur gajah)

The riverside simpur (*Dilennia*).

Rajah Brooke's birdwings: males gathering at a seepage.

Symmetrical internal structure of the simpur fruit.

such as a fungus, can amount to 40 million nucleotide pairs. In more complex life forms the number of nucleotides can exceed one billion. In man the number of nucleotide pairs is about three billion, although only

WHAT IS A SPECIES?

For practical purposes, the definition of species of plants coined long ago by the English botanist, John Ray, is still valid:

"After a long and considerable investigation, no surer criterion for determining species has occurred to me than the distinguishing features that perpetuate themselves in propagation from seed. Thus, no matter what variations occur in the individual or the species, if they spring from the seed of one and the same plant, they are accidental variations and not such as to distinguish a species."

John Ray (1686) Historia plantarum

The Green lantern bug (*Pyrops sultan*), a member of the numerous and diverse insect Order, Hemiptera.

The dragonfly *Trithemis aurora*, a widespread lowland species in South East Asia.

about 2% of this is 'useful' DNA containing gene sequences. Although attainable in theory, it is clear that a total genetic catalogue would be too vast and unwieldy to be useful.

Naturalists in the forest will al-ways need to work with complete organisms, the whole animals, plants, fungus or micro-organisms that they encounter.

SPECIES DIVERSITY

Among the vast numbers of individuals that make up the marvellous variety of natural life, at any one place (such as the Belalong forest) it is possible to recognise groups with shared resemblances. Scientists apply the term **species** (a Latin word) to these recognisable sets, whether plant, animal, fungus or micro-organism. The processes that maintain the separateness of species have operated since life first

A SAMPLE OF BIODIVERSITY

The chief groups of living organisms that contribute to biodiversity at Belalong:

BACTERIA
> **Prokaryotes** including
> **Cyanobacteria**

EUCARYA
> **Protists**   Unicellular
>   eukaryotes
>   of mixed character

Micro-organisms

Plants
Chlorophytes: green algae; diatoms
Bryophytes: mosses; liverworts

Lower plants

Pteridophytes: ferns; club mosses
Spermatophytes: the seed plants, comprising
                    gymnosperms and angiosperms
                    (=flowering plants), divided
                    into monocotyledons and
                    dicotyledons

Vascular plants

Fungi
Ascomycotina
Basidiomycotina   mushrooms, moulds and yeasts

Animals
Flatworms: flukes; tapeworms; turbellarians
Roundworms: nematodes
Annelids: earthworms; leeches
Arthropods: crustaceans; myriapods; spiders,
                    ticks, mites; scorpions; insects
Molluscs: snails and slugs

Invertebrates

Chordates: fish; amphibians; reptiles;
                    birds; mammals

Vertebrates

arose on earth. The concept of 'species' has existed in biology for centuries. In modern terms we can define a living species as a set of populations of interbreeding individuals, reproductively, morphologically or geographically isolated from other such sets.

Biodiversity can only be quantified with a knowledge of taxonomy. At present, there is no definitive world list of the named living species of plants, animals, fungi or micro-organisms. For plants, botanists attempt to keep up to date through the annual compilation

NEW DISCOVERIES

New species are continually being discovered and named. The numbers of new flowering plants and ferns described during four years, taken from *Index Kewensis*:

Year	1986	1987	1988	1989	1990
Flowering plants	2,832	2,526	2,859	2,752	2,635
Ferns	238	142	159	170	116

The leaves of a moss, no more than a few cells thick, can absorb water and nutrients directly (*Leucobryum bowringii*).

Some insects have bizarre shapes, such as this violin beetle (*Mormolyce phyllodes*) at Belalong.

MICRO-ORGANISMS

A most fundamental division among living things is that between the simplest, the **prokaryotes** (Bacteria), in which the genetic material in each cell is not contained within a **nucleus** (a central structure enclosed in a double membrane), and the **eukaryotes** (Eucarya), in which the genetic material is so contained. The plants, fungi and animals are the three Kingdoms of eukaryotes; within each of these Kingdoms there is a mixed assemblage of very small organisms, several of which combine characters of plants and animals, to which the name **protist** (Protista) is given.

The term **micro-organism** is used to signify an unrelated assemblage of small organisms, including bacteria, protists and others. Most of these organisims can only be studied and identified when magnified by lens or microscope. Others are included if identification requires microscopic examination or another laboratory process.

No inventory of micro-organisms of the world exists, but they are undoubtedly a major component of global biodiversity. They are responsible for many, varied biological activities, especially those involved in decomposition and other degradation processes. Many of them inhabit animal alimentary systems, where they are essential for processing their host's food intake. Many are symbiotic in other ways and many are pathogenic.

Hundreds of species occur in the most extreme environments of the world: at abyssal depths of the oceans, in strong chemical solutions, or at very high or very low temperatures. An estimate of a global total of 2-3,000,000 species of prokaryotes has been made by H G Trueper (1992. *Biodiversity and Conservation* 1:227-236).

Decomposition processes, starting with the action of micro-organisms and fungi, recycle the nutrients in a fallen tree and make them available again to other life forms.

of *Index Kewensis,* and for animals, zoologists through the *Zoological Record.* The total number of named species, estimated from these and other sources, falls in the range 1.4 - 1.8 million.

Some groups have been better studied than others. Best known are those plants and animals that are large or conspicuous, or endowed with showy features: for example, flowering plants, vertebrate animals or bright and attractive invertebrates such as butterflies or dragonflies. Because of the effort applied to these groups, it

ESTIMATES OF BIODIVERSITY

Known and estimated world totals of living species of selected groups of plants, fungi and animals, showing numbers already described and best estimates of the total numbers likely to exist.

Group	Described species	Estimated total species	Percentage of total already described
Micro-organisms			
Bacteria	3,000	2,500,000	0.1
Plants			
Algae	40,000	350,000	11
Bryophytes	17,000	25,000	68
Vascular plants	220,000	270,000	81
Fungi			
(including lichens)	69,000	1,500,000	5
Animals			
Nematodes	15,000	500,000	3
Arthropods	80,000	6,000,000	13
Fish	22,500	35,000	64
Birds	9,040	9,100	99
Mammals	4,000	4,020	>99

ALPHA DIVERSITY

The species diversity of a stated group at a particular place and time is termed **alpha diversity**. When all species cannot be enumerated for practical reasons, the species richness of a sample may be expressed by a diversity index which is independent of sample size.

One such index is Williams' alpha, derived from the equation:

$$\alpha = S/\log_e(1 + N/\alpha)$$

where N is the number of individuals and S the number of species in the sample.

has become difficult to find undescribed species. It is therefore reasonable to assume that the numbers known and named are close to the true world total. For the other less well-known groups, collecting has provided an overall sample, but the numbers of species remain a matter for conjecture. Taking account of totals already described and named, plus expected new discoveries, a reasonable estimate of the overall number of species of living organisms of all kinds in the world is around 10 million.

In the tropical world, vascular plants (that is, pteridophytes plus spermatophytes) and chordate animals account for about half of the number of species described and named. Taking into account other less well-known groups, a huge upward revision of the total must be expected. For example, in a Sulawesi national park, 1,690 species of one order of insects, the bugs (Hemiptera), were found, of which 63% were unknown. In Mulu National Park, Sarawak, of 4,000 species of beetles

77

Birdwing caterpillars of swallowtail Family Papilionidae on their food plant (*Aristolochia*).

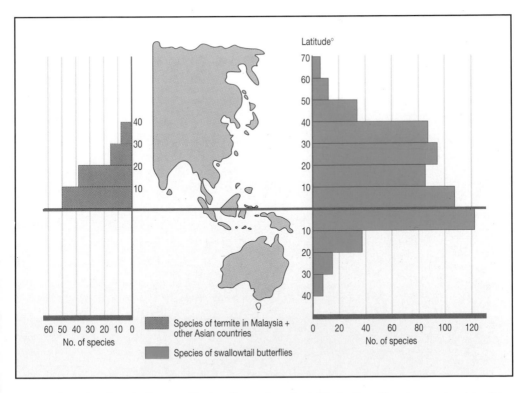

Tropical species diversity illustrated by termites and swallowtail butterflies. The step graphs show the number of species of the two groups recorded at sample localities within each 10° band of latitude. Species richness in termites peaks in lowland dipterocarp forests in Sarawak and Peninsular Malaysia.
[Adapted with permission from original data by N M Collins]

BIODIVERSITY TRENDS: SOME EXAMPLES

Vascular plants: The flora of Europe, a large north temperate zone continental and island area, comprises about 13,000 species. In the tropics, worldwide, about 250,000 species are known (about 50,000 being trees).

Butterflies: 70 species in Britain (of about 380 species in all of Western Europe); in Peninsular Malaysia, a smaller area, 1,014 species.

Breeding birds: on the North American continent, around 20 species along the northern shore of Alaska and Canada; about 150 species at mid-temperate latitudes; 600 species in Panama.

Mammals: contrast Peninsular Malaysia and Denmark, roughly comparable in area but projecting at opposite diagonals from the Eurasian continental block: total land mammal species (PM) 203/ (D) 45; bats 83/12, rodents 54/14 and carnivores 29/8.

collected, some 75% (that is, about 3,000) proved to be new to science and undescribed.

Among the well-known groups, there is a general trend for species rich-ness to increase from the polar regions towards the equator. The swallowtail butterflies (Family Papilionidae) in eastern Asia and Australasia, peaking at equatorial latitudes, provide a strik-

Processional termites (*Hospitalitermes*) are common at Belalong.

The estuarine mud of the southern shore of Brunei Bay supports a distinctive community of specialised plants and animals.

ing illustration; so do the termites (Order Isoptera) of eastern Asia.

This trend culminates in the tropical rainforests of all continents, which are renowned for an extraordinary richness of species. As a working rule of thumb, for any given taxonomic group, equivalent areas in the tropics can be expected to support four to ten times the number of species found at temperate latitudes.

It is this richness which fascinated the explorer naturalists of the 19th century, including Charles Darwin and Alfred R. Wallace, and triggered in their inventive minds, new and fundamental theories of biological evolution.

ECOSYSTEM DIVERSITY

Theory predicts and experience confirms that, within close geographical limits, natural undisturbed sites with similar environmental characters (in terms of climate, geology, topography, soils, etc.) will normally be inhabited by assemblages of plants and animals that show predictable resemblances, both in the species present and in the relative frequency of those species.

The term **ecosystem** is a name for this combination of living things together with their non-living habitat. The units of diversity at this level are therefore these consistent associations

Dysphania fenestra (Geometridae), one of approximately 10,000 moth species in Borneo.

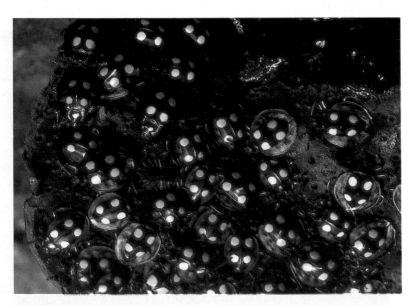

Eumorphus marginatus, a specialised fungus-eater, one beetle (Coleoptera) among thousands of species in Borneo.

or **communities** of species.

Observation shows that such communities are formed by natural processes in response to identifiable features of the environment. Sometimes these features are distinctive: for instance, a river bed, a cliff face or estuarine mud. In other cases, the critical features may be less obvious, and careful analysis of the distributions of species and an understanding of their ecological needs are necessary to estab-

Moths (Lepidoptera): numerous and diverse in the Belalong forest.

Caloptilia baringi

Moca auxobathra

Glanycus tricolor

Nemophora secisella

Syncratomorpha euthetodes

Ophiorrhabda quartaria

Twenty-nine species of Phasmida have been collected in the Belalong forest: *Anarchoides lyratus* (a male) was taken on Bukit Belalong .

Trees are the dominant form of plant life in tropical rainforests. At Belalong, trees extend from ridge to ridge.

On the west slope of the
Belalong valley, the total basal
area of trees of >10 cm dbh
occupied 40.79 sq m (0.41%)
of the 1 ha Plot AAU1.

lish ecosystem boundaries.

It is the aim of ecologists, by applying scientific methods, to recognise and describe the different communities. Such studies have been most intensively applied to plant communities. Because there is no formal evolutionary scheme against which to set a classification, the recognisable communities are arranged by ecological groupings rather than in a hierarchic system. It is usual to give these communities names, based on one, two or three of the most frequent species; code

letters and numbers may also be used. Each community or subcommunity is linked to geographic, **edaphic**, climatic or **biotic** factors on which it appears to be dependent. These are the units of an ecosystem classification.

In temperate regions, including Britain, description of vegetation types has provided an objective classification of forests or woodlands by which ecologists can make meaningful records of biodiversity at the ecosystem level. In this comparatively species-poor environment, the categorisation of forest

NUTRITION

From an ecological standpoint, living organisms can be grouped according to their mode of nutrition:

Autotrophs

These are organisms which manufacture the materials needed to live and grow from simple inorganic substances, utilising sunlight energy to fuel the process. In the key process, they make sugars from water and carbon dioxide, releasing oxygen as a waste product. The principal examples are plants in which green pigments, **chlorophylls**, act to capture light energy. Autotrophs are also able to synthesise complex proteins and fats. For this, they require simple mineral nutrients, such as phosphorus, nitrogen and potassium.

Saprophytes

Saprophytes lack the ability to synthesise certain key substances, including carbohydrates. They derive nutrition from dead organic material, like wood, twigs, leaves, animal remains or waste. Saprophytes normally release **enzymes** into the dead material and selectively re-absorb decomposed products. Saprophytes include many types of fungus, and a few vascular plants that lack chlorophyll.

Heterotrophs

This is the general name for organisms which cannot synthesise the materials they need to live and grow, and consequently have to derive these from other organisms, which may be autotrophs or other heterotrophs. Animals are heterotrophs, broadly divided among herbivores (which eat only plants), carnivores (which eat

WHAT IS A TREE?

By the term, **tree**, we mean a long-lived vascular plant which increases in size and stem thickness by the growth of woody tissue, and can (in favourable circumstances) achieve large stature. A tree would normally have a single main stem and be able to exceed 10 metres in height, whereas a woody **shrub** would be multi-stemmed and of lesser stature. Neither of these terms, tree or shrub, has taxonomic significance and it is sometimes difficult to decide whether a particular plant is a tree or a shrub. Indeed, many vascular plant families include some species that are trees, some that are shrubs and others that are short-lived, soft-stemmed **herbs**.

NICHE

The **niche** can be defined as the functional position of an organism in its environment, that is, the physical features of the place in which it lives, the periods of time in which it occurs and is active there, and the resources it obtains. It is a key concept in ecology (often called Gause's law) that two related species with identical niches cannot co-exist; one would inevitably oust the other. In the high species diversity of the tropical rainforest, does this rule apply?

other animals) and omnivores (which eat both plants and animals).

Parasites

Parasites include plants, fungi and animals that derive nutrition from other organisms which are known as the **hosts**. The host is harmed to some extent, but is not immediately killed - and may, indeed, survive for a normal expectation of life. Some fungi start as parasites, and become saprophytes when the host organism dies. Some higher plants lack the ability to produce chlorophyll and are obligatory parasites. *Rafflesia* is a well-known parasitic plant; less familiar is *Rhizanthes*, found in Belalong forest. Both are composed of a long-lived mass of tissue within the host, periodically producing external blooms. Others, notably the mistletoes such as dedalu (*Loranthus*), retain an external body of stem and leaves with photosynthetic ability and are attached by a root-like absorptive structure to a host, on which they depend for water and miner-als. These are called **hemi-parasites**. Some animal parasites live mainly outside the host's body, these are called **ectoparasites.** Others, such as intestinal worms or the microfilaria of blood, live within the host's body; these are **endoparasites**.

Symbiosis

Symbiosis is the term applied to two different organisms (**symbionts**) living together. Sometimes both derive benefit from this relationship, which can then be called **mutualism**. Lichens are remarkable examples. They appear to be one plant, but are an integral relationship between a fungus and an alga. In other symbiotic relationships, only one partner may be the principal beneficiary, while the other is not harmed; this is **commensalism**.

It may not be easy to distinguish between symbiosis, commensalism and parasitism in a relationship between organisms.

The hollow vestiges of a forest giant, now largely decomposed by the action of saprophytes and decomposers.

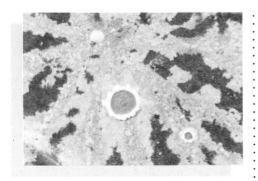

An encrusting lichen, a symbiont of alga and fungus.

and woodland vegetation types can take account of all plants in the community, large and small: tree, shrub, herb, moss or lichen.

In the species-rich tropical environment, ecological work has been led by foresters and, as we shall see, they have produced a classification of vegetation types based largely on trees.

ECOLOGY OF ECOSYSTEMS

The populations of species of an ecosystem are interdependent with one another and with the non-living environment, through an immensely complex network of interactions. The functional position of any individual (and, by extrapolation, the species of which it is a member) is termed its **niche**.

Fundamental processes include the flow of energy through the system via food chains and food webs, and the cycling of nutrients. The initial step is the extraction of gaseous carbon-dioxide from the atmosphere and its chemical combination with water, within the cells of green plants, to produce carbohydrate which is incorporated in the living matter of the plant. Plants that obtain nutrition by this means are known as **autotrophs.**

Autotrophic green plants thrive, grow and die, whereupon the processes of decay and decomposition return carbon dioxide to the environment. In many cases, however, these plants are fed upon by animals which digest the plant matter to provide nourishment for themselves.

Plant-eating animals are known as **primary consumers**. These animals may be fed upon by others, the **secondary consumers**, which in turn may fall prey to other animals (**tertiary consumers**) and so on.

This succession is termed a **food chain**, but real life is rarely so straightforward and most animals prey and are preyed upon as elements of an intricate **food web.**

More complicated interactions include symbiosis and parasitism. After death, another group of organisms, the **saprophytes** and **decomposers** break down the dead matter once again, to simpler components which are available to be recycled.

Other nutrients are obtained from the non-living environment. Essential elements, including metallic ions and phosphorus, are derived from soil minerals. The earth's main reserves of nitrogen are in the atmosphere. This can

A rainstorm sweeps across the Belalong valleys.

be converted to usable form (nitrate ions) under natural circumstances by electrical discharges during thunderstorms. Nowadays, the burning of fossil fuels (oil or coal) in power stations or motor engines, is a major source of air-borne nitrate. Rain is naturally slightly acidic, due to the presence of carbonate ions. It also carries dissolved nitrogen (as nitrate) and sulphur; these are plant nutrients and are subsequently transported in the flow of ground or surface-waters. In addition, some plants, by association with bacteria, are capable of fixing gaseous nitrogen directly from the atmosphere.

Other bacteria in the soil break down dead nitrogenous organic matter and thereby release gaseous nitrogen and return it to the atmosphere.

In similar ways, there is a multitude of processes by which carbon and other mineral nutrients are brought into, cycled and exported from the ecosystem.

A fundamental step, indispensable to all these processes, is the capture of energy from sunlight by the operation of photosynthesis in the tissue of green plants. These autotrophs comprise the bulk of living matter in the forest.

To understand the origin of high tropical biodiversity we need to look first at the green plants of the rainforest ecosystem at Belalong.

The belt of ru laut (*Casuarina equisetifolia*) fringes the sandy shore of Brunei Darussalam.

CHAPTER 6

TROPICAL RAINFOREST FORMATIONS

To study the characteristics of biodiversity, it is important to discover how many species occur in a particular place, and to investigate the links between species and particular environments. We must search for regular associations between species and discover the factors that limit the distributions of species. In tropical regions, forest ecologists have been able to establish a broad classification of tree communities, or **forest formations.** Work carried out in Sarawak and Brunei Darussalam has led to a practical classification of major formations, matching field experience.

A forest formation can be related to one or more features of its location, notably soil quality, aspect and elevation. For instance, on the open, sandy coasts of Brunei, the **Beach Forest** group contains four types according to site and successional stage: Ru laut (*Casuarina equisetifolia*), a narrow belt fringing the shore; Mixed Beach Forest, on dry soils behind the shore line;

The margin of the Mangal in the Temburong estuary is marked by a line of bakau (*Rhizophora*) seedlings.

FOREST FORMATIONS IN BRUNEI DARUSSALAM

This general classification recognises seven major forest formations, each with subdivisions based on predominant representative species.

1. **Beach Forest**
   - Ru laut (*Casuarina equisetifolia*) Forest
   - Mixed Beach Forest
   - Nibung (*Oncosperma*) Forest
   - Beach Scrub

2. **Mangal** (Mangrove) **Forest**
   - Pedada (*Sonneratia*) Forest
   - Api-api (*Avicennia*) Forest
   - Bakau (*Rhizophora*) Forest
   - Nyireh (*Xylocarpus*)/Berus or Linggadai (*Bruguiera*) Forest
   - Nipah *(Nypa)* swamp
   - Nibung (*Oncosperma*) swamp

3. **Peatswamp Forest**
   - Ramin (*Gonostylus*)/Jongkong (*Dactylocladus*) Forest
   - Terentang (*Campnosperma*)/Pulai (*Alstonia*) Forest
   - Meranti (*Shorea* sp.)/Pulai Forest
   - Alan (*Shorea albida*) Forest
   - Alan Bunga (*Shorea albida*) Forest
   - Padang Alan Forest
   - Padang Paya Pole Forest

4. **Riparian Forests**
   - Brackish-water Forest
   - Freshwater tidal Forest
   - Gallery Forest: ensurai (*Dipterocarpus oblongifolius*)/gapis (*Saraca)*
   - Alluvial (*Octomeles*) Forest

Mangal is a forest formation of mangrove trees growing on the tidal mudflats.

5. Mixed Dipterocarp Forests
• Lowland Mixed Dipterocarp Forests

a. Humult (humus-rich) soils
    Sandstone or clay
	b. Udult (humus-poor) soils
	    Clays or shales

Kapur peringgi (*Dryobalanops aromatica*) assn.	Meranti sarang punai (*Shorea parvifolia*) assn.
Slope & Valley Meranti raya (*Shorea flemmichii*) assn.	Hill-slope, Kapur paji (*Dryobalanops lanceolata*) assn.

} Lowland Forests

• Hill Dipterocarp Forests

Hill Bencaloi (*Anisoptera grossivenia*) assn.	Ridge Keruing merah (*Dipterocarpus verrucosus*) assn.

• Upper Dipterocarp Forest ⎤
          High ridge (*Shorea coriacea*) assn. ⎤ Lower
                                                Montane
• Oak/Laurel (Mixed) Forest ⎦   Forest
• Montane ericaceous   ⊢ Upper Montane Forest ⎦

6. Heath Forests
• Lowland Heath Forests
   Kerapah (impeded drainage)
   Kerangas (free-draining)
      a. Tolong (*Agathis*) Forest (deep soil)
      b. Resak (*Cotylelobium lanceolatum*) Forest (shallow soil)
• Hill Kerangas
• Upper Kerangas
• Escarpment/ridge-top Kerangas

7. Secondary Forests (belukar)

> Derived from P S Ashton (1964. *Oxford Forestry Memoirs*, 25), E F Bruenig (1969. *Malayan Forester* 32 2, 143-179), Anderson & Marsden Ltd (1988. *Brunei forest resources & strategy planning study*), in consultation with P S Ashton.

Nibung (*Oncosperma*) Forest, on unconsolidated, moist sites; Beach Scrub, on rocky outcrops.

MANGAL

Another group of forest formations are those associated with coastal and estuarine muddy soils, the **mangal** or mangrove communities. These are poor in tree species but constant in occurrence throughout the Sunda Shelf region of which Brunei is a part.

Along the sheltered muddy shores of Brunei Bay, Mangal Forest is well developed and shows pronounced ecosystem zonation related to the character of the substrate, tidal levels and degree of salinity.

Four formations are constant in Brunei mangals. The open flats are

Nipah palms form a dense stand bordering the Temburong estuary where the heads of nibung palms are silhouetted on the skyline.

colonised by a pioneer community in which pedada (*Sonneratia*) or api-api (*Avicennia*) dominate. The middle zone from mid-tidal level (mean sea level) is dominated by the stilt-rooted bakau (*Rhizophora*), and the higher, less frequently inundated zone by a mix of nyireh (*Xylocarpus*) with berus or linggadai *(Bruguiera)*. The Bakau also lines the banks of the seaward river channels.

Where the salinity is reduced by fresh water, at the inland margin of the mangal and along tidal riverine stretches, swamp forests develop: either Nipah swamp, dominated by the stemless palm, nipah, or, on the landward edge reached by sea-water only at the higher tides, by Nibung swamp, a transitional community in which the nibung palm raises its aery head above a viciously thorny trunk.

PEATSWAMP FOREST

Further inland, behind these coastal forest formations, where the land is low-lying and hence poorly drained, freshwater **Peatswamp Forests** form the natural climax vegetation. These forests developed on land that was formerly mangal. From about 11,000 years ago, as sea levels rose, the coastline advanced and the landward margin of the mangrove became less saline. The mangal was then replaced, first by the Terentang/Pulai forest and later by the Alan Forest, Alan Bunga Forest, Padang Alan Forest and lastly the Padang Paya Pole Forest. The surface of the Peatswamp Forest has built

Api-api (*Avicennia*) forms the seaward zone of some areas of the mangal.

An aerial view of the mangal forest of the lower Temburong river shows the zonation in response to tidal levels and salinity. The side creek is bordered by a dense fringe of nipah.

Alan Bunga Forest in which the dipterocarp tree alan (*Shorea albida*) forms nearly pure stands.

Alan Forest; the giant alan (*Shorea albida*) trees are often hollow and with stag-headed crowns.

up over at least 4,500 years into a convex dome of peat, as much as 20 m deep, in the centre of the largest swamps and with plants of its central portion isolated from all external sources of water and nutrients, other than those obtained from rainwater.

The different forest types show a concentric zonation, with Ramin and Terentang towards the margin of the swamp, and the sequence culminating in the very stunted Padang Paya Pole Forest, with a canopy height of only 10-12 m, in the centre. The forest at the swamp margins is of far greater stature and Alan Bunga Forest includes some of the tallest trees in the tropics, at nearly 80 m high. Unlike most other lowland tropical forests, which consist of a large number of tree species, each with few individuals, the Peatswamp Forest, particularly Alan Forest, Alan Bunga Forest and Padang Alan Forest, have a single species, the alan (*Shorea albida*), dominating the community. This is well developed in Belait District where large areas of this forest and its unique composition make it a significant timber resource, second only to the Mixed Dipterocarp Forest in importance. The Peatswamp Forest has been much studied in parts of Sarawak, where nine or more types have been recognised.

RIPARIAN FOREST

The river journey from Brunei Bay up the Temburong to Bangar gives fleeting views of **Riparian** (river bank) **Forest**, across the transition from brackish to freshwater tidal reaches. Nipah, dominant in the brackish water zone, becomes scarce some distance before Bangar town is reached. In many places, human activity has altered the natural community, but in a brief stretch key indicator species of the Freshwater Tidal community appear: notably rasau or screwpine (*Pandanus*), with putat (*Barringtonia*), perius-perius (*Elaeocarpus*), simpur (*Dillenia*) and kasai (*Pometia pinnata*).

Along the Temburong river upstream of Kampong Batang Duri, the natural vegetation of the riparian fringe is Gallery Forest, dominated by huge ensurai (*Dipterocarpus oblongifolius*) trees, which overhang the river. Much of this gallery forest below the Forest Reserve boundary has been cleared for shifting cultivation, but along the river bank smaller members of this association can still be seen: simpur, kasai and ubah (*Eugenia*), with tufted white blossoms, attractive to nectarivorous bats. Above the river junction at Kuala Belalong, Gallery Forest survives in its pristine glory. Huge ensurai and other trees arch over the course of the Sungai Belalong. Flanking the river on either side and extending into the tributary

Stilt roots are developed by trees of several different genera to provide support on unstable waterlogged substrates, in Mangal (as shown) or in freshwater Swamp Forest.

Alluvial forest beside Sungai Temburong,
the ground largely bare of herbs and
trees of small size.

Rasau, the pandan, appears among other
riparian vegetation on the bank of the tidal
Temburong, below Bangar town.

Stilt roots provide support in the muddy
conditions of alluvial forest.

Huge ensurai trees (*Dipterocarpus oblongifolius*)
overhang Sungai Temburong.

The golden yellow blossom of gapis (*Saraca*).

The big pinnate leaf of kasai (*Pometia pinnata*),
a characteristic tree of riparian forest,
pink in colour when young.

The rippled leaves of langkap or aping (*Arenga undulatifolia*) are conspicuous in riparian forest flanking Sungai Belalong.

valleys are narrow bands of riparian forest in which gapis (*Saraca*) is a prominent waterside tree. Another conspicuous member of the association is the langkap, or aping, palm (*Arenga undulatifolia*), easily identified by its corrugated leaves.

ALLUVIAL FOREST

Alluvial forest develops on flat land beside the river meanders; it is usually limited in extent, with deposits of fine-grain silt and mud preventing the development of any extensive ground cover. The development of stilt roots, knee roots and sinuous plank buttresses by various tree species is characteristic, as is the generally open nature of the forest. At Belalong, alluvial forest is uncommon, due to the generally steep gorges through which the major rivers flow. It is only found beside the lower reaches of the Sungai Temburong.

HEATH FOREST

Heath Forests are more species-rich than the mangrove associations. Heath forests in different places show physiognomic resemblances but not necessarily any close similarity in spe-

Plots 01 and 02 were established
on the East Ridge.

Curation of voucher specimens, collected
by tree-climbing.

cies composition. All heath forests grow on nutrient-poor, acidic soils. Not frequently found at Belalong, the only examples are small patches of Hill Kerangas, on the higher ridges leading up to the Bukit Belalong area.

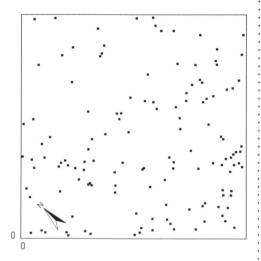

The distribution of the 28 species (133 individuals) of dipterocarp trees above 10 cm dbh in Plot AAU1.

MIXED DIPTEROCARP FOREST

The trend to high species diversity in humid tropical regions is expressed most strikingly in interior forests and on better soils. In this environment there is a gradient of changing species composition with aspect, slope and, especially, with altitude reflecting related changes in environmental variables, such as rainfall, exposure and temperature. Across the continents of the tropical world, these interior rainforests consist of very different assemblages of species of disparate origins. Nonetheless, there are recognisable similarities in overall appearance, and forest ecologists have subdivided the altitudinally limited forests into Low-

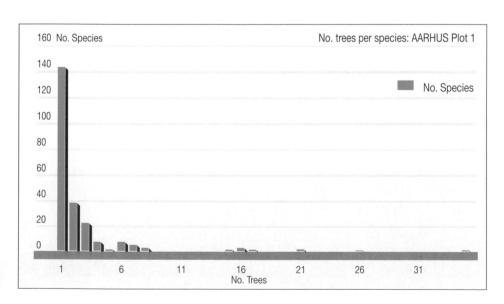

Species frequency histogram for Plot AAU1.

THE ASHTON TRAIL

Peter S. Ashton worked in Brunei forests as a graduate student in the 1960s. He has since spent much of the rest of his life investigating the underlying ecology of the rainforest, its biodiversity and its dynamics. His name and one of his first study plots are preserved in the Ashton Trail at Kuala Belalong Field Studies Centre.

Pelawan (*Tristania*) on the Ashton trail.

land, Lower Montane and Upper Montane formations.

In the Sunda region, trees of the family Dipterocarpaceae predominate to a marked degree in the local representatives of the Lowland and Lower Montane formations. These are there-

Ridge on ridge, the Belalong river system is vegetated by continuous forest.

In the Belalong forest.

fore known as **Mixed Dipterocarp Forests**. At Belalong, we see a pristine example. Three lowland 1 ha sample plots have been enumerated at Belalong: Plot 01 and Plot 02 by Sylvester Tan Kheng San of the Sarawak Forest Department and Plot AAU1 by Ivan Neilsen, Henrik Balslev and Axel Dalberg Poulsen of Aarhus University. In these three plots, dipterocarps accounted for 17% (Plot 01), 13% (Plot 02) and 24% (Plot AAU1) of all trees above a standard minimum diameter of 10 cm.

The botanical interest of dipterocarp forests has attracted much scientific research. Their commercial importance has prompted widespread survey and study, directed predominantly towards forestry management and maximising timber potential.

In the Belalong forest, the taxonomic composition of three 1 ha plots of lowland Mixed Dipterocarp Forest was as follows: Plot 01, 592 trees, 42 Families; Plot 02, 656 trees, 41 Families; Plot AAU1, 550 trees of 43 Families, represented by 231 species.

Elsewhere in the region, larger plots have shown that, as the sampling area enlarges, the number of species also increases. At Bukit Raya, Sarawak, 711 tree species (>10 cm dbh) were enumerated in a set of plots cumulatively totalling 6.6 ha; a 22.3 ha (50 acre) plot in Jengka Forest Reserve, Peninsular Malaysia, contained 337 species (> 28 cm dbh); and a 50 ha plot at

Pasoh, also in Peninsular Malaysia, contained some 830 species of trees (> 1 cm dbh).

This high diversity involves large numbers of rare species. In the 1 ha Belalong Plot AAU1, 143 species were represented by single individuals (62% of all species). In the much larger plot at Jengka, there were still 38% of species which were represented by single trees, and only three species represented by 20 or more individuals.

Species richness (termed **alpha diversity**) of this striking degree has challenged forest ecologists. For instance, the counterpart of tropical species richness is the rarity of individual representatives of those species. How are commonness or rarity controlled? What controls the genetical diversity of species in an ecosystem? How does diversity relate to the survival of species in ecosystems, and the persistence of ecosystems themselves?

Within the Lowland Mixed Dipterocarp formation, detailed comparisons of forests in Brunei and Sarawak have failed to identify subcommunities, other than a broad division based on soil types. This separates forests on soils classified by the US Dept. of Agriculture system as udult ultisols (acrisols in the FAO classification. See Chapter 4) from those on

Treefall is frequent at Belalong where storms bring strong gusts of wind. Slopes are steep and unstable, landslips are commonplace and tree root systems are largely superficial.

humult (humic) ultisols. Soils of the first type are generally rich in clay, with relatively high surface pH, while the latter have a surface horizon of raw humus and generally lower pH (3.5 - 4.1), low mineral clay and low nutrient concentrations. Peter Ashton has found that forests on udult soils are more uniform in species composition than those on humults.

There is still no final explanation for species richness in tropical forests. Some ecologists assume that the selective processes operating in temperate

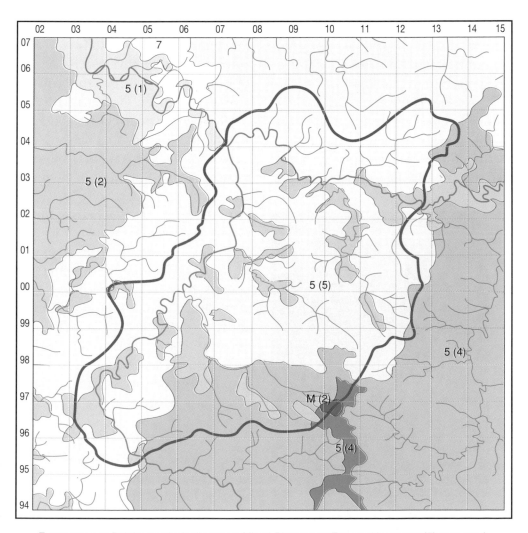

Forest types at Belalong: principally type **5** Mixed Dipterocarp Forest with stratum **(5)** over much of the area, **(2)** in the tributary valleys of the Belalong and Temburong, succeeded by **(4)** on the upper slopes and extending into **M** Montane Forest, strata **(4)** on the summit ridge and **(2)** at the summit of Bukit Belalong itself. Small patches of Secondary Forest, type **7** are seen in the northwest, alongside Sungai Belalong, together with some Dipterocarp Forest of stratum **(1).**
(Refer to pp.92 and 108)

ecosystems are applicable. If this is so, a forest tree community, in terms of floristic composition and the relative abundance of species, will be predictable in terms of the non-living habitat and therefore constant over long periods (the equilibrium model). Others hold that the local composition of species at any given time and place is the mixed consequence of the opportunities for immigration and accidents of extinction (non-equilibrium).

All explanations stress the dynamic nature of the forest environment, in which the incidence and severity of disturbance – through windfall or landslide, for example – is criti-

The bases of trees are covered with mosses and ferns near the summit of Bukit Belalong .

cal. We must accept that in this environment there is intense competition for space, nutrients and light.

Peter Ashton's work in Brunei and Sarawak suggests that species richness is primarily determined by physical resources of the environment and is enhanced by small scale **heterogeneity** in factors that are limiting to survival and growth. On soils with high nutrient content, diversity reflects the frequency and scale of gap formation in the tree cover. On soils with relatively low nutrient content, notably where phosphorus is scarce (soil concentrations below 200 ppm) and magnesium low (<1,200 ppm), then species richness is positively correlated with the latter. Diversity is maximal at about these values; at higher levels it becomes negatively correlated with both nutrients, that is, on richer soils species diversity is reduced.

Other factors that may contribute to diversity operate during the early stages of a tree's life cycle. Host-specific seed predation may lead to low population densities, thus allowing many otherwise ecologically competitive species to co-exist.

Over wide ranges throughout Borneo, certain tree species are consistently the most abundant in any comparable forest. Differences in the composition of tree communities on different soils largely reflect the occurrence of rare species. The presence of compatible mycorrhizae may also be influential (See Chapter 9).

TIMBER RESOURCES OF BELALONG

Commercial foresters are more concerned with forests as found on the ground than with ecological theories. Their surveys itemise the timber resource in terms of large trees of economically important species or species groups. For pragmatic reasons, they need to simplify the process of categorisation. A survey of the forest resources of Brunei Darussalam recognised five **strata**, determined by canopy features seen in aerial photography. The classification also took note of four terrain classes, from I (flat to gently undulating slope generally less than 15°), through II (slope 15-24°), III (slope 25-35°), to IV (very steep terrain; average slopes in excess of 35°).

In the Belalong forest, according to this classification, in the three Mixed Dipterocarp Forest strata, (2), (4) and (5) (See p. 108), meranti sarang punai *(Shorea parvifolia)* was the most frequent timber-tree species, averaging 12.5% of all such trees.

Ranking second or third in strata (4) and (5) were kapur paji *(Dryobalanops lanceolata)* / meranti majau = selangan pelanduk *(Shorea leptoclados)*, and fourth was mengaris *(Koompassia excelsa)*. It is noteworthy that two of these four species are those used in the classification of Mixed Dipterocarp Forest. When the comparison is extended to cover the ten species contributing the most in volumetric terms to each strata, differences in the community composition begin to appear. (Refer to p.108).

Comparison of species composition of more distantly separated plots within Mixed Dipterocarp Forest are given by detailed samples taken in 1964 by P. S. Ashton, in his pioneering eco-

107

Nepenthes tentaculata, one of the upland pitcher plants on Bukit Belalong.

FOREST STRATA

Forest strata, as used in the classification of Mixed Dipterocarp Forest and Montane Forest in the Batu Apoi Forest Reserve (after Anderson & Marsden).

Stratum	Characteristics
(0)	Unforested.
(1)	Dense even, or semi-open, canopy of mainly small crowned trees.
(2)	Canopy uneven, or moderately open; some medium or large emergents.
(3)	Dense even canopy of medium crowns.
(4)	Dense uneven canopy, of medium sized and large crowns.
(5)	Dense uneven canopy, mainly large crowns.

IMPORTANT SPECIES

The ten volumetrically most important species within each of the three sampled strata of Mixed Dipterocarp Forest in the Batu Apoi Forest Reserve:

Vernacular name	Botanical name	Strata Rank order (2)	(4)	(5)
Meranti sarang punai	*Shorea parvifolia*	1	1	1
Kapur paji	*Dryobalanops lanceolata*	11	3	2
Meranti majau	*Shorea leptoclados*	4	2	3
Kumus	*Shorea laevis*	8	4	4
Mengaris (Tualang)	*Koompassia excelsa*	2	6	6
Urat mata	*Parashorea smythiesii*	3	12	5
Meranti menalit	*Shorea ferruginea*	15	5	10
Kempas	*Koompassia malaccensis*	46	7	9
Meranti melantai	*Shorea macroptera*	7	33	6
Kapur bukit	*Dryobalanops beccarii*	56=	22	8
Meranti binatuh	*Shorea argentifolia*	5	15	13
Nemesu	*Shorea pauciflora*	9	17	13
Meranti paya	*Shorea platyclados*	-	10	19
Selangan batu padi	*Shorea obscura*	-	9	21=
Selangan merah bukit	*Shorea flaviflora*	26	8	33=
Selangan batu tulang ikan	*Shorea superba*	6	-	32
Nyatoh	Sapotaceae	10	-	80=

[Adapted from Anderson & Marsden Ltd 1988. *Brunei forest resources & strategy planning study*. Unpublished report].

Upper pitcher of *Nepenthes lowii*, only found on the highest peaks of Bukit Retak and Gunung Pagon in Brunei.

logical studies. All trees exceeding 12 inches girth at breast height (10 cm dbh) were enumerated in two sets of fifty 0.41 ha (1 acre) plots. One set was in Andalau Forest Reserve, and the other above Kuala Belalong, extending along the axial ridge running south from the river junction, now known as Jalan Tengah. Ashton, found 760 tree species in his plots, 472 at Andalau and 420 at Kuala Belalong, with only 132 species occurring in both areas. [Ashton, P.S. 1964. Ecological Studies in the Mixed Dipterocarp forests of Brunei State. *Oxford Forestry Memoirs* No. 25].

The most spectacular trees in Mixed Dipterocarp Forest are the towering giants, with spreading buttresses and stupendous columnar trunks. In Belalong forest, such large trees (exceeding 40 cm dbh) amounted to 59 /

592 (10%) in Plot 1 and 69 / 657 (10.5%) in Plot 2. Along the ridge plotted by Ashton, mean numbers for 2.1 ha (5 acre) sectors lie in the range 16 – 43, averaging 7.7–20.8 giant trees per hectare. Peter Ashton found that six species, all dipterocarps, were the most abundant in one or more of these sectors, but none of these six exceeded 12.2% in relative abundance.

MONTANE FORESTS

With increasing altitude the climate becomes progressively cooler and more moist. These changes are reflected by changes in the forest, with tropical lowland forests of massive trees with large buttresses and high canopies being progressively replaced by forests of smaller trees of lower stature.

In short facies montane forest, the boulders and tree trunks are covered with mosses and ferns.

In the Batu Apoi Forest Reserve there is no sudden transition from Mixed Dipterocarp Forest to Montane Forest, which develops at an altitude of between 700 and 900 m, according to topography. Two, or possibly three types of Lower Montane Forest can be recognised in Batu Apoi Forest Reserve. A dipterocarp-dominated forest in which a meranti (*Shorea coriacea*) is a major component, develops on ridges with shallow white sandy soils. In some areas in the south of the reserve, tolong (*Agathis dammara*) forms almost pure stands of limited extent; this is usually considered to be a type of Upper Kerangas Forest. However, most Lower Montane Forest in Batu Apoi is of the Oak-Laurel type, which lacks a dominant species, but in which the oaks (*Quercus, Lithocarpus*), Sapotaceae and *Podocarpus neriifolius* are significant components. Laurels (Lauraceae), while present, are of less importance than in other comparable forests in South East Asia.

Upper Montane Forest develops at altitudes between 1,000 m (on ridges and knolls) and 1,200 m (on broader ridges). Two facies can be distinguished. Tall facies montane forest consists of small trees with a canopy height of 10-15 m; important species include a sempili (*Dacrydium beccarii*), celery pine (*Phyllocladus hypophyllus*) and the true oak (*Quercus percoriacea*). Short facies

Montane Forest includes similar species growing as gnarled and bushy shrubs on peat-covered soils in exposed situations. Ericaceous shrubs (*Rhododendron* spp. and *Vaccinium* spp.) and pitcher plants (*Nepenthes* spp., including *Nepenthes lowii* and *Nepenthes stenophylla*) are noticeable components.

Although most of the Lower Montane or Upper Montane Forest types are not dipterocarp-dominated, they have been included under Mixed Dipterocarp Forests in the classification table to emphasise the continuity between the forest types and increasing altitude. A strict demarcation between Upper Dipterocarp and Oak/Laurel Forest does not exist as the change is usually rather gradual.

Apart from changes in species composition, there is a very definite change in the physiognomy of the forest with increasing altitude. As indicated, the forest becomes of smaller stature, but there is also a concomitant decrease in biomass of the forest as a whole. Leaves become smaller, tougher and more leathery and there is a very noticeable increase in the number and range of epiphytes, especially of mosses, liverworts and ferns.

The Upper Montane Forest, in particular, is extremely rich in bryophytes with both the ground and the trees smothered in long skeins of trailing moss – a feature which has led to its often being called 'moss forest' or 'elfin' woodland.

In the Belalong forest, changes in the structure are evident as the path ascends towards Bukit Belalong, with the trees becoming shorter, buttresses rarer and mosses and other epiphytes increasing in number. On the summit ridge of Bukit Belalong, Oak-Laurel forest predominates, with some small areas on the knolls more comparable to Upper Montane (tall facies) Forest. At 913 m, Bukit Belalong is too low to permit the development of short-facies Montane Forest, but the continuity of the forest types from Lowland Mixed Dipterocarp to Lower Montane make it an ideal subject for further study.

In Upper Montane Forest the moss thickly clothes the tree boles above the height of a man.

In its wild state the sealing wax palm, pinang laka (*Cyrtostachys renda*), grows in coastal and swamp forests of Brunei.

CHAPTER 7

TREES AND WOODY SHRUBS

Within the great variation of life-forms among forest plants, we can recognise taxonomic divisions and also functional groupings. The term **synusia** has been applied to these functional groups. Among green plants, two major divisions have been drawn between mechanically independent plants, comprising trees, woody shrubs and herbs; and mechanically dependent plants, comprising climbers, stranglers and epiphytes (including some hemiparasites). Some plant Families include members of several synusiae: thus, aroids (Araceae) include herbs, climbers and epiphytes. Others are restricted to one: the dipterocarps, for example, are all trees. Some single genera, such as figs (*Ficus*) are very variable. Clearly, these groupings are of little or no taxonomic significance. Their importance lies in the way they illustrate the complex physical structure of the tropical rainforest.

Of the mechanically independent plants, trees and shrubs comprise the bulk of the forest and this synusia forms the subject of this chapter.

In tropical rainforest true shrubs (profusely branching low woody plants with many growing tips) are rare, their place being taken by small tree-like plants with **monopodial** branching. Many of these treelets grow very slowly in the low light of the

Blossoms of the hemiparasite *Aeschynanthus* (Gesneriaceae).

understorey, where they flower and fruit; others are the arrested juveniles of the forest giants.

The variation in form of trees and treelets is extremely broad; the present review concentrates only on a few of the more important groups in the Belalong forest.

MONOCOTYLEDONS

Monocotyledons are defined as a subclass of flowering plants having a single embryonic seed leaf, leaves with parallel veins, and flowers with parts in threes. The group includes grasses, lilies, palms and orchids.

PALMS

The palms (Family Arecaceae) form a large, diverse and very ancient group of the subclass of monocotyledons, of mostly tropical and subtropical distribution. At present, about 2,700 species are recognised. The greatest diversity in number of species and growth forms occurs in the rainforests of South and Central America, and from South East Asia to the West Pacific. Many palms have useful products, and they

Biru (*Licuala*), the beautiful fan palms of the undergrowth.

The fishtail palms (*Caryota*) take their name from the irregular triangular form of the leaflets.

The undulant leaflets of aping or langkap (*Arenga undulatifolia*).

Aping or langkap (*Arenga undulatifolia*) is conspicuous along the riverbanks.

The crown of the wild sago palm, luba or pantu' (*Eugeissona utilis*), rears above the ridge forest.

The palms of Belalong include more than half of those known in Brunei. The most important absences are palms of coastal and peatswamp forests, extreme kerangas habitats and montane forest, habitats that do not occur within this forest. The majestic fan palm (*Borassodendron borneense*) has not yet been found at Belalong, although it occurs not far away on low hills near Selapon.

The fan palms are represented by three species of biru (*Licuala*), exquisitely photogenic palms of the forest undergrowth, with unmistakable wedge-shaped leaflets.

More diverse and variable are the feather palms. Of these, one group is characterised by scaly fruits and, usually, spiny leaves. The rattans belong to this group; so do salak (*Salacca*) and pantu' or luba (*Eugeissona utilis*), the wild Bornean sago that forms the staple for the Penan people. Salak is mainly confined to the bottom of swampy valleys and stream sides, where the thorny fronds are notable. Pantu' is abundant on well drained, poor soils, on ridge tops and steep slopes, including the summit ridges of Bukit Belalong. The massive leaves, armed with vicious black spines, and the robust flowering spires that terminate the growth of individual stems, are distinctive.

Rattans abound: 49 different species have been found, varying from robust climbers that reach the forest canopy to

The flowering stem of pantu' accumulates a store of edible starch. After flowering the fruit is set and the stem dies.

The viciously thorny leaf bases of salak (*Salacca*).

short-stemmed plants of the undergrowth. Most rattans are armed with barbed whips that act as aids to climbing. It is these that form occasional impenetrable entanglements in the undergrowth.

The fishtail and sugar palms, distinguished by their jagged-margined leaflets, are represented in the Belalong forest by mudur (*Caryota*) with doubly-pinnate leaves and aping (*Arenga*). *Arenga undulatifolia* is common along the banks of Sungai Temburong and Sungai Belalong, and is conspicuous with its large dull green leaves and leaflets with striking wavy margins. In marked contrast, *Arenga distincta* and *Arenga borneensis* are small palms of the forest undergrowth with slender reed-like stems and small fish-tailed leaflets.

Also found is the massive tree palm, nibung (*Oncosperma horridum*), which is immediately recognisable by its hideously spiny trunk and spiny green crownshaft of leaf-sheaths. The growing point or "cabbage" (umbut) of nibung makes good eating and hunters in the forest have taken their toll, even in the remote areas.

The most frequent thornless palms of the forest undergrowth are the wild pinang (*Pinanga*), richly represented at Belalong. One of the first palms to be encountered at Kuala Belalong is *Pinanga tenella* var. *tenella*, a beautiful small clustering palm that grows along the banks of the main rivers. This palm is a rheophyte, a plant growing within the flood zone of a river and adapted to withstand the effects of flowing water. The narrow leathery leaflets present little resistance to water current and the densely clustering behaviour allows the plant to replace any stems damaged by the turbulence of high water levels.

Other species of *Pinanga* tend to occur as scattered individuals. Perhaps the most unusual species is *Pinanga veitchii*, immediately distinguishable by the astonishing colour of its juvenile leaves which are strongly mottled dark and pale liver-coloured, and purplish on the undersurface.

The related genus *Areca* is represented in the Belalong area by a single species, *A. minuta*, a very small thornless palm of the undergrowth which, when not in flower, could easily be misidentified as a species of *Pinanga*. However, when flowering, the fact that female flowers are restricted to the base of the inflorescence, rather than throughout, as in *Pinanga*, allows easy identification.

The bright red fruits of a small pinang (*Pinanga*) on Bukit Belalong are borne at the base of the plant.

are widely cultivated. The important cultivated species, such as coconut (*Cocos nucifera*), the betel palm, pinang (*Areca catechu*), the oil palm, kelapa sawit (*Elaeis guineensis*) and the sago palm (*Metroxylon sagu*) are all grown in Brunei Darussalam. Most palms planted along roadsides or in gardens are of foreign origin; only the fishtail, mudur belukar (*Caryota mitis*) and sealing wax palm, pinang laka (*Cyrtostachys renda*) have been successfully taken into cultivation from local sources.

The wild palms of Brunei provide a good representation of a rich Sunda regional flora. All are plants of forest (including mangal). Few seem capable of tolerating severe disturbance and, as a consequence, few are naturally found in secondary growth. For instance, any tall palms left standing in farm clearings may produce fruit, but no regeneration takes place in the cleared land. One unusual palm, the nipah (*Nypa fruticans*), has adapted to the demanding environment of brackish water coastal habitats; its huge leaves rise from a branching stem which creeps over the mangrove mud.

The central ridge and margins of the long pandan leaf carry recurved spines.

PANDANS

There are some 700 species of pandans or screw-pines (Pandanaceae), distributed throughout the Old World tropics from Africa to Oceania, about 600 species within the genus *Pandanus*. Their habitats range from the mari-

Pandans are recognised by their long, strap-shaped leaves, arranged spirally on the stem.

The epiphytic pandan, *Freycinetia*, forms large clumps on the boles of forest trees.

A bamboo clump (*Schizostachyum* sp.) on the river bank.

time strand to the rainforest, where they are numerous and diverse, and include epiphytes, climbers and free-standing plants, often with prominent stilt roots. The leaves are elongated and strap-like, arranged spirally on the stem and bearing recurved spines on the margins and the median ridge.

BAMBOOS

Bamboos (subfamily Bambusoideae of the grass Family, Poaceae) share common features with the grasses, such as flower structure. Bamboos are distinguished by their size and woody growth and, for this reason, are placed here among shrubs rather than herbs.

Flowering spikes of *Schizostachyum*.

BAMBOOS OF BELALONG

Four species of bamboos have been found growing wild in the Belalong forest: *Schizostachyum latifolium*, not common, an erect bamboo with slender culms of 1- 2 cm in diameter with drooping tips. This bamboo occurs widely in Brunei, Sabah and Sarawak (Malaysia). *Schizostachyum* aff. *brachycladum*, found growing along the banks of Sungai Belalong and also in villages of the lower Temburong, is an erect bamboo with moderately large leaf blades. *Dinochloa* (related to *D. trichogona*), a climbing bamboo grows in the forest. Fourth, a previously undescribed species belonging to a new genus, is a scrambling bamboo not yet found outside the Temburong region. This grows along river banks and on hillsides up to Bukit Belalong.

The graceful branches of the new Temburong bamboo overhang the Sungai Belalong.

The leaves and inflorescence of the Temburong bamboo.

A bamboo plant has no central trunk but consists of a ramifying system which can be differentiated as **rhizome**, **culm** and **branches**. Each part is divided into segments, marked by nodes and internodes. Each internode is enveloped by a sheath originating from the node. These enveloping sheaths are alternate at successive nodes.

The rhizome is generally subterranean and forms the foundation of the bamboo plant. The culm is the main axis of the plant above ground. It is usually hollow between the nodes; in some *Dinochloa* species it is solid. Many bamboos have erèct, straight culms with pendulous tips. Some have scrambling culms; in these, the internodes are usually long with thin walls. Branches are many at each node, so that the culms cannot support them-

The crowns of trees of the Mixed Dipterocarp Forest form a closed canopy, the only part of the forest subjected to the full intensity of incident sunlight. The canopy breaks the fall of raindrops and is battered and buffeted by the winds that sweep through these valleys.

selves, but need to lean on trees or scramble between trees. Some, such as *Dinochloa*, have climbing culms.

DICOTYLEDONS

Dicotyledons are defined as flowering plants having two embryonic seed leaves.

THE DIPTEROCARPS

The tree Family of dipterocarps (Dipterocarpaceae) is pan-tropical in distribution but best represented in Asia, with 12 genera comprising some 470 species. The greatest diversity of dipterocarps is in Borneo, with 267 species in all, consisting of members of the genera *Anisoptera* (5 species), *Cotylelobium* (3), *Dipterocarpus* (41), *Dryobalanops* (7), *Hopea* (42), *Parashorea* (6), *Shorea* (127), *Upuna* (1) and *Vatica* (35). Of these, 155 species are **endemic** to the island, that is, being found nowhere else.

Dipterocarps have simple, penninerved leaves with articulated stalks. Their flowers are bisexual and star-shaped, with five sepals and five petals. When flowering, many exude a rich scent. Asian species possess resin canals and some produce copious resin or damar.

This technical description does

Humans are dwarfed by the stature of these huge trees.

The aerial parts of mature trees in the Mixed Dipterocarp Forest are often territorial. In the canopy, each crown fills its own place. From above or from below, this separation shows as a pattern of irregular polygons.

Young meranti (*Shorea* sp.) seedlings are shade tolerant, and form a dense clump under the parent tree on the West Ridge of Belalong.

Dry dipterocarp fruits showing the variety of size and shape with two, three or five wings.

Feeding roots form dense superficial mats in the forest soil, and are dependent on association with mycorrhizal fungi (See Chapter 9).

Huge surface roots ramify over the soil. Little is known about the extent
of the underground territories of these forest trees.

Foliage and blossom of an ensurai (*Dipterocarpus oblongifolius*) overhang Sungai Temburong.

DAMAR

Damar is the resin characterising dipterocarps and a few other, unrelated broad-leafed (dicotyledenous) trees including kedondong (*Canarium*). Damar exudes as a result of injury to the bark. As it first runs from the tree, damar is a stiff fluid. The outer surface hardens by the loss of volatile components, forming a crust often marvellously sculpted into the form of drops, ripples and runnels. Fresh damar is clear but old damar, as can be found in the soil on Belalong hillsides, is opaque and hard. Fresh damar is collected by stingless bees (Meloponinae), and utilised to form the nest entrance tube (See Chapter 11).

Historically, the flame from burning damar provided lighting in Borneo longhouses. Damar was also used to caulk boats, usually mixed with a binding material such as bark fibre. In the 19th and early 20th centuries, there was an important export trade in damar, as the chief constituent of varnishes, especially protective boat varnishes, and it was customary to tap forest dipterocarp trees to increase their yield. Changes in boat construction, especially the introduction of fibre-glass, and the development of synthetic resin substitutes have diminished the commercial value of damar. Its use is now limited to the manufacture of specialised paints and coatings.

Damar covering the buttress of a giant meranti (*Shorea*).

little justice to these towering emergent trees, whose vast, often buttressed trunks seem to hold up the forest and whose huge, cauliflower-like evergreen crowns dominate the canopy and emergent layers. On ridge tops the surface roots of the giant dipterocarps spread widely to cling to this precarious perch.

The flowering cycles of dipterocarps are synchronised within species and are frequently gregarious. This is termed **mast flowering**, and involves many species in an area blooming together or in close sequence. A tree can produce four million flowers over two weeks, each flower lasting less than a day.

The known pollinators include bees – the big *Apis dorsata*, as well as Asian honey bees and the abundant

KINGS OF THE FOREST

Professor John Corner FRS, Emeritus Professor of Tropical Botany at Cambridge, has written of:

"the lofty dipterocarp tree, which represents the culmination of tropical rainforest in Malaysia, where many species of the family Dipterocarpaceae construct the most luxuriant forest on earth. The immense trunk, superbly engineered and, consequently for its destruction, in high demand for timber, branches at a height of 100 ft into the large canopy of small leaves, many twigs, and spreading limbs along which animals may travel from tree to tree, and eat, sleep, and give birth without returning to the ground. That is tree life. The small leaves glitter, reflecting light and transmitting sun flecks into the depths beneath, where the slanting rays of the ascending and descending sun penetrate."

E.J.H. Corner (1964)
The Life of Plants p. 151

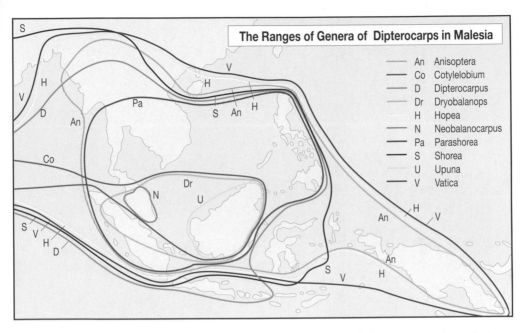

The ranges of genera of dipterocarps in Malesia [Modified with permission and advice from T. C. Whitmore (1981. *Wallace's Line and Plate Tectonics*, fig. 8.3)].

and diverse stingless bees – and, among the commercially important meranti (*Shorea* species), the small, feebly flying thrips (Thysanoptera). Thrips lay their eggs in the bud, and their young feed on the growing petals. Within a short generation period, one female can produce up to 4,000 descendants by the time the flowers are mature. The petals are so arranged that this juvenile thrip population is largely trapped within a chamber into which the anthers open. Adults feed on the pollen, which is sticky and adheres to them. Some escape, but most remain in the flower until it falls. Juveniles can survive in the fallen corolla (with stamens attached) for five days, during which time the pollen remains viable. Adults, some bearing pollen, fly up to the canopy each evening and repeat the cycle.

After flowering, in most (but not all) species of dipterocarps, some or all sepals enlarge in the mature fruit, becoming wing-like: two sepals in *Anisoptera, Dipterocarpus, Vatica, Cotylelobium* and *Hopea*, three in *Shorea* and all five in *Dryobalanops* and *Parashorea*. These wings are coloured red (most frequently), green or yellow, and are exposed in the canopy and have a photosynthetic function. They do not seem to be effective aids to long-range dispersal, and most fruits fall within 50 m of the parent butt.

Fruits of the dipterocarps of this forest lack a dormant period and ger-

The colour and appearance of bark provides a guide for identification.
The bark of kapur (*Dryobalanops*) has large, coarse flakes.

minate promptly, forming dense patches of seedlings on the forest floor. Both before and after falling, the seeds are vulnerable to attack, especially by beetles of the Family Scolytidae, and by ground feeding mammals, especially rodents. Survival rates vary from 10% to 90%. Successful establishment also depends on the presence of appropriate mycorrhizae. It may be advantageous to remain clumped, close to the parent tree, to facilitate cross infection of the **mycobiont** from the roots.

PELAWAN

Pelawan trees (*Tristania*, Family Myrtaceae) can be recognised from their beautiful, smooth, orange-brown to pinkish-grey bark peeling off in large, scroll-like pieces which fall and pile up around the base of the trunk. This feature explains the local Brunei name, selunsor, meaning 'to slip down'. There are many huge examples on the ridges

Buttress roots characterise many of the largest trees. The size and shape is variable, in response to soil conditions and the position of the tree.

The hard, fine-grained buttress wood is valued for craft uses: a section has been taken from this tree for machete/parang sheaths, turnery or craftwork.

Pelawan (*Tristania*) has a beautiful smooth bark, which sheds long, scroll-like pieces.

Koompassia on the Sungai Temburong bank. A comb of the giant bee (*Apis dorsata*) hangs below the branch.

and hillsides of Belalong forest. Pelawan trees are evergreen but seasonal in flowering. They have unbuttressed trunks and dense, round crowns of small, rather upright, glossy leaves which tend to be tufted at the ends of the twigs. Their young leaves are pink and the blossoms white.

MENGARIS & KEMPAS

There are two species of *Koompassia* (Leguminosae) at Belalong: mengaris or tualang (*Koompassia excelsa*) and kempas (*Koompassia malaccensis*). Both are conspicuous by virtue of their lofty form, with spreading crowns of compound leaves with small leaflets. Mengaris is one of the tallest trees in the forest, with recorded examples exceeding 80 m. It has enormous buttresses, and a columnar trunk with smooth, greyish-green or olive bark. Combs of giant bees (*Apis dorsata*) often hang under the branches. The delicate green foliage is shed once a year, between February and May, when the trees become bare. In fecund years (such as 1992) blossom is borne as the new leaves erupt and bees are intensely attracted to the scent and nectar.

Mengaris wood is hard and heavy, at 50-54 lbs per cubic foot air-dried, but not durable. Severe ring-shake commonly occurs when the tree is felled. This, on top of the labour involved in felling such enormous trees, and the fact that customary rights to particular trees (for the honey harvest) are frequently held by individuals, discourages the removal of these trees. They often stand in farm clearings as remnants of the forest.

Kempas is identified by grey or dark grey bark with fine, closely-spaced fissures and by sharp, narrow buttresses. Because of the value of this fine wood for craft work, it is often found with a piece hacked out to make knife handles, tops, etc.

DURIANS

The durians (*Durio,* Bombacaceae) are confined to tropical Asia. Their centre of distribution is Borneo, where 19 of

A durian pulu (*Durio kutejensis*) tree bearing fruits on its upper branches grown in a plantation.

Leaves (upper and lower surface) of different durian species.

134

The flowers of durian pulu are bright red, unlike those of most durians which are white.

Durian pulu is ramiflorous, and the fruits are borne directly on the branches.

the 27 known species occur. Durian trees are fairly well distributed throughout Mixed Dipterocarp Forests. They are medium to large trees, typically with sharp buttresses and bark which is sculpted into small, shallow, more or less rectangular flakes. Their leaves are alternate, in most species showing a coppery sheen on the underside.

Durians are **cauliflorous** or **ramiflorous** in habit, that is, bearing flowers directly on the trunk, or on the branches, respectively. The flowers open in the evening and secrete copious nectar, attracting bees, beetles, moths and small fruit bats, which serve as pollinators. The fruits are big and spiny, splitting segmentally when ripe, to expose the fleshy **aril** which encloses the large seeds, one to half a dozen (the upper number varying with species) in each compartment or **locule**.

There are durians in great variety in Brunei Darussalam, several of which appear seasonally in local markets. Within the Belalong forest, some edible species have been found as well as others with small, tasteless fruits, known collectively as durian burung. Four trees grow in Plot AAU 1: one durian pulu *Durio kutejensis*, one *Durio excelsus* and two of another species, as yet undetermined.

UBAH

Ubah, kayu kelat and jambu are Malay names for members of the genus *Eugenia* (Family Myrtaceae) which is named after Prince Eugene of Savoy, 1663-1736, a patron of science. This is one of the largest genera of flowering plants of any description in this region and remarkable in the abundance of individuals and numbers of species.

At Belalong, there were 16 trees (> 10 cm dbh) of 11 species of *Eugenia* in Plot AAU1, but many individuals of the same or different species were not included as they were small trees or shrubs. It is easy to recognise a eugenia by the simple, opposite, leathery, short-stalked leaves that generally point down and have upcurled sides, by the absence of stipules (so that there is no line or scar connecting the stalks of a pair of leaves across the twig) and, in season, by the tufted, 'shaving

The brush-like flower of the riverside ubah (*Eugenia*) is pollinated by bats.

brush' flowers.

Eugenias are evergreen. They shed their leaves gradually throughout the year, but new leaves and flowers develop at seasonal intervals. Some flower once a year after pronounced dry weather; most seem to flower twice a year after each dry spell and a few flower three or more times.

FIGS

Fig plants (all of the one genus, *Ficus*, Family Moraceae) may be large or small trees, bushes, scrambling climbers, creepers or epiphytes. A remarkable fig tree-form is the **strangler**. This begins life as an epiphyte on another host tree, to which it attaches by encircling roots. These roots join and divide, extending progressively down the host trunk until they reach the ground. Other roots will drop straight to the soil from any part of the plant. The host trunk becomes enclosed in a basket of fig roots and, once it has access to soil nutrients, the ramifying fig crown grows out through that of its support. A vigorous strangler kills by shading out its host, rather than by squeezing, and ultimately stands on its massive column of roots, in the heart of which the decaying remains of the host can usually be seen.

The fig itself is a flower-head, turned outside in. It is formed from the expanded inflorescence base which curves over and inwards; the true flow-ers line the inside. The shape of the figs, whether sessile or stalked, round or oblong, smooth or ribbed, hairy or glabrous, the colour when ripe, and the part of the plant on which they are produced are characteristic of the species. Ripening figs may remain green, or turn yellow, brown, pink, orange, red, purple or black. Figs may be borne in the leaf axils, on the twigs just behind the leaves, on the branches or the trunk, where they may be arranged in clusters on woody knobs or on short, pendant leafless twigs; geocarpic figs are produced on underground runners.

Within the fig the minute flowers are of three kinds: male flowers (with stamens), female flowers that set seed, and gall flowers which are sterile female flowers. Among stranglers, the three kinds of flowers occur inside all figs. In other forms there are two kinds of figs, one containing male and gall-flowers, the other only female flowers. Commonly, a tree will bear figs of only one kind.

Fig-flowers are pollinated by tiny wasps (*Blastophaga*), with which they have a unique relationship — each being dependent on the other. There are many species of fig-wasps, each restricted to one or a few allied species of fig.

The wasp larvae develop inside gall-flowers. The males, strange wingless creatures, emerge first and live as adults for a few hours during which they seek out their female companions and inseminate them as they lie curled

The spreading crown of the strangling fig competes with the host tree in which it is lodged.

This strangling fig established itself in the crown of a large pelawan; its roots have grown down to the ground.

A young strangler (right) attached to its host by encircling roots.

within the gall-flowers. The females, which are wasp-like in appearance, later push their way out past the male flowers, picking up pollen on the way, and fly to another, younger fig of the same species. Here they attempt to lay in the ovaries of morphologically female flowers, whether in a gall fig or a female fig, by passing the ovipositor down the style. The relative shapes of ovipositor and style are such that laying can only be achieved in gall-flowers and not in fertile female flowers which are, however, pollinated in the attempt!

The fig-wasps are parasitised by other, even smaller wasps which have immensely long ovipositors capable of penetrating the fig wall; these in turn may be hyperparasitised. Cut open a ripe gall fig or strangler fig and you will find a microcosm of interdependent insect life.

Fig trees produce large crops with variable periodicities. In the Belalong forest, stranglers provide vital food sources for frugivorous animals, especially birds and mammals. Hornbills gather to feed on ripe figs and Hose's leaf monkeys and gibbons join the feast. Giant squirrels can be seen in the canopy and pigs, mouse-deer and porcupines relish the fallen figs on the forest floor. The animals, in turn, play an essential role in seed dispersal.

Although most fig trees and bushes inhabit both primary and sec-

Ripe figs have an opening at the top for pollinators to reach the flowers.

A ripe fig in section; most flowers are the gall-flower type.

The copious crops of strangler figs are an important resource for many fruit-eating animals.

Strangling figs are common in towns where they gain a foothold on walls, or older buildings.

glers are ubiquitous and have even adapted to urban life, where cracks in old walls provide suitable places for seeds to germinate. Severe damage can be caused to buildings if they are not completely removed.

HEATHS

The heaths and allies (Family Ericaceae) comprise a cosmopolitan group of woody shrubs and shrublets, many of which have brightly coloured, showy flowers. Notable members are the heaths (*Erica*) which reach their greatest diversity in southern Africa, the rhododendrons which are concentrated in the Himalayan region, and the cranberries and bilberries (*Vaccinium*) distributed across the north temperate zone of the world. The numerous species in the Malesian region mostly grow on ridges and mountains. Not surprisingly, few have been found in the Belalong forest.

Few species of Ericaceae have been recorded in the Belalong forest. Of these, two rhododendrons, *Rhododendron malayanum* and *R.longiflorum*, are epiphytes on large trees overhanging the river. Both also probably occur in the trees on Bukit Belalong although only the orange-red flowers of *R. longiflorum* were seen on the ground on the hillsides.

Rhododendron javanicum, a widespread and very variable species in Borneo.

Kelam padang, *Vaccinium kemulense* was collected once from a fallen branch on Bukit Belalong. It is one of the commonest species of the sect. *Rigiolepis*, a rather poorly known and taxonomically difficult group of the bilberries (*Vaccinium*) with small flowers, has bright red fruit avidly taken by birds.

WOODY SHRUBS

Senduduk and allies (Family Melastomataceae) are mainly woody shrubs but also trees, epiphytes and herbs. All have opposite, simple, entire leaves, tapered at each end, normally showing three or five more or less equally prominent longitudinal veins. Their flowers tend to be showy, in pink, purple or blue, with four or five petals and twice as many stamens. The fruits are berries, often pulpy when ripe and attractive to animals. At Belalong, 13 genera have been identified. Most immediately noticeable are the Straits rhododendrons, senduduk (*Melastoma*) which flourish at the forest edge, in clearings or landslips, along the riversides and in open

141

A senduduk (*Melastoma* sp.) flourishes in the scrubby vegetation at the summit of Bukit Belalong.

There are many species of senduduk. One, *Melastoma malabathricum*, is a familiar roadside plant.

The orange flowers of jarum-jarum (*Ixora*, Family Rubiaceae), one of the few flowering woody shrubs of the Belalong forest.

scrub on the summit of Bukit Belalong.

The bright pink flowers seem to be in bloom all year, each lasting only a day. The fruits are sweet and avidly eaten by small mammals and birds; hence the seeds are widely dispersed. Epiphytic melastomes are common in riverside trees. *Medinilla* is one genus; another, *Pachycentria*, has bulbs on the roots, probably as an adaptation to the rigours of epiphytic life.

Flowers of jarum-jarum, attractive to understorey butterflies.

143

Other genera at Belalong are plants of the forest, widespread and easily recognised by their characteristic leaves. Five species of the montane genus *Sonerila*, herbs less than 10 cm tall, have been found on Bukit Belalong above 800 m. Two other genera reach tree stature: sial menahun (*Pternandra*), with three-veined leaves and four-petalled blue flowers, and nipis kulit (*Memecylon*), with paper-thin bark and rather untypical, leathery leaves bearing a prominent central vein and inconspicuous side veins. The largest examples measured at Belalong were nipis kulit, 54 cm dbh in Plot 01 and 24 cm dbh (26 m tall) in Plot AAU1; and sial menahun, 50 cm dbh (24 m tall) in Plot AAU1. Many Melastomataceae are credited with herbal or therapeutic properties, but the wood of sial menahun is believed by some to harbour perennial misfortune (as its Malay name implies).

An epiphyte (*Medinilla* or *Pachycentria*, Family Melastomataceae) on a riverside tree.

Axel Dalberg Poulsen and Draman observing plant life in Plot AAUI.

CHAPTER 8

OTHER PLANT LIFE

The remaining synusia of mechanically independent green, (photosynthesising) plants are the herbs, plants which in general do not develop significant amounts of wood in the stem, except at their base. As well as flowering plants, mosses, liverworts, ferns and fern allies are also included in this synusia. Like many flowering plant families, these also have representatives in other synusiae.

Stranglers, climbers and epiphytes comprise the three synusiae of mechanically dependent green plants, well-represented in the Belalong forest.

Plants which lack chlorophyll include the synusiae of saprophytes and parasites; examples of both these groups can be found at Belalong. In lacking development of woody tissues in their stems, flowering plant parasites and saprophytes resemble herbs, and are often also considered within that synusia.

Mosses make an important contribution to the biodiversity of Belalong forest.

Liverworts form dense patches on riverside trees.

A cushion of moss, the green gametophytes bearing brown sporophytes, each with a terminal sporangium.

148

MOSSES AND LIVERWORTS

Bryophytes (mosses and liverworts) are the most simple of land plants. They lack conducting (**vascular**) tissue and roots, although they may be anchored to the substrate by filamentous **rhizoids**. They are able to absorb water directly through their leaves, and can also lose it just as easily, and are therefore able to thrive in damp places within the forest.

 Mosses may be tufted or frondose; their minute leaves are mostly a single cell thick and arranged spirally round the stem. At Belalong, they are ubiquitous, clothing tree bases, encrusting twigs and are even epiphytic on the surfaces of leaves in shady places. On Bukit Belalong, in its damp and peaty places, clumps of bog-moss (*Sphagnum*) occur in this, their special habitat worldwide. Liverworts may be erect and branched, with regular leaflets ar-

The sporangium of a moss, containing hundreds of minute spores.

Club-mosses, like this *Lycopodium* are not true mosses, but are related to ferns.

A terrestrial orchid (*Cystorchis variegata*) with variegated brown leaves found in Plot 02.

ranged in two ranks, or flattened and irregular in shape.

In both groups there is a regular alternation of generations, with the familiar moss or liverwort plant (known as the **gametophyte**) which produces the sex organs. These in turn produce the **gametes** – the 'male' sperm and the 'female' egg. The sperm swims to the egg and fuses with it, forming a **zygote**, which germinates whilst still attached to the parent gametophyte to form a small upright **sporophyte**. Hundreds of **spores** are produced by the sporophyte within a structure called **sporangium**; these are released to float about in the wind, and if they land in a suitable place, grow into a new gametophyte plant.

GROUND HERBS

Ground herbs are non-woody plants rooted on the forest floor. Herbs in the tropical rainforest are perennial and therefore some species become rather woody at the base with age but still remain herbaceous towards the apex. Ground herbs include some that can become climbers and others that are normally epiphytes.

The most important families contributing to the ground herb flora are gingers (Zingiberaceae), aroids (Araceae), Gesneriaceae, Marantaceae, begonias (Begoniaceae), orchids (Orchidaceae) and sedges (Cyperaceae). Ferns are also an important component. Ground herbs are adapted to the low light intensities on the forest floor which can be only about 1-2% of the incoming radiation. Features such as broad leaves, a purple lower leaf surface, and iridescence (a blue-green bloom from the leaves) are general features of herbs in tropical rainforests. The survey of a 1 ha plot reveals 92 species of ground herbs. This number is much lower than the number of woody species per ha, but herbs still contribute significantly to the total diversity.

149

HERB INVENTORIES

On the West Ridge, a plot (AAU1) was selected by the team from Aarhus University (Denmark). In this plot all individual vascular herbs were registered, a voucher of each species being collected in each 10 m x 10 m quadrat. An estimate of cover, height, reproductive state and life form strategy was noted. The exercise was repeated in Plot 02 on

Saprophytic ground herbs lack the green pigment chlorophyll and may also have reduced leaves. *Petrosavia stellaris* in flower on Bukit Belalong in February 1992.

The sporangia of a tree fern (*Cyathea* sp., Cyatheaceae), are arranged in sori, each protected by a cup-shaped indusium.

Pronephrium hosei (Thelypteridaceae), a terrestrial fern growing on the banks of the Sungai Temburong.

the East Ridge.

FERNS AND FERN ALLIES

The pteridophytes (ferns and fern allies), are vascular plants with a well-developed conducting system and true roots. They exhibit an alternation of generations, as do the bryophytes, but in the ferns and fern allies the larger, dominant generation is the sporophyte, which produces sporangia containing spores. The spores germinate to form a diminutive free-living gametophyte, which in most pteridophytes is only 1-2 cm across, and which bears the male and female sex organs. The sperm swim through a film of water to reach the egg; once fertilised, the zygote develops into a new sporophyte. The need for free water for fertilisation restricts ferns to habitats which are at least seasonally damp, but they are found all over the world, apart from deserts, snow-covered mountains and the ice-caps of polar regions. Ferns and fern allies are particularly well-devel-

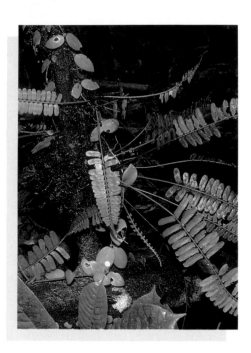

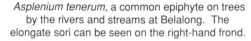

Asplenium tenerum, a common epiphyte on trees by the rivers and streams at Belalong. The elongate sori can be seen on the right-hand frond.

A massive stag's horn fern (*Platycerium*, Polypodiaceae), a nest epiphyte with pendulous fertile fronds and upright fronds forming the 'nest'.

oped in the tropics. Borneo, including Brunei Darussalam, has a rich fern flora.

Ferns can be recognised by the groups of sporangia, called **sori**, on the backs of leaves (rarely on the margins). The sori may be round, midway between the margin and the mid-vein (many Polypodiaceae, Cyatheaceae), elongate along the veins (e.g. Aspleniaceae), elongate and marginal (e.g. Vittariaceae) or coalescing to cover the whole lower surface (e.g. *Platycerium*, Polypodiaceae). In some ferns the individual sori are protected by a flap of tissue, the **indusium**, the presence or absence of which, and its shape, is of taxonomic importance.

The leaves of ferns, known as fronds, are very varied, from minute simple leaves only 1-2 cm long to massive dissected fronds up to 3 m long. Stems also vary from creeping to upright, with the tree ferns (*Cyathea* sp.) bearing a crown of large fronds on an upright trunk as much as 4 m high (See Chapter 6). Many ferns are terrestrial, growing on the forest floor; others are climbers, rooted in the ground and with high-climbing stems reaching for the canopy. Many species are epiphytes, growing amongst moss on the boles and branches of the trees, where they form an important habitat for arboreal animals. Among these, the 'nest' epiphytes are unusual in producing two sorts of leaves, one which hugs the

Mesophlebion oligodictyon (Thelypteridaceae) grows on river banks. The two narrow central fronds are fertile and bear sporangia on the lower side.

The simple-fronded *Lemmaphyllum accedens* (Polypodiaceae) grows with the long pinnate fronds of *Ctenopteris alata* (Grammitidaceae). Both are low-level epiphytes on trees by rivers.

On Bukit Belalong the pendulous bright green fronds of *Acrosorus* (Grammitidaceae) stand out from the smaller dull green fronds of the filmy fern *Hymenophyllum lobii* (Hymenophyllaceae).

support and accumulates dead leaves, twigs and other debris, into which the roots penetrate, and the more normal fronds which bear the sori.

The fern allies include horsetails (Equisetaceae, not yet found in Brunei) and the club-mosses (Lycopodiaceae and Selaginellaceae). Unlike the true ferns, the club mosses have small, often needle-like, leaves on an upright or creeping stem. The sporangia are usually borne singly on the upper surface of a leaf, these fertile leaves frequently being aggregated into cones on the ends of the branches.

FERNS AT BELALONG

Of the estimated 400 species of ferns and fern allies in Brunei Darussalam, about 172 have been found in the 5,000 ha of the Belalong forest. 101 species are terrestrial, of which 12 are rheophytes, confined to river banks and stream beds. Nine species are climbers or scramblers, while the remainder, 62 species, are epiphytes. This is a lower percentage of epiphytes (36%) than recorded from Gunung Mulu or Gunung Kinabalu, and reflects the limited extent of montane forest on Bukit Belalong.

Twenty-four Families are found at Belalong, the most speciose being the largely epiphytic Polypodiaceae (29 species) and the filmy ferns, Hymenophyllaceae (21 species, of which all but six are epiphytes). Well-represented Families with predominantly or wholly terrestrial species include the Thelypteridaceae (15 species), the Dryopteridaceae and Woodsiaceae (12 species each). The club-mosses (Selaginellaceae) are also diverse, with 12 species recorded from the area.

FLOWERING PLANTS - MONOCOTYLEDONOUS HERBS

BANANAS

Largest of the herbaceous flowering plants are wild bananas, pisang (*Musa*, Musaceae). Bananas are quick to colonise landslips and gaps, particularly in the alluvial soil along the riverside. Their flowers are important nectar sources, especially for the long-billed spiderhunters (*Arachnothera*). Their fruits are eaten and the seeds consequently dispersed by squirrels, rats, civets and fruit bats. The rolled leaf of the banana as it begins to open is the favoured roost site of whiskered bats and, once fully expanded, also provides shelter for the small fruit bats (*Cynopterus*). Accumulated litter around the base of the culms is an important invertebrate habitat.

Three species of wild bananas are recorded in these valleys. All three occur as rainforest 'weeds' in temporarily open sites such as landslides or shifting gravel banks in changing water courses. *Musa campestris* probably has the greatest drought tolerance and occurs most frequently in large openings but all three species can become common plants when the forest is disturbed, and are often seen elsewhere in Brunei along roadsides.

Three species of banana can be seen close to the Field Studies Centre: (1) *Musa campestris*, 1.5-3 m high, with bright purple bracts, orange-yellow flowers and very pale whitish-green fruit irregularly mottled with purple; (2) *Musa borneensis*, a large species up to 7 m high which appears mostly, if not totally, in the cream to yellow-bracted form (*M. "flavida"*), a colour variant of a widespread Borneo species that elsewhere has purplish or reddish bracts. *Musa borneensis* is distinctive in having highly rugose leaf auricles, a

This field banana (*Musa campestris*) is an early coloniser of landslips on the riparian fringe.

This large banana plant (*Musa borneensis*) grows at the Field Studies Centre.

The inflorescence of *Musa borneensis*.

hanging influorescence with uniseriate flowers which stand clear of the bracts, and is visited and probably pollinated by birds. (3) The third species, *Musa textilis* (or *M. muluensis*, a closely allied species), also up to 7 m high, has a hanging influorescence with much laxer fruit than *M. borneensis*, and does not have rugose auricles but has a shiny reddish-purple imbricate male bud with biseriate flowers.

GRASSES AND SEDGES

With the exception of the bamboos, the grasses (Poaceae) are not prominent members of the rainforest flora. Weed species have colonised many clearings, but only three species of grasses occur naturally in the true forest environment. Sedges (Cyperaceae), however, are better represented with

The sedge *Mapania monostachya*, a very abundant species on steep slopes with bare soil surfaces.

ten species, six of which belong to the single genus *Mapania. M. monostachya* was found to have more than 100 individuals in each of the two 1 ha plots censused by the Aarhus University team, and is one of the commonest ground herbs on the steep upper slopes with exposed mineral soils. Other species grow beside rivers and streams.

GINGERS

The pantropical Family of gingers, Zingiberaceae, is particularly species-rich in Asia. Here, gingers are important constituents of the undergrowth of the tropical rainforest. The plants are perennial and grow mostly in damp and humid shady places but some can stand full exposure to the sun, harsh conditions and high elevations. A few species are epiphytic. In many terrestrial species, flowers are borne directly on underground rhizomes, a consider-

Alpinia glabra, an upright ginger with a terminal inflorescence.

Etlingera sp., with basal inflorescences appearing directly from the underground rhizomes.

The flowers of *Alpinia glabra*.

Etlingera brevilabris with basal inflorescences appearing metres away from the leaf-bearing stem.

The terminal inflorescence of *Plagiostachys strobilifera* bursts through the side of the pseudostem.

The creeping, broad-leaved *Boesenbergia orbiculata* near the river.

able distance from the upright leaves.

Around the tropical world, the gingers include about 1,300 herbaceous species from 49 genera. In Borneo the gingers are represented by 19 genera and at least 152 species. About a third of the Bornean species were found in the Belalong forest making the gingers the most species-rich Family contributing to the ground herb vegetation in that area. Most of the species are perennial terrestrials, but a few species of *Burbidgea* and *Hedychium* occur as epiphytes.

The gingers occur in various habitats from near the rivers to the top of Bukit Belalong. Some of the largest species, *Etlingera fimbribracteata* and *E. punicea* are found in gaps near the river. Many terrestrial species have long rhizomes. These allow any plant to spread through the forest. If one reaches

A few gingers are epiphytes, for instance, *Burbidgea stenantha.*

A new species of ginger, *Boesenbergia belalongensis* discovered at Belalong in 1991.

an area of better light, the plant can flower and seed vigorously.

The flowers are often very spectacular. Little is known of their pollination but in many cases bees or butterflies are probably involved. The gingers are not only attractive ornamentals but many species are also used as spices (ginger, turmeric, cardamon), perfumes, dyes, medicines, or as food plants.

157

AROIDS

Most aroids (Family Araceae) are recognisable by the characteristic spike-shaped inflorescence consisting of very small flowers, enclosed by a spathe, usually cream or greenish in colour. The peculiar *Amorphophallus* produces a single leaf at a time, with a much divided tripartite frond borne on a tall, mottled stem. In old plants, the leaf blade exceeds 2 m in width. Other aroids characteristically have entire,

Etlingera sp. aff. *muluensis*, an abundant species in Plot 02 on the East Ridge at Belalong.

A juvenile plant of *Epipremnum falcifolium* on the forest floor.

The huge leaves of birah (*Alocasia*) growing in the clearing of KBFSC.

The flowers of birah at KBFSC. Each inflorescence has a spike of flowers enclosed by a purplish spathe.

Mature plant of *Epipremnum falcifolium*, flowering 10 m up a tree trunk.

fleshy, arrow-shaped to rounded leaves; on some climbing aroids, there is a progressive change in leaf shape as they ascend the trees.

The Araceae is the second most diverse herbaceous Family in the Belalong forest. Aroids are found on the ground and also as climbers and epiphytes. Many of the climbing species, such as *Amydrium medium* and *Epipremnum falcifolium*, germinate on the forest floor and will grow towards darkness with an almost leafless shoot; an ability that raises the chance of finding a tree trunk to climb. The aroid will then change its growth form and produce bigger leaves and eventually flowers as it grows up the trunk and into a better lit environment.

The largest aroid at Belalong is a species of *Alocasia*, which grows in disturbed habitats near the river. The leaves grow up to 4 m and produce many inflorescences. As with many other Araceae it produces a nasty irritant sap. The emerging leaves are rolled lengthwise and offer a temporary shelter to whiskered bats (*Myotis muricola*). The seeds, which have a sweet, red outer layer, are eaten by the Little spiderhunter (*Arachnothera longirostra*).

DICOTYLEDONOUS HERBS

Although many of the forest floor herbs are monocotyledons, several dicotyledon Families are well-represented. Within the study area, the Gesneriaceae, Rubiaceae and Begoniaceae each have more than ten species.

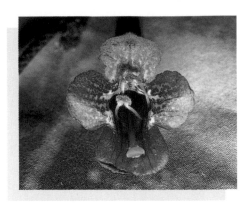

Flower of the epiphytic *Aeschynanthus vinaceus* (Gesneriaceae).

159

GESNERIACEAE

This Family is important among the herbaceous flora in the Forest Reserve. The largest genera of the terrestrial gesners are *Cyrtandra* and *Didymocarpus*, but the Family is also well represented as epiphytes, such as *Aeschynanthus*, overhanging the river, often with bright red flowers. The Gesneriaceae, with approximately 16 species, arc only surpassed in diversity by some fern Families and gingers and aroids, both monocotyledons.

Didymocarpus amaenus (Gesneriaceae), a terrestrial herb with variegated leaves.

BEGONIACEAE

The Family Begoniaceae is probably unique in having more than a thousand species, all but a few of which are included within one vast genus, *Begonia*. Despite numerous unusual or specialised features, all *Begonia* species are characterised by asymmetrical leaves, often broader towards the base. They frequently have a larger basal lobe on one side; separate male and female flowers with petals and sepals generally the same colour and texture and indistinguishable (**tepals**) – and an inferior, usually three-winged ovary with the styles often branched and coiled. In many species it is leaf-characteristics, rather than the flowers, that are the more striking and diagnostic.

Borneo is rich in *Begonia* species and Brunei, only a small part of the island, is now believed to have 17 species within its boundaries, the major-

Begonia baramensis (A)

Begonia (C)

Begonia (B)

Begonias of Batu Apoi Forest Reserve,
identified by Dr Martin Sands.

Begonia (D)

This begonia grows in microhabitats with exposed mineral soil.

ity collected only since 1989, in the course of fieldwork associated with the Kew/Brunei Forestry Department or UBD/RGS Projects. All but one of the species, *Begonia baramensis* (A), are apparently new to science and several may be endemic to Brunei.

Dr Martin Sands reports 12 species in the catchments of Sungai Temburong and Sungai Belalong. Of these, eight grow on the Setap/Temburong shales in the Batu Apoi Forest Reserve, within a few kilometres of Kuala Belalong. All are markedly distinct from one another.

In the upper catchment of the Temburong, a *Begonia*, which belongs to a group of species with leaves broadest towards the apex, grows on steep earth slopes or almost vertical cliffs up to 1,150 m elevation, the highest altitude so far at which a begonia is known to occur in Brunei. It is distinctive in having sharply-winged fruits, usually borne close to the ground on the rooting portion of the lower stem. Below

about 1,000 m this is replaced by different species, few growing far from the river.

Two are fairly common but distinctive. First, *Begonia baramensis* is unique among Bruneian species in having peltate leaves with the petiole of the leaf joining the blade in the middle. This fine species, known from several localities in Brunei and Sarawak, can reach a height of 2.5 m, the dark, velvety green leaves having red veins beneath and often an attractive silver band along the margin (A).

The second common species, which also occurs in Sarawak and Sabah, is distinctive in possessing scattered but conspicuous red or black stiff hairs on the upper surface of the leaf and seems to prefer a lighter habitat, often growing on or between river-bed boulders (B).

Also close to the river, but more usually in the shade, are two particularly attractive and interesting begonias. One of them is a low-growing species, scarcely exceeding 15 cm high, which has white flowers and long, blue-green, pointed leaves that are coarsely bullate and densely covered with long hairs (C). The other is much taller, up to 1 m high, having large, yellowish green, more rounded leaves with a covering of white hairs on both surfaces and is unusual in that the tepals of the female flowers are lime-green with long hairs around the margin.

Perhaps the most striking Brunei begonia discovered so far is to be found at its best on the steep flanks of river-bank gullies in the deepest shade. Gleaming like jewels in the darkness and impossible to capture adequately on film, its iridescent, turquoise-blue leaves are truly astonishing and, even in rather lighter situations, their glossy, hairless surface complements the delicate pink-flushed flowers (D).

CLIMBERS

Climbers can be defined as plants rooted in the ground, with aerial parts supported by other plants. Some flourish only when they reach the sunlit upper canopy; others are adapted to the shady understorey. Taxonomically, climbers are diverse; at least 24 Families have this habit in Sarawak and Brunei forests. The woody stems of the group, commonly known as lianas (akar), are prominent in the forest, and are looped and festooned at all levels. Mean counts of stem densities in Lambir National Park, Sarawak, by Dr Paul Chai were in the range of 500-3,000 per ha. The camel's foot, akar katup-katup (*Bauhinia*, Leguminosae) can spread across the canopies of several trees and its brilliant orange coloured blossoms form showy masses, while the gnetum, akar seburek (*Gnetum*, Gnetaceae) bears its flowers on raised rings throughout the length of its sturdy stem.

Many climbers bear specialised

Tropical rainforests are characterised by a wealth of woody climbers.

The stem of this climber is twisted in a series of alternating reversed turns around its support.

For many climbers a spiral growth form attaches them to supporting vegetation.

Bole climbers attach directly to the trunk of the host tree.

Herbaceous climbers (*Merremia*) grow and sprawl over cleared ground.

The orange coloured blossoms of katup-katup (*Bauhinia*) are among the more glorious sights of the forest.

The festooning stem of akar seburek (*Gnetum*) is marked by raised rings throughout its length.

Katup-katup flowers in the upper canopy.

Akar seburek cones, in this case male cones, are borne on raised rings round the stem.

All rattans produce scaly fruits. Often the inflorescence is also armed with recurved spines.

The crown of a rattan is anchored in the canopy by the extended rachis of the leaf which bears many recurved spines.

The scaly fruits and dense thorns of a rattan (*Pogonotium*).

RATTANS

In Belalong forest, 72 taxonomic collections were made along trails and in areas adjoining KBFSC and camps Wakwak, Busiri, Bukit, Engkiang and Babi. Small (10 x 10 m) sample plots were set up to test for factors affecting the distribution of rattans; data provided information on species' habitat preferences.

On the slope of the east bank of the Belalong at KBFSC a 1.5 ha plot (50 x 300 m) was fully enumerated. Twenty-five species of rattan were identified among 135 clumps, the most common being, in order: *Daemonorops periacantha*, *Calamus flabellatus*, *C. pogonacanthus*, *C. sordidus*, *C. marginatus*, *Ceratobolus concolor* and *D. oxycarpa*. Sixty stems with above ground length >3 m were tagged, mapped and measured.

---

climbing structures, such as hooks or tendrils. These and others have twining stems or branches by which they grip the trunks and branches of the trees that support them. Another group, the bole climbers, are closely attached to their support, often by adventitious roots. Several of these show progressive variation in leaf shape as they ascend.

The rattans are an important group of woody climbers in the Belalong forests. The genera present include *Calamus*, *Ceratobolus*, *Daemonorops*, *Korthalsia* and *Plectocomiopsis*. All are spiny, and rely on thorny extensions to serve as climbing organs. In many, the rachis of the leaf is prolonged as a hooked whip; some *Calamus* have hooked inflorescences, both fertile and sterile, growing from the stem. These climbing organs are designed to hook onto other vegetation, and in this manner to support the rattan stem as it strives upwards to the sunlight of the forest canopy.

The rattan *Korthalsia* can be recognised by fishtail leaflets, whitish on the underside.

The swollen sheathing leaf-base of *Korthalsia* is often inhabited by ants.

The fishtail rattans, rotan dahan or rotan semut (*Korthalsia*) have branched stems. The leaf sheath and stalk are prickly; the leaflets fishtail shape, shortly stalked, whitish beneath. *Korthalsia* species are very common rattans, easily recognised from the grey to chalky white fishtail leaflets and big sheathy leaf bases which, in several species, are inhabited by ants. When present, the ants respond to disturbance by tapping their legs, producing a low, hiss-like noise. The benefits to the plant are uncertain.

EPIPHYTES

Among some bole climbers, the older, lower part dies as the plant progressively climbs its host tree. It thus becomes an **epiphyte**, one of the important groups of forest plants that live attached to the aerial parts of trees and shrubs. Shade-adapted epiphytes thrive

Epiphytes crowd the bole of this tree including the bird's nest fern (*Asplenium*), stag's horn fern (*Platycerium*), other ferns and a climbing aroid.

Many orchids are epiphytic and are adapted to survive exposure in the forest canopy.

The orchid *Trichoglottis* in flower.

Water and humus are trapped and enclosed within the ring of fronds of the birds' nest fern (*Asplenium nidus*) encircling the trunk of a small tree.

The bole of this forest giant is clad in epiphytic mosses, ferns and flowering plants.

ANT PLANTS

The swollen ant-inhabited stem of *Hydnophytum* on a tree in kerangas forest.

Many plants attract ants and other insects by producing nectar from special glands (extra-floral nectaries) on their stems and leaves. Plants may also provide some smaller ant species with nesting sites consisting of small chambers or groups of hairs, known as **domatia**, on the leaves. In the ant-plants this relationship has developed further, with the plant providing nesting sites, and often food for the ants within the tissues. In return the ants are thought to protect the plant from herbivores and in some cases supply the plant with essential nutrients.

Terrestrial ant-plants include *Macaranga* (Chapter 11), some rattans, including *Korthalsia*, the unusual rheophyte *Myrmeconauclea* (Chapter 13), and at least one species of the pitcher plant, *Nepenthes*. Epiphytic ant-plants, known as myrmecophytes, are best-developed in for-

ests growing on nutrient-poor soils (kerangas, peatswamp and montane forest) but can be found in all forest types in

The ant-inhabited chambers occupy most of the swollen stem of *Hydnophytum*.

Brunei, including the Belalong forest.

Representatives of several different plant families are myrmecophytes, including ferns (*Lecanopteris*, Polypodiaceae). Flowering plant myrmecophytes include *Dischidia* (Asclepiadaceae), *Hydnophytum* and *Myrmecodia* (Rubiaceae). The stem of many species is hollowed into a series of large chambers which the ants inhabit; some produce food-bodies while others are used for nesting. Dead and decomposing ants and other detritus provide the plant with a source of minerals. In *Dischidia* sp., leaves are hollow; old leaves become filled with a mass of compost-like material into which the roots grow.

The relationship between ants and their myrmecophyte hosts is often described as a symbiosis. As with many plant-animal interactions the extent of the symbiosis varies in different pairs of organisms, from simple exploitation to true symbiosis. In the case of *Myrmecodia* and *Hydnophytum* it has been demonstrated, by using radioactive **isotopes**, that the plant can absorb both organic and inorganic compounds through the stem cavities; these thus appear to be examples of true symbiosis. The relationship in other cases is less clear.

Licuala (Arecaceae) leaf with a heavy cover of lichens and algae.

An old leaf of kapur paji (*Dryobalanops lanceolata*) with a cover of liverworts, lichens, fungi and algae.

in the lower levels of the forest, in the poorly lit, highly humid environment. On the upper boles and branches, light-demanding epiphytes abound, among which aroids, orchids and ferns are notable. These plants are exposed to bright sunlight, high temperatures, strong winds and frequent low humidity of the upper canopy environment. Many of them show adaptations to minimise evaporative water loss, such as thick, leathery leaves, or to store

The trailing myrmecophyte *Dischidia rafflesiana* has hollow leaves which enclose the roots (bottom right) and offer a home for ants.

170

EPIPHYLLS

In the perpetually moist environment of the rainforest, mosses, fungi, lichens, algae, liverworts and cyanobacteria establish themselves on the upper surfaces of all but the youngest of still photosynthesising host leaves. These usually very small epiphytes adapted to grow on leaves are known as epiphylls, and their occurrence is limited to the more humid rainforests around the world.

Some leaves bear a heavy covering of epiphylls, which have low growth and respiration rates, well suited to the low light environment of the understorey. It is not clear whether the presence of epiphylls is damaging to their hosts. Although they certainly interfere with the light 'harvest' of their supporting leaves, there is evidence that some may transfer nitrogen and minerals to their hosts. A common epiphyll is *Trentepohlia*, a green alga (Chlorophyceae) with a high concentration of carotene which colours it orange.

A filamentous green alga (*Trentepohlia*) on kapur paji (as seen under the microscope).

Under fluorescent light, the light-trapping chlorophyll pigments of an epiphyllous alga fluoresce bright red.

Nepenthes reinwardtiana is an epiphytic pitcher plant in the Temburong valley.

water, such as the swollen pseudobulbs of orchids.

The variety of epiphytes is enormous, and includes microscopic algae, lichens, mosses, ferns and herbaceous and woody flowering plants. Some of these epiphytes are designed to trap falling leaves and other detritus to provide a store of humus into which their roots can grow.

Lichen colonies spread by slow growth over the surfaces of trunks, twigs and leaves, and produce brightly coloured marbled patterns. Encrusting growths of algae, lichens and mosses can progressively cover the surfaces of leaves; these are epiphylls.

PITCHER PLANTS

Pitcher plants, somboi-somboi (*Nepenthes*, Family Nepenthaceae) range across the eastern tropics, from Madagascar eastward to Australia and New Caledonia. Of the 80 or so species described, over 30 occur in Borneo; Brunei is particularly rich with over 20 species. *Nepenthes* are climbing plants, growing on poor or waterlogged soils, low in such essential nutrients as nitrogen and phosphorus. The mid-rib of the narrow leathery leaf is prolonged to form a tendril which wraps around the stems of supporting vegetation termi-

171

One of the common pitcher plants,
Nepenthes gracilis.

A pitcher plant begins life as a rosette
on the forest floor.

PREY OF PITCHER PLANTS

Among *Nepenthes* (except *Nepenthes ampullaria*), the plant produces two distinct forms of pitcher. The terrestrial, or lower pitcher, is squat and robust, with a pair of 'wings' at the front.

As the plant grows and the stem clambers up neighbouring vegetation, it produces upper, or aerial pitchers, which are usually slimmer than the lower pitchers. They do not possess 'wings', and may produce a strong sickly sweet perfume.

Analysis of pitcher contents of *Nepenthes rafflesiana* plants, growing in the kerangas forest of Brunei Darussalam showed that although ants formed the greatest part of insects captured in both pitcher types, the upper pitchers caught significantly more insects such as bees (especially trigonids), moths, flies and beetles, than did the lower pitchers on the same plant. It appears that a combination of ultraviolet pattern and scent in the upper pitchers was responsible for the greater attraction of flying prey. However, it is not evident that the upper pitchers are mimicking flowers. In the sites studied, there was no model flower that the pitchers resembled. In many areas, the pitchers are highly abundant, and dominate the landscape in terms of colour and scent. A true mimic should not provide a reward, whereas the pitchers do produce nectar. In fact, the pitchers of *N. rafflesiana* appeared to represent one of the major perennial sources of nectar in the areas studied, feeding a large and varied invertebrate population. Only a small proportion of the invertebrates visiting the pitchers actually fell prey to the plant. Most of them successfully collected the nectar and then safely left the pitcher.

In effect, it seems that pitcher plants may be mutualistic rather than mimetic and that the similarities between flowers and pitchers are a result of convergent evolution.

Lower pitchers of *N. rafflesiana* are typically round and squat.

The upper pitchers of *N. rafflesiana* are more elongated.

The flowers of pitcher plants play no part in capture; they are pollinated by beetles.

The pitcher itself expands from the tip of the climbing tendril. This species, *Nepenthes hirsuta*, grows on Bukit Belalong.

173

Tetrastigma, the host plant of *Rhizanthes* at Belalong.

Rhizanthes lowii in bud.

nating in a pitcher. They attract and catch insects and invertebrates seeking nectar. Nectaries are situated around the pitcher mouth; in order to gain access, the prey is tempted to venture inside the body of the pitcher. Once here, its feet become clogged with waxy scales which detach from the pitcher wall. Eventually, it may lose its grip and fall into the fluid within the pitcher, where it drowns, decomposes and ultimately provides supplementary nutrients to be absorbed through the pitcher wall. At the same time, there are other organisms (including mosquito larvae) which are able to live and grow within the pitcher fluid, evidently immune to any enzyme activity within it. For these, the pitchers provide an important resource.

When fully opened, the petals of *Rhizanthes lowii* are reflexed and have long hairs.

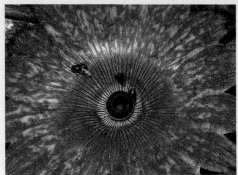

Flies are attracted to the centre of the flower, where the stamens or pistil are located.

SAPROPHYTES

Lecanorhis multiflora, a common saprophytic orchid on ridge tops.

Epirixanthes pallida (Polygalaceae), a common saprophyte in moist localities.

In the rainforest the vast majority of saprophytes are lower organisms – bacteria and fungi – but saprophytic (or, more precisely, mycrotrophic) flowering plants are also present. They are most often found in moist, dark habitats, and are small and inconspicuous plants and therefore difficult to spot. In Belalong forest ten species, of five Families, of saprophytic flowering plants were encountered: *Burmannia* (Burmanniaceae), *Petrosavia* (Liliaceae), *Aphyllorchis, Lecanorchis, Tropidia* (Orchidaceae), *Epirixanthes* (Polygalaceae) and *Sciaphila* (Triuridaceae).

Flowers of *Lecanorhis multiflora*.

FLOWERING PLANT PARASITES

Only two families of root and stem parasites are found in the tropical rainforest: Balanophoraceae and Rafflesiaceae. In both families the body of the parasite exists as a network ramifying through the tissues of the host; no leaves or other external organs are formed, apart from the inflorescence and flowers. Examples of both the Balanophoraceae and the Rafflesiaceae have been found in Brunei, the Balanophoraceae represented by a single species found on the slopes of Gunung Pagon to the south of the Belalong forest.

The Rafflesiaceae are better known, including the plant with the largest flower in the world, *Rafflesia arnoldii*, first found in Sumatra. In Brunei, a similar species, *Rafflesia pricei*, with smaller flowers (up to 30 cm across) has been found near Bukit Retak.

At Belalong a less well-known genus, *Rhizanthes*, represented by a single species, *Rhizanthes lowii*, has been found on the West Ridge. *Rhizanthes* is parasitic on a vine, *Tetrastigma*, and, like *Rafflesia*, does not show any external signs of its presence until it flowers. These, produced on surface or sub-surface roots and stems of the vine, break through the tissue of the host and when fully expanded may be 8-10 cm across. The colour, texture and smell of the flower are reminiscent of rotting meat, and several species of flies are attracted to the open flowers. It is likely that these are the pollinators.

Balanophora, a flowering plant parasite, found on the slopes of Gunung Pagon.

A bud of *Rafflesia pricei*, parasitic on the vine *Tetrastigma*.

175

The fruiting body of a fungus can take many forms. Among the more bizarre at Belalong is *Pholiota*.

CHAPTER 9

FUNGI

Although superficially plant-like, the fungi are very different in their biology and hence recognised as a separate Kingdom. The familiar manifestation of a fungus is its fruiting body, such as mushrooms, toadstools, etc. These are often short-lived extensions of the main mass of tissue, the ramifying thread-like mycelium.

The introductory spread pages show *Leucocoprinus caepistipes*.

FUNGUS BIOLOGY

Fungi are very numerous and almost ubiquitous throughout the world. Many species form inconspicuous, cobweb-like growths, and develop fruit bodies which may be only discernible under the microscope. All fungi lack the pigment chlorophyll found in green plants and therefore cannot utilise light en-

The fruit-body of *Lentinus connatus* is characterised by a long, smooth stem.

The fruit-bodies of *Lentinus squarrosulus* grow from dead timber on the forest floor.

tissue of the host organism, or (if saprophytic) within dead matter. Not infrequently, at Belalong, the dead leaves, twigs and other plant remains on the forest floor are lightly bound together by this covering of active, living mycelium. The hyphal threads in some species may also band together to form thick strands (**rhizomorphs**). From the mycelium arise the fruit-bodies. These are built up of densely interwoven hyphae, modified in different ways. Fruit-bodies produce microscopically small spores which, on germination, give rise to new mycelium.

ergy for the production of carbon compounds from carbon dioxide and water. They are, however, capable of synthesising many other organic compounds. Fungi therefore live either as parasites on other living organisms, or as saprophytes drawing nutrients from dead remains.

The absorption of nutrients takes place via the mycelium which consists of fine thread-like **hyphae** which may spread in soil, or (if parasitic) within the

Fungi play an enormously important role in recycling the organic matter of the tropical rainforest, ultimately renewing its component nutrients and energy value in forms available to growing plants. Saprophytic fungi break down dead organic matter – leaves, wood or animal remains or dung. In simple forms the mycelium grows freely in the soil, weaving its way over these minutely fragmented remains.

The asymmetrical, almost bracket shaped fruit-bodies of a saprophytic fungus (*Hohenbuehelia* sp).

The red fruit body of a *Cordyceps* (Ascomycotina) arises from a dead giant ant (*Camponotus*).

trients for their own growth, and also convert the plant material into a form more easily assimilated by the small animals that feed on it in the next stages of the decomposition cycle.

Fungi are food for many animals. For instance, the giant ant *Camponotus* is a specialised feeder on fungal tissue. The processional termite *Hospitalitermes* harvests fungi and lichens. Fungi are utilised by other termites to bring otherwise indigestible woody tissue into the animal food chain. For the living forest plants, fungi play an equally essential part in nutrition via the root-fungus association known as **mycorrhizal symbiosis**, in which the fungus takes on the role of conveying nutrients from the soil to the host plant.

Pathogenic and parasitic species, including many bracket fungi, must play a significant part in the ecology of Belalong forest. The evolution of systems protective against these fungi may have great selective significance among plants.

Saprophytic fungi invade dead leaves in the litter layer of the forest floor or submerged in the water of streams or pools. Others attack decaying wood such as tree stumps or branches. Some species are restricted to the woods of certain groups of trees or to a single tree genus or even to one species. In the aquatic environment, fungi are equally important as decomposers of dead organic matter – leaves, twigs and pieces of wood.

All these fungi produce **enzymes** that can degrade the tough cell-walls of plant tissue. In this manner fungi obtain nu-

Brown and white brackets of *Rigidoporus lineatus*, which may be a wound parasite, although usually saprophytic.

181

One toppled *Lepiota pulverulenta* (Basidiomycotina) shows its gills.

The fruiting body of a typical agaric, *Amanita princeps* (Basidiomycotina), member of an important mycorrhizal genus.

FUNGUS GARDENERS

Certain insects, notably ambrosia beetles, certain ants and termites, actually cultivate fungi as food crops. Fungus-cultivating habits probably evolved as the natural result of their close association with fungi in the soil. It is natural that ants or termites nesting in subter-

---

MYCORRHIZAE

Mycorrhizae, the close association of the roots of vascular plants with soil fungi, are very widespread, pervading many different habitats and communities. The mycelium of mycorrhizal fungi extends from the plant root into the soil and transfers nutrients directly to the plant. Because there is mutual benefit, the association is classed as a symbiosis. A great taxonomic variety is involved, both of fungi (the **mycobionts**) and of plants (the **phytobionts**). The relationship of fungus and root leads to the recognition of two major kinds of mycorrhiza:-

Endomycorrhizae

In this form of the symbiosis, the fungus penetrates the tissue of the roots and forms characteristic vesicles within the cells. Endomycorrhizae are regularly formed by perhaps four-fifths of all vascular plants. They have actually been recorded in some 200 families and more than 1, 000 genera. The fungi involved are ubiquitous in distribution and physiologically unspecialised.

Ectomycorrhizae

In this form, the fungus surrounds the root but does not penetrate the living cells. Ectomycorrhizae are specialised, and often host specific, mostly formed with basidiomycetes, and sometimes with ascomycetes.

Among dicotyledonous plants occurring in Belalong forest, ectomycorrhizae are probably characteristic of all dipterocarps (Dipterocarpaceae) and most Myrtaceae. In the legumes (Leguminosae), many tropical members are involved with ectomycorrhizae. Ectomycorrhizae may have the ability, lacking in higher plants, to absorb and utilise organic nitrogen (such as ammonium) taken directly from decaying organic matter.

ranean locations should sometimes have used them as food. The next evolutionary step would be the development of habits involved with the care and cultivation of the fungi.

FUNGUS BIODIVERSITY

The larger fungi are divided into two main groups: ascomycetes (Ascomycotina) and basidiomycetes (Basidiomycotina). In ascomycetes, fruit-bodies take many forms. Some are more or less cup-shaped; these are commonly referred to as discomycetes, or cup fungi. Some ascomycetes have tuberous fruit-bodies and grow below soil surface; these are the truffles and their allies. Yeasts, so widely used in baking and brewing, are also ascomycetes.

Frondose brackets of *Stereum* sp.

183

FUNGI OF BRUNEI DARUSSALAM

Taxonomic and floristic investigation of the fungi of Brunei Darussalam is still in its early stages. The ascomycetes (cup-and-flask fungi), in particular, require intensive collection and study. The smaller discomycetes comprise a vast group, those from tropical areas being little known. Few species have yet to be collected in the country, and it is anticipated that fieldwork here will produce undescribed species, which will add to the knowledge of the taxonomy of these fungi, and provide new ecological and geographical data for species whose biology and distribution remains poorly known.

Although the ascomycetes are most numerous, the basidiomycetes include the highest number of the familiar larger fungi. The stalked, umbrella-like type of fructification, with spores developed on and shed from gills or pores on the undersurface, is common among the basidiomycetes and has reached a high degree of elaboration and variability in 'gill fungi', the Agaricales or agarics.

It has been said that most woody plants require mycorrhizae to survive, and most herbaceous plants need them to thrive. Under tropical conditions, in which individuals of a given plant species are often widely spaced and rare, dependence on endomycorrhizal fungi may be essential. In these groups, the phytobionts may be too rare to allow a specialized mycorrhizal association. In effect, the low diversity among these fungi may be a factor that permits high diversity in the vascular plants depending on them.

For ectomycorrhizal fungi, sym-

The coral-like *Lentaria surculus* (Ascomycotina).

184

The dry black fruiting body of *Xylaria ianthino-velutina* (Ascomycotina).

The bright yellow *Guepinia spathularia* (Ascomycotina).

The furry cups of *Cookeina tricholoma* (Ascomycotina, discomycetes).

The stalked stromata of *Xylaria fockei* (Ascomycotina, pyrenomycetes).

The graceful lady's veil fungus (*Phallus indusiatus*).

The familiar gilled 'umbrella' of *Volvariella terastia* (Basidiomycotina, Agaricales) grows from the soil.

The frail tentacles of *Gibellula pulchra* (Ascomycotina) are growing from the carcase of a dead spider.

Bracket fungi (*Hymenochaete villosa*) (Basidiomycotina).

Lentinus connatus
(Basidiomycotina) is also
a saprophyte.

187

The largest fruit body growing in the soil
at Belalong was this solitary *Strobilomyces*
at 20 cm tall.

biosis is usually obligatory, and the fungus may be specific to one or only a few kinds of phytobiont. The plants, however, may have the capacity of symbiosis with a wide range of fungi, usually simultaneously. Moreover, seedlings may have fungal symbionts different to those of established plants, so that the mycobionts evidently replace one another as the plant matures. In such communities, there may be high diversity among fungal symbionts on roots of the same species of trees. In Mixed Dipterocarp Forest, as at Belalong, several genera of dipterocarps possibly share the same species of mycorrhizal symbionts.

The mycobiont may constitute 35-45% of the dry weight of ectomycorrhizal roots, in contrast to perhaps only 10-15% of endomycorrhiza. In the heaths, etc. (Ericaceae) the fungus constitutes up to 80% of the symbiotic association by weight. Although this partnership is expensive in terms of energy, it may have permitted the Ericaceae to colonize poor, acidic soils, such as the kerangas or montane soils of Brunei Darussalam.

Orchids (Orchidaceae) are charac-

LICHENS

Lichens are composite organisms, consisting of a dominant fungal partner and one or more photosynthetic partners. The resulting composite, organised structures behave as independent entities. The fungal partner (mycobiont) in most cases is an ascomycete, whilst the autotrophic partner (photobiont) on which the success and longevity of the lichen symbiosis depends, may be a green alga or a cyanobacterium. Photobionts, in lichens, come from a small number of genera, most of which occur widely in nature, whilst lichen mycobionts are exclusively lichen-forming and are taxonomically diverse, many coming from groups which also include non-lichen-forming taxa.

The lichen symbiosis is one of the most successful known in nature. Lichens are extremely widespread, being found in all parts of the world, occupying many different habitats, some very inhospitable in terms of exposure to extremes of temperature or dryness. Lichens are often very sensitive to pollution and some are key indicators of unspoilt habitats.

Lichens are very variable in appearance and may be encrusting (**crustose**), scaly or leaf-like (**foliose**), or tufted like a miniature shrub (**fruticose**), and may grow directly in soil, or be attached to stones or rock, or colonise tree bark or leaf surfaces. Lichens are abundant in forest environments.

Many orchids, such as this flowering *Dendrobium cinnabarinum*, cannot grow without a fungal partner.

teristically associated with fungi usually basidiomycetes. The seeds of many orchids will germinate only in the presence of suitable fungi. The orchid mycorrhiza is unique because the endophytic fungus also supplies the plant with carbon, at least during the orchid's seedling stage. Mature orchid plants, however, appear to be non-mycorrhizal and are autotrophic.

Distinct from mycorrhizae are the **rhizomorphs**, aggregations of the hyphae into thicker threads or strings which are produced by various species. The rhizomorph may develop as a preliminary to the formation of the fruit body and may thus have a root-like function, leading from some underground source such as a termite nest, e.g. the agaric genus *Termitomyces*. Other rhizomorphs extend across the substrate and help to spread the fungus.

Also notable in Belalong forest are the tangled, tough, dark brown or black threads of the horse-hair fungi, which often bind together dead twigs, leaves and living stems, particularly in damp gullies. These represent several species, notably of the genus *Marasmius*. Their small fruit-bodies are borne at intervals along these threads.

Luminescent fungi offer a visual treat at night in the Belalong forest. The luminous structure may be a dense patch of hyphae spread over the forest floor or investing a dead twig, steadily glowing a mysterious blue green light, vanishing into invisibility when illuminated by torchlight. Some may involve the entire fruit body; others, the cap only, shining atop a dark stalk. The function of luminescence is uncertain.

SEASONALITY OF FUNGI

While the fruit-bodies of the harder bracket fungi (polypores) are often perennial, repeatedly adding new layers of growth, those of many other fungi appear only at certain times of year. In the tropical rainforest of Brunei Darussalam, seasonal flushes may be associated with the return of wet weather after periods of low rainfall. Wetting of the substrate apparently stimulates the formation of fruit-bodies, which then emerge in striking mass fructifications throughout the forest. Different genera or species may respond at different times, forming a succession during the season. The expanded fruit bodies may individually last only a few days before collapsing, their decay often hastened by infestation by the mycelium of other fungi while their invisible spores are dispersed by wind or water.

An encrusting lichen forms large rounded patches
on the bole of a tree in the Belalong forest.

The canopy can be considered the external skin of the tropical rainforest.

CHAPTER 10

THE FOREST ENVIRONMENT

The tropical moist forest, which we have called **rainforest**, presents many different habitats, constantly changing, as trees grow and flourish, set or shed flowers or fruit, drop branches, and die or fall. To this huge variability the great diversity of species can be linked.

Let us therefore consider Belalong forest as an environment, not forgetting that this environment extends above the upper canopy and below the soil surface, and that its present state reflects a long evolutionary history.

THE ANCIENT VEGETATION OF BORNEO

Fifteen million years ago, a tropical rainforest of some kind extended across South East Asia to land that is now Borneo, but there are few clues as to its structure and composition. Later, alternating cold (glacial) and warm periods of the last few million years of earth history had important consequences on the local vegetation. Episodes of global cooling by 2-6 °C brought about

An ancient ice-cap moulded the summit of Mount Kinabalu.

PROFILE DIAGRAM

A profile diagram is a side-on sketch of all the trees on a narrow strip of forest, usually about 60 m long by about 7.5 m wide. The land is first surveyed, then all the trees within the strip are measured – their total height, height to first branch, diameter at breast height (**dbh**: conventionally at 130 cm above the ground, or immediately above the buttresses, if present) and their positions along the strip are recorded. The

Kuala Belalong 200 x 25ft.
profile diagram along ridge,
1800 ft (c. 550m).
Trees exceeding 15ft. only.

Profile diagram of Belalong forest by P. S. Ashton. In total, 92 trees are shown representing 45 species, in 24 Families. D1–D7 show 18 dipterocarps, of 7 species.
[Reproduced with permission from P. S. Ashton. 1964].

huge extensions of the continental glaciers of polar and temperate regions, locking up the surface water of the world as ice, and thereby lowering the level of the sea. At the height of the final Ice Age, some 18,000 years ago, position of each tree relative to the 'front' of the strip is also noted, so that trees may be placed behind each other as necessary. For each tree a sketch of the shape of the crown with the main branches is also made. The profile may be simplified by omitting all plants below 4.5 or 6 m high.

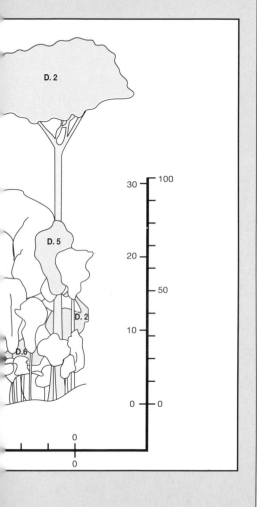

Sea and Java Sea were exposed as dry land (the Sunda Shelf), joining Borneo, Sumatra and Java with continental Asia.

At this time a permanent ice cap covered the summit of Mount Kinabalu and evidence of ancient pollen, preserved in wet peat deposits and lake sediments, clearly shows that montane forest occupied lower elevations and must have expanded to cover areas much greater than its present extent.

It also appears that rainfall was reduced and more seasonal in incidence, creating conditions in which open woodland or savannah vegetated much of this huge extension of lowland habitat on the Sunda Shelf. High-canopy closed forest probably persisted only on damp soils and in river valleys. Such vegetation, akin to present lowland rainforest, must have been restricted to scattered, fragmentary stands, perhaps stressed and locally depleted.

The last glacial period ended some 12,000 years ago, or Before Present (BP). It was followed by rapid climatic warming which reached a peak about 5,000 BP, when sea levels stood 5-10 m above present chart datum.

195

RE-INVASION OF THE LOWLAND

At this time the shoreline of northwestern Borneo must have retreated behind the inland margin of the present coastal swamps and river deltas. A small marine recession and the accumulation of alluvial sediments and peat deposits have subsequently enlarged the lowland area suitable for rainforest.

the sea surface was as much as 120 m below its present level and, as a result, the Gulf of Siam, southern South China

Given the long life expectancy of

The soil surface is covered with a thin layer of leaf litter.

Among other plants of the forest floor, seedling selangan batu (*Dipterocarpus*) are distinguished by their pale green first leaves, with elongated drip tips.

trees, and the long generation time, it may be plausible to explain some of the complex diversity seen in these forests as a reflection of the fresh re-invasion of present lowland habitat.

STRUCTURE OF THE FOREST

The upper leaf layer of the forest canopy is an efficient capturer of incident light and radiant heat, while the lower layers act as a progressively intensifying filter. Moisture, as mist or rain, is also progressively captured in the forest profile. Winds, which have both desiccating and mechanical effects, act more strongly at upper levels. There are thus important local gradients in micro-climatic factors including light, relative humidity, air temperature and

WEST RIDGE PLOT

In Plot AAU1, the Dipterocarpaceae are the most important family (derived by summing measures of relative density, diversity and dominance), followed by the Euphorbiaceae. The most numerous species within 1 ha plot was perah (*Elateriospermum tapos*, Euphorbiaceae) with 35 trees, followed by rengas (*Gluta laxiflora*, Anacardiaceae), 26 trees and resak (*Vatica odorata*, Dipterocarpaceae), 21. The most diverse Family was Dipterocarpaceae, with 28 species in the plot, followed by Euphorbiaceae, 21 species and four other families with more than 10 species (Myristicaceae, Burseraceae, Ebenaceae and Myrtaceae). In basal area, out of a total of 40.79 sq. m, meranti (*Shorea parviflora*) and kumus (*Shorea laevis*) (Dipterocarpaceae) were the dominant species (12.3% and 14.7% respectively); the Family Dipterocarpaceae accounted for over half the basal area in the plot. The tallest tree measured was a kumus, nearly 62 m high, emergent above the canopy at 30-40 m above the ground.

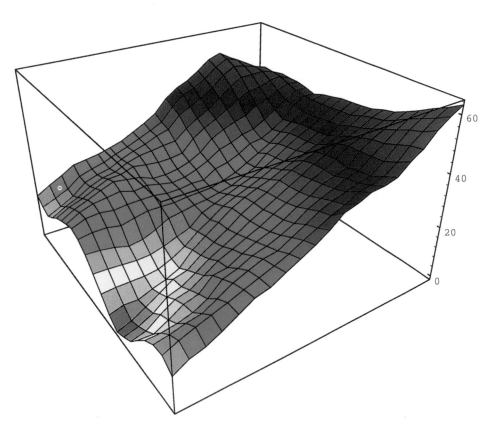

Three dimensional topographical representation of Plot AAU1. The vertical scale is in metres and the near side is to the north.

air movements. The forest has an insulating effect, so that climatic variability is moderated towards the ground. Near the forest floor, prevailing conditions are most constant, with low light intensity, moderate temperature and high humidity.

The forest is multi-layered. In mature lowland Mixed Dipterocarp Forest, as many as five vertical layers or storeys can be recognised: a discontinuous **emergent** layer of the crowns of very tall trees which stand above the more uniform **canopy**, which also consists of the massive crowns of large trees. Below the canopy, and often merging with it, is a shaded **subcanopy**, composed of smaller trees adapted to the lower light regime beneath the canopy. An **understorey** or shrub layer, consisting of small trees and shrubs is often distinct immediately above the lowest, the **herb** or ground layer, which includes the rather sparse forest floor vegetation of seedlings and herbs.

The soil surface is covered in litter, the fallen leaves, twigs and bigger limbs of trees, among which grow herbaceous plants. Pockets of decayed organic matter provide a rooting medium for small plants at any height above ground: in fissures, crevices, forks, leaf axils and in the foliage of epiphytes themselves.

This layered structure can be seen in the profile diagram (pp. 194-5), which represents a section through a portion of the Belalong forest. Three tall emergents are included in the profile, the tallest, a kumus (*Shorea laevis*), 54 m high. These stand above the main canopy which, in this profile, is at about 30 m. The subcanopy layer merges with the canopy except at the left hand end where it is distinct. The shrub and herb layers have not been included in the profile, which is limited to plants over about 4.5 m high. While this notion of layering does not take into account the dynamic nature of the forest, it has proved useful in describing the vertical distribution of other plants and animals.

The profile illustrates one aspect of the structure of the forest. A plan survey presents an alternative view. On the East Ridge at Belalong two 1 ha permanent plots were established in 1991/92: Plot 01 (near Pondok Bujat) and 02 (alongside Jalan Tengah), in which all trees exceeding 10 cm dbh were enumerated and their positions mapped; in Plot 02, all herbaceous plants were also

The tallest tree in Plot AAU1, a kumus (*Shorea laevis*), at nearly 62 m.

Diplazium crenatoserratum (Woodsiaceae) confined to the dry upper ridge tops at Belalong.

Diplazium cordifolium, confined to moist slopes or valleys.

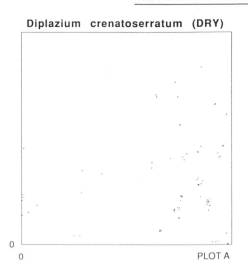

Diplazium crenatoserratum (DRY)

0
0   PLOT A

D. crenatoserratum in Plot AAU1; orientation as on p.101. Each dot represents one plant.

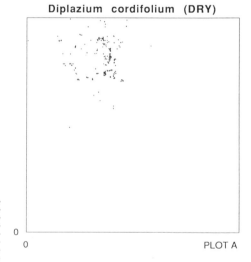

Diplazium cordifolium (DRY)

0
0   PLOT A

Distribution of *D. cordifolium* in Plot AAU1; orientation as on p.101. This plant is restricted to the moist valley (compare topographic map p.197).

enumerated. Another 1 ha Plot (AAU1) was set up on the West Ridge by a team from Aarhus University, in which all trees above 10 cm dbh were enumerated, as were all herbs. The East Ridge plots occupy the top of the ridge, while Plot AAU1 is situated on the slope immediately below the ridge. Other plots were also set up for special studies, including a 6 ha plot to study the distribution and ecology of trees of the genus *Macaranga*.

Topography influences herb diversity and abundance. Plot AAU1 drops some 60 m towards the northeast (See topographic map, p. 197) and the majority of individuals and species occur on the lower slopes rather than near the ridge top. Some species, such as *Begonia*

GAPS AND FOREST DYNAMICS

Trees die and fall from disease or old age, or from windblow or landslip, and make gaps of varying size in the forest. These gaps are gradually filled by new trees and eventually the mature forest profile is restored on that spot. This cycle is endlessly repeated so that the forest as a whole forms a mosaic of different stages of maturity. Three stages can be recognised in this cycle - gap, building and mature phases. The forest profile shown illustrates the mature phase at the ends, and the building phase in the central portion. The occurrence of gaps of various sizes and various ages in the forest is one of the most important factors contributing to heterogeneity and to species richness of the forest as a whole.

Shallow-rooted on the thin soils, trees fall every day in these steep valleys. One fallen, creeper-tangled giant can smash a score of smaller trees in its shade.

sp. and the terrestrial filmy fern *Trichomanes singaporeanum* are confined to bare, steeply inclined soil surfaces between roots of trees. Others are restricted to a floodstream extending through the lower centre of the plot. Different species have different habitat requirements, as indicated in the two distribution maps of two ferns of the same genus, *Diplazium* in Plot AAU1.

Gaps may be of any size. At Belalong rather large gaps form as a result of landslips on the steep unstable terrain (See Chapter 3), while smaller gaps result from windblow or tree-death. Gap size influences the species which will grow in the next phase of forest regeneration. In small gaps, the seedlings already established in the shade of the understorey may fill the space available but in large gaps a dif-

A small landslide creates a gap in the forest.

ferent group becomes important. These are the so-called **pioneer** species – plants whose seeds germinate only in the open conditions of large gaps, and then generally grow faster but are shorter-lived than the species forming the mature forest (known as **non-pioneer** or **climax** species). Although there is no absolute division but, rather, a continuum of requirements for seedling establishment, it is possible to recognise these two groups of trees which differ broadly in their ecological requirements.

Pioneers usually grow in gaps open to the sky, in which full sunlight reaches the ground at least part of the day. Many pioneer species produce large numbers of small, well-dispersed seeds which will increase their chances of colonising new gaps. The trees generally grow rapidly on establishment within a gap, and many have light soft

201

Where treefall has created a gap allowing sunlight to penetrate, pioneer species, including *Mallotus,* have responded with rapid growth.

wood. In South East Asia the genus *Macaranga* are well known pioneers.

In Mixed Dipterocarp Forest the seedlings of canopy dominants and emergents can germinate and establish themselves in the shade. The seedlings

Sunflecks on the forest floor.

The contrast between gap (in the foreground) and the understorey is clear.

LEAF DYNAMICS OF GAP AND UNDERSTOREY SEEDLINGS

The morphology and rates of stomatal conductance, net photosynthesis and respiration of leaves of gap and forest understorey seedlings have been compared to give an insight into the growth strategies of seedlings in these two contrasting environments.

The species investigated included four emergent dipterocarps (*Shorea falciferoides, Shorea leprosula, Para-*

Juvenile kapur paji (*Dryobalanops lanceolata*) in a gap.

shorea macrophylla and *Dryobalanops lanceolata*), two canopy species (*Drypetes* sp. and *Aporosa lunata*, both Euphorbiaceae), and two pioneer species, a mahang, or sedaman (*Macaranga trachyphylla*, Euphorbiaceae), and a banana (*Musa* sp., Musaceae). The pioneer species were confined to the gap while all other species were present both in the gap and understorey.

The leaves of the gap seedlings were significantly thicker than those of the understorey. In each case the **specific leaf area** (that is, the area in sq. cm per g) of gap seedlings was substantially less than that of the plants of the same species growing in the shade of the forest understorey. The stomatal density was on average 40% greater. These patterns are consistent with those expected of typical 'shade' and 'sun' plants, where differences in levels of photosynthetically active radiation are associated with such differences in leaf morphology.

Stomatal conductances for leaves of gap seedlings fell into two categories – high rates for the pioneers and more conservative rates for the non-pioneers. In the understorey the stomatal conductances although lower than gap values were surprisingly high considering the associated very low level of photosynthetically active radiation.

All seedlings in the gap had high rates of net photosynthesis, although those of the pioneer species were again significantly higher than those of the canopy and emergent species, giving the pioneers an advantage at this early phase of gap colonisation.

Based on apparent quantum yields, understorey seedlings tended to be photosynthetically more efficient than gap plants; also light compensation points and rates of dark respiration were lower for understorey plants than for those of the same species growing in the gap. These features may be important in allowing the emergent and canopy seedlings to establish in the very low light of the understorey.

Physiological comparisons were made of tree seedlings and understorey plants in sunlight and in shade.

Measuring photosynthetic rates using a cuvette attached to an Infra-Red Gas Analyser.

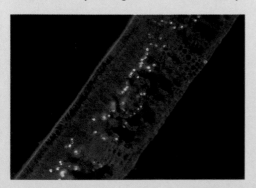
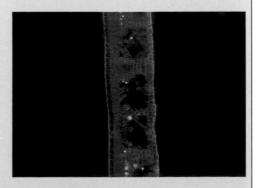

Transverse sections of the leaves of gap (left) and understorey (right) seedlings showing thicker leaves and more chlorophyll-containing tissue in gap seedlings (micrograph showing autoflorescence – red indicates chlorophyll *a*, gold – oil droplets, lime-green – cellulose).

of these non-pioneer trees survive and grow, albeit very slowly, under low light levels and such seedlings may exist for many years under these conditions. Some respond to very small increases in light, perhaps caused by the creation of a tiny break in the canopy far above. These typically grow rather slowly and have hard, dense timber. Other climax species will only start a growth spurt if there is a substantial increase in light, as when large gaps are formed. Some climax species can then grow rapidly and produce light, low-density wood.

Thus, whenever a gap in the canopy is created, by whatever means, there is a substantial increase in the light energy reaching the seedlings

VARIATIONS IN LEAF PHYSIOLOGY AND MORPHOLOGY WITHIN A SINGLE TREE

At Belalong, a brief study was conducted on a 32 m tall kapur paji (*Dryobalanops lanceolata*) canopy tree, using a single-rope technique to gain access to leaves in different vertical positions. The tree selected was monopodial, and had distinct layers of leaves at 31 m, 28 m, 25 m, 21 m and 19 m, corresponding to the main lateral branch pattern. Morphological and physiological comparisons were made between young, fully expanded leaves from the different layers, and also from leaves sampled from 10 randomly selected understorey kapur paji seedlings (=0m) adjacent to the main study tree.

There were distinct morphological and physiological differences between leaves from the top canopy and the understorey, for all measured parameters. Characteristics of leaves from intermediate height positions within the canopy tree were generally similar to those of the top canopy leaves, though intermediate values were apparent for mean leaf area and specific leaf area (lower in top canopy leaves).

Anatomical comparisons revealed substantially greater thickness of total leaf, upper epidermis and palisade layers in top canopy compared with understorey leaves (intermediate leaves were not examined). Drip tips were considerably longer in the understorey leaves.

Mid-day water potentials were lowest in the canopy leaves and highest in understorey leaves. Morning and afternoon stomatal conductances were higher in canopy compared with understorey leaves; afternoon closure occurred in canopy leaves. Stomatal density was lowest in the understorey group and highest (approximately double) in the top canopy leaves. Leaf water content was highest in the understorey leaves, with no height effect within the main tree.

Studying the morphological and physiological characters of leaves from the forest floor to the upper canopy.

SPECIES RICHNESS IN TROPICAL FORESTS

One of the great unresolved challenges facing tropical ecologists is the explanation of how species richness arises, and how ecologically similar species are able to co-exist. Simply stated, why are some species rare and others common, and what factors prevent the extinction of the rarer species?

Two broad approaches to the problem exist. The first school invokes resource partitioning, and according to this view, a species will ultimately be eliminated from the community unless it is competitively superior for some resources at least some of the time. A second school emphasises the role of local history instead and chance processes in determining the composition of tropical plant communities. According to this view, competition among species, as a community-shaping process, is of minor importance.

'marking time' on the forest floor, giving them a chance to realise their full potential. The seedlings must change their physiology to meet the new resource conditions, especially those of increased light intensity and different light quality. At the same time some components of the soil **seed bank** also respond to the change in the conditions and pioneer species, adapted to grow in these gaps, join in the rush to utilise the newly available resources. In such a large opening, the seedlings of climax species are in competition with those of the pioneer species which may rapidly colonise the gap and temporarily overtake them. As time passes, climax species eventually come to dominate as the pioneer species become moribund and die.

The growth rate of these young

Juvenile leaves, in the shade, may be a very different shape to those of the mature tree.
Leaves of this young terap (*Artocarpus*) have deeply dissected margins; those of the mature tree
in the upper canopy are shallowly emarginated or entire.

SPECIES RICHNESS – STUDIES ON MACARANGA

In Belalong forest, the eight species of *Macaranga* provide an ideal model for studying the problem of how species richness arises. The eight species are closely related and ecologically similar. Most grow in well-lit patches of forest created by treefalls and landslides, or cling precariously to riverbanks. They grow fast and die young. Their seeds are covered with a thin red pulp and are eaten and dispersed by small forest birds. In these and other ways they are superficially alike but on closer inspection, differences are apparent. Whereas one species grows 30 m tall, with a trunk as wide as a man, another barely reaches 10 m. One species has huge rounded leaves, while others have small leaves with three deep lobes. The seeds of one species are less than a tenth the weight of seeds of close relatives. These differences accord with Gause's principle, that sympatric species must have different niches to coexist: each species exploits limiting resources in a subtly different way. It is equally possible, however, to interpret the results as different evolutionary 'solutions' to the same diffuse selection pressures and to believe that chance events have allowed the mix of species to persist.

To investigate the processes of forest gap formation and forest regeneration on these steep unstable hillsides, a plot was established flanking the Belalong. It covers 6 ha, varying in slope from 30° – 60° and is transected by two small streams. All gaps were plotted, as were fallen trees > 20 cm diameter and all individual old and young trees of the pioneer genus *Macaranga*, the mahang or sedaman.

This work yielded evidence for patchiness in distribution of different species both within the soil seed bank, and in the subsequent adult population. When a tree fruits, many of the seeds fall beneath the parent crown, or are dropped close to their source by bird dispersers. Some of these seeds may remain dormant in the soil until, by chance, a light gap is formed by a treefall above them. Hence most of the seeds which germinate will be of the parent species which previously occupied the site. Competition, if it occurs, will therefore be among individuals of the same, rather than different species, and competitive exclusion will be prevented. We may conclude that niche separation, chance events and local history all have roles to play in species coexistence in this rainforest.

Macaranga trachyphylla, one of the common pioneer species of mahang or sedaman.

giants-in-waiting is suppressed in the shady conditions. On average, less than 2% of the sunlight falling on the canopy reaches the forest floor, and the distribution of this filtered light is uneven in space and time.

A striking pattern of light variation is seen as a result of sunflecks, created by shafts of sunlight that penetrate small openings in the canopy. Sunflecks are important resources for understorey plants and may constitute

Macaranga beccariana, another mahang common in the Belalong forest.

On ridgetops where soils are shallow, sprawling extensions of the buttress roots provide anchorage for the large forest trees.

As shown by the flat root plate of a toppled tree, the roots of forest trees are very superficial.

Underneath the leaf litter a dense mat of fine, actively feeding roots enmesh the soil surface, taking up nutrients released by decomposition.

more than 50% of the daily light energy requirements of the slow growing seedlings.

During their development from seedlings to maturity, trees face different physiological challenges, such as the need to adapt to the contrasting environments of the understorey and the canopy. Adaptations are likely to include differences in the physiology of leaves occupying different levels in the vertical forest profile, where increased water and temperature stresses may be expected with increasing height

NUTRIENT CYCLING

There are many mechanisms in tropical forest soils to limit the loss of nutrients from the ecosystem.

Firstly, a rich community of decomposer organisms break down the litter, taking up nutrients into their own structures (**immobilisation**) while simultaneously releasing nutrients for root uptake (**mobilisation**).

Secondly, the mineral soil surface becomes completely enmeshed in a feeding root mat which grows into and through the litter layer as it decays, taking up nutrients as soon as they are released through decomposition.

Thirdly, there are many biological associations that maximise nutrient usage, including mycorrhizae and symbiotic nitrogen-fixing bacteria. All these mechanisms act to minimise losses of scarce nutrients from the forest system by leaching to soil drainage waters and thence to streams.

The forest floor is often densely covered in dead litter. Nutrient-rich root bags, inserted into the surface soil, were used to measure root growth under different types of rainforest at Belalong.

above ground.

In some mature trees there are also morphological differences between the canopy and understorey leaves and there may be differences in the physiology of leaves at the different levels, even on the same plant.

Mahang (*Macaranga*) species are pioneers, most often growing in secondary habitats, or in gaps or by river-

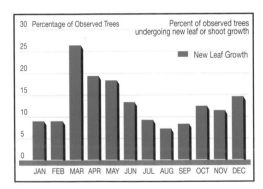

New leaf growth among canopy trees in Mixed Dipterocarp Forest at Ulu Gombak, Peninsular Malaysia (latitude 3° 20'N). Bars show the percentage of observed trees producing new growth, by month, averaged over six years.

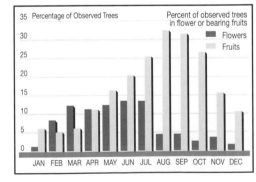

Flowering and fruiting in Mixed Dipterocarp Forest at Ulu Gombak, Peninsular Malaysia. Bars show the percentage of trees under observation that flowered, or carried fruits (ripe or unripe), by month, averaged over six years.

The flush of new red leaves of kasai (*Pometia*).

Perah (*Elateriospermum tapos*) is an annual leaf-exchanger; the old leaves fall as the flush of new red shoots break out (See p. 216).

banks in primary forest.

Eight species commonly occur in Belalong forest: *Macaranga aëtheadenia, M. trachyphylla, M. hypoleuca, M. beccariana, M. kingii, M. winkleri, M. hosei* and *M. hullettii*. They are easily recognised by their segmented, nodose stems, conspicuous stipules and, in many species, large broad leaves.

NUTRIENT CONSERVATION

Except in the narrow riparian zone subject to flooding by the rivers, most mineral nutrients essential for plant growth derive from the weathering of soil parent material and subsequent recycling within the ecosystem. The

The five-sepaled fruits of rengas littered the forest floor in January 1991 and 1992.

In these dipterocarp fruit scattered on the forest floor those of three genera can be distinguished: a two-winged fruit of *Dipterocarpus*, a three-winged fruit of *Shorea* and a five-winged fruit of *Dryobalanops*.

Their ripe fruits borne on the terminal shoots colour the crowns of dipterocarp trees yellow and red all across the Belalong forest.

key element, nitrogen (as nitrate) is highly soluble and readily lost by leaching. It may be replenished by the activity of micro-organisms in the soil or in the root nodules of certain plant species. Atmospheric nitrogen may also be converted into a form available to plant life by electrical discharges (lightning) during thunderstorms and then be carried in solution during rain.

Rain is therefore a significant route by which nutrients are imported. Light rainfall (less than 4-5 mm) may be entirely intercepted by the canopy; nutrients thereby become available directly to epiphytes and to other plants whereas heavy rainfall drips through the foliage or runs down the tree stems to reach the ground, carrying dissolved nutrients with it.

Seedlings of meranti (*Shorea* sp.) cluster round the parent tree.

est plants are highly successful at scavenging chemical nutrients from all sources: rainfall, throughfall, soil and from decaying leaf litter at the soil surface. Success depends on features including aerial growth and root architecture, the soil type and soil biology, local topography and climate. Nutrients in rainfall are taken up by direct absorption or by epiphytes, but the main source of nutrients for plant uptake is by the decomposition and recycling of the dead matter of the forest itself. Decomposition processes occur rapidly in the rainforest soils. Layers of leaf litter at the soil surface are thin, but are maintained by more or less continuous litterfall from the canopy.

The fine mesh of active feeding roots of forest trees do not penetrate far below the soil surface. Structural roots may be deeper, and are important for

Seasonal burning of forest clearings for shifting cultivation can also cause the airborne transfer of large amounts of nutrient-rich ash. In August 1991, large areas of forest were cleared and burnt in parts of Sarawak adjoining Temburong district. As a result, Belalong forest was shrouded in thick smoke, and fragments of charred leaf fell as pale grey flakes.

Tropical rainfor-

Oaks, mempening (such as *Lithocarpus*, bearing acorns in February 1992) occur throughout the Belalong forest, proportionately in greater number at high altitudes.

At 600 m, the trees are smaller than at lower altitudes and buttresses are less pronounced.

Altitudinal zonation determines the physiognomy and species composition of climatic climax forests. It is a feature of the distributions of many groups of plants and animals found within them.

anchorage and for water uptake in dry conditions. On the superficial soils of ridgetops surrounding the Belalong valley, the dipterocarp trees have gigantic woody structural roots which spread widely on the soil surface and in cracks of the rocks to provide anchorage. Treefalls expose vast, shallow root plates where the tree has toppled over.

SEASONALITY

As we have seen at Belalong (See Chapter 2), there is generally a dry period in the early part of each calendar year, followed by a variable season of moderate rainfall, a second less rigorous dry spell and finally, in the closing months,

The hypothesis tested on Bukit Belalong was that lower temperatures and increased moisture reduce decomposition, restricting nutrient cycling and limiting growth.

The forest was studied at three altitudes (200 m, 500 m, and 850 m) and at each of these altitudes three 0.25 ha plots were laid out. In each plot all trees greater than 10 cm dbh were measured, tagged and identified and features such as buttressing and presence of adventitious roots were noted.

Floristic differences are slight between the low and mid plots, but in the lower montane forest at the highest altitude the Dipterocarpaceae decline markedly in importance, with the complete disappearance of genera of large trees such as *Dryobalanops* and *Dipterocarpus*. The Myrtaceae and Fagaceae become more prominent and the conifer *Podocarpus* is found in one plot. Epiphytic bryophytes and terrestrial herbs are much more abundant, both good indications of the more humid climate.

The stature of the montane forest also changes; the tallest tree in the top plots was found to be only 32 m high compared with 60 m in the low plots. The canopy surface is much more even, without the giant emergents of the lowland forest. The maximum dbh measured in the top plots was 80 cm compared with 160 cm in the low plots, and stem density increases from about 500 per ha to about 700 per ha in the top plots.

Small litterfall was measured for one year to determine relative productivities and examine nutrient cycling. Forty metal litter traps were set out at each altitude and these were emptied

Conifers, such as *Podocarpus motleyi*, are characteristic of ridge and montane forest.

at 2-3 weekly intervals. After collection the litter was dried quickly and sorted into four fractions: leaves, small wood, reproductive parts and trash.

Litterfall was unevenly distributed through the year with a major peak in April 1992, following a dry period at the beginning of the year. At about this time there was also a spectacular mass flowering of the forest trees, particularly at the lower altitudes. The rates of litterfall were 10.7, 10.4 and 8.3 t per ha per year, respectively; the reduction in the top plots is statistically significant.

However, when compared with data from other South East Asian forests it is found that this montane forest is more productive than any other montane forest, and even more so than lowland forests.

Measurement of the standing litter crop and comparison with the annual input

In the lower montane forest the trees are generally smaller and pole-like.

The lowland plots at 200 m have larger trees (the pole has 20 cm scale).

treatments (N, P, K and NPK). In total, 240 bags were buried at random co-ordinates in the plots and recovered after eight months. Fewer roots were produced in the montane forest, but fertilisation did not significantly promote productivity.

If the montane forest has adequate nutrients and solar radiation what is limiting its growth? Drought has been shown to stunt montane forest in the Philippines. As soils at the top of Bukit Belalong are shallower and stonier than at low altitudes, this might be considered a factor. It should be remembered, however, that rainfall is 20% higher at the summit and the profusion of mosses and herbs indicates a consistently damp environment. There are tall trees growing in the shallow soils of ridgetops at low altitudes, so it seems unlikely that drought is stunting the trees of the montane forest. Temperature differences seem the most likely explanation for the change in forest type on Bukit Belalong, slightly reducing productivity and eliminating lowland species that prefer warmer conditions.

of fresh litter can be used to determine rates of decomposition. The litter layer decomposition quotient (litter input/standing litter crop) is an index that can be easily compared between sites. The values measured on Bukit Belalong were 3.3, 2.7 and 2.6 which indicate a slight slowing of decomposition at the higher altitudes, but they are still comparatively rapid and do not indicate a tendency to accumulate undecomposed litter.

Since work on other tropical mountains has shown nitrogen to be the nutrient most likely to limit montane forests, its cycling was studied most intensively on Bukit Belalong. Chemical analyses showed a 20% reduction in litterfall nitrogen in the top plots, but the actual concentration of nitrogen does not change with altitude, so the montane forest does not use nitrogen more efficiently which would be expected if nitrogen was in particularly short supply. It therefore appears that the montane forest is not limited by nitrogen and this conclusion is supported by several other lines of work.

A study of nitrogen mineralisation and nitrification was carried out on soils from each of the plots and it was found that there were no significant differences in either the levels of soil nitrate or ammonium or their rates of production. Fine root productivity was measured using mesh bags filled with Perlite with different fertilisation

The litter crop was collected using traps which were emptied every month.

A mahang (*Macaranga*) grows amongst the montane vegetation.

tent, it may occur at intervals determined by internal factors such as the age and health of the tree, and influenced by external events including daylength, temperature or the availability of water and nutrients.

Among most tree species of this forest, a mature leaf will survive for longer than a year while succeeding generations of leaves are produced; such trees are evergreen.

Among some of the species in which leaf growth is intermittent, the old leaves will all fall together, to be replaced by a fresh crop of new growth; these have been called **leaf-exchangers**. The old leaves may fall before, during or after the growth of the re-

a pronounced wet season. There is certainly no time at which plant growth is wholly inhibited but this climatic cycle does evidently impose matching patterns of seasonal activity. We can expect that these are similar to those found elsewhere at comparable latitudes under similar climatic regimes in the Sunda region, for instance, as in Peninsular Malaysia.

In such forest there is great variation in patterns of growth between species of trees and, within species, between trees of different ages and states of growth. Shoot growth and the production of new leaves by a tree may be continuous or intermittent; if intermit-

placement crop. In some species, relative timing of leaf-loss and replacement may vary at different places or in different years.

Those trees which are periodically bare between the fall of one generation of leaves and the growth of the next have been called **deciduous**; this represents no more than delayed leaf exchange. Examples of leaf exchangers in Belalong forest are petai (*Parkia*), perah and mengaris.

The pattern of flowering and fruiting among the forest trees at Ulu Gombak, averaged over the years, showed a single annual peak. Observations in Belalong forest have been too

SOILS BIOASSAY

A bioassay was carried out, using local hill rice, padi bukit (*Oryza sativa*). About 6 kg of soil were collected from six positions within 1 m of the edge of plots at 153 m and 887 m elevation. Unshaded experimental sites were chosen at KBFSC (61 m) and on Bukit Belalong (913 m).

Soil from the two elevations was divided, and half of each sample used at each of the two experimental sites. At each site, 500 ml of soil was put into each of 48 14-cm pots. Into each pot, seven pregerminated rice seeds were placed at 3 cm depth. Eight fertiliser treatments, each replicated six times, were made for each soil at each altitude, with untreated water from the nearest stream as control. Once they appeared above ground, the number of plants was reduced to five in each pot.

After 14 days, the plants were removed from the pots, and their roots washed with water before air drying.

At both altitudes, shoots were larger when grown in soils from 153 m, but this effect was overshadowed by the much greater mean height of plants grown in both soils at 61 m compared with those at 913 m.

Root/shoot quotients were markedly greater in all plants grown at 913 m. Some fertilisation treatments did cause statistically significant increases in growth, but the increases at the summit were never enough to match the growth at the lower site.

It was concluded that differences between the climates were more important than any effects of soil fertility in reducing growth at the summit.

217

Studying rice seedlings.

scanty to confirm a similar pattern, but there was some evidence of an annual fruiting peak coinciding with the later months of the year. Twice in succession in November-January, fruits of rengas were scattered on the forest floor. In one year the jungle durians were ripe at this season, falling in January 1991; but there was no fruiting 12 months later. Conversely, we noted widespread flowering among the *Koompassia* trees (mengaris and kempas) in the early months of 1992, not recorded in 1991.

The dipterocarps of these forests also flower to some extent in the early part of each year and, from time to time, there is massed gregarious flowering activity among many (or all) species in an area. The intervals between mass flowering can be from one to eight years. Again, at Belalong, observations are limited, it was found that many dipterocarps fruited abundantly at the end of 1990, flowered in early 1991 and again fruited heavily at the end of that year. The exceptional species was the riparian ensurai, which flowered along the river banks in broad synchrony, at half yearly intervals corresponding to the two dry seasons.

The wings of most dipterocarp fruit when ripe are brightly coloured, in shades of yellow or red. Borne at the ends of the twigs, they make a showy display. Their function in dispersal is limited. Most fruits land less than 50 m from the parent tree although they can be blown much further by the gusting winds associated with rainstorms. The crop can be vast, so that the colourful winged fruits of dipterocarps carpet the forest floor in patches.

Dipterocarp seeds, like those of most other trees sharing these tropical rainforests with them, have limited powers of dormancy. If conditions are not suitable for prompt germination, they remain viable for only a few weeks. In several dipterocarp species, the seed carries reserves in the form of oil. These provide a rich food source for animals, vertebrate and invertebrate and, in the case of the illipe or engkabang (certain *Shorea* species) are of commercial value. It is commonplace to find that a high proportion of the seed crop is damaged, mostly by the depredations of weevils and other beetle larvae. In one example, a mersawa (*Anisoptera*) in Peninsular Malaysia, P. F. Burgess found that, as a result of insect attack, only 8% of the fruit crop was viable.

In normal seasons, as a consequence of high seed predation and un-favourable conditions for germination, the numbers of seedlings produced are low. 1992 was exceptional at Belalong. In November of that year, dense patches of young seedling dipterocarps and mengaris/kempas (*Koompassia* species) were spread over the hillsides. However, many of the strangely shaped cotyledons of the young dipterocarps were being consumed by insect larvae. The ultimate success of this new generation of trees remains to be seen.

EFFECTS OF ALTITUDINAL ZONATION

As we have noted, on tropical mountains increasing altitude brings progressive changes, of which the Mixed forest at Belalong is an example. These changes involve structure and appearance, as well as the species mix of trees and other plants.

Sunlight increases in intensity with altitude and has a dwarfing effect by preventing the lengthening of internodes. Winds increase and will alter conditions of evaporation and shoot temperature. Drying winds will shrivel young shoots, stunt growth on the windward side, and generally cause bushy and flat tops by accentuating the growth of side shoots. On the other mountains it has been considered that probably the most important factor at high altitude is the thinning and impoverishment of the soil under the increased frequency and intensity of rain. At lowered temperatures and under water-logged conditions, decomposition slows and peat accumulates. Towards any summit there is less hold for

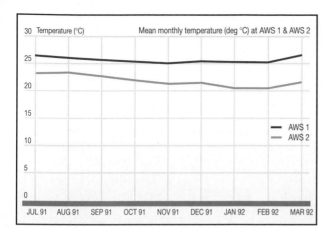

Temperature and rainfall variation
at the two automatic weather
stations (AWS 1 & 2)

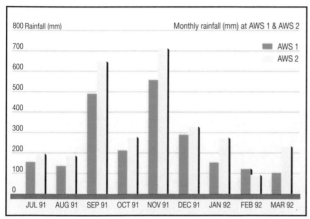

the roots and less for them to grow in; furthermore water drains more rapidly. There may be neither enough soil nor, in dry weather, enough water for large trees to survive.

The climatic differences between the lowlands and uplands were shown by the contrast between simultaneous records taken at the two automatic weather stations, AWS 1 at Kuala Belalong (61 m) and AWS 2 on Bukit Belalong (913 m). The plots show increased rainfall and lower temperatures that typify the montane zone.

Between the two elevations, 61 m and 913 m, the computed lapse rate in mean daily maximum air temperatures was 0.35°C/100 m and in mean daily minimum air temperatures was 0.22°C /100 m. Mean daily totals of solar radiation were virtually identical at the two stations, but more variable at the summit due to the intermittent formation of a cloud cap.

The mechanisms involved in the changes seen on moving from lowland to montane forest are unclear, but certainly vary from mountain to mountain. The primary influence on vegetation is climate, with cooler wetter conditions at higher altitudes. Other factors, such as soil acidity or nutrient status, may however, have secondary effects.

A group of plant-sucking bugs (Flatidae, Homoptera). Inset: a detail.

CHAPTER 11

INVERTEBRATE BIODIVERSITY

As the tabulation in Chapter 5 showed, in numbers of species worldwide, animals greatly exceed plants. We have also seen how species diversity among several groups of animals is higher at equatorial latitudes than elsewhere. These trends peak in the tropical rainforests.

DIVERSITY IN THE FOREST

The term **invertebrate** is applied to animals that are larger than microscopic but which lack an internal jointed bony skeleton (a defining character of the **vertebrates**). For these animals, none of which reach a large size, the forest provides an enormous variety of places to live or shelter: the soil; the litter layer of the ground surface; streams and standing water; the trunks, bark and wood of trees, externally and internally; branches, twigs, leaves and flowers; and the air around, and above the canopy. High species diversity is reflected in many, varied adaptations for specialism in diet and mode of life, in places of rest or concealment, and in nesting or breeding sites.

All animals are heterotrophs. For many, the forest vegetation provides the primary food source, offering a huge variety of hard and soft tissue, including wood, bark, leaves, flowers and fruits, alive or dead. Also eaten are

223

VIRUSES

The viruses are minute and non-cellular, consisting simply of nucleic acid genetic material enclosed by protein. In order to replicate and multiply, a virus must enter a cell of a suitable host. Once there, it redirects the activities of the host cell to produce more virus particles, which are released and can then infect other cells. Different viruses vary in their capacity to survive outside their hosts; this affects the mode and ease of transmission. In some cases the virus may be resistant to the hazards of the external environment but in others, direct host-to-host contact is required. In many cases, however, the virus is carried by an intermediary, the **vector**, such as an arthropod that feeds by sucking plant juices or animal blood. All types of organism, including bacteria, fungi, plants and animals, are susceptible to infection. Most viruses are highly host-specific. Some are pathogenic, injurious or lethal to the host, but many are only mildly incapacitating or harmless. As a consequence, viral infections are probably normal and universal among living organisms, and it must be the case that a huge diversity of viruses exist in Belalong forest.

Caterpillar (*Thliptocerus* sp.) feeding on the fern *Nephrolepis hirsutula*.

Moth larvae of one group, the Lithini, are among the few insects able to deal with the protective chemicals in fern leaves.

Caterpillars of one species, *Entomopteryx amputata*, were successfully reared on ferns at KBFSC. During two months in 1992, over 100 fern-feeding individual insect larvae were collected at Belalong, including 13 species of moths. These represent several Families, and use a variety of different feeding methods, emphasising that the ability to overcome the effects of the ferns' chemical protection must be spread among a diversity of species.

Adult geometrid moth
(*Entomopteryx amputata*).

Fern-feeding caterpillar (Geometridae) immediately after ecdysis (note shed skin in centre of frame).

Land planarians (*Bipalium* sp., Turbellaria) move slowly, producing a sheet of mucus.

THE ECOLOGICAL SIGNIFICANCE OF PROTOZOA

Protozoa are single-celled heterotrophs and, hence, the smallest animals. Free-living protozoa occur in most aquatic habitats (freshwater or marine) and are very numerous in soils. They are also widespread symbionts, parasites or pathogens of animals and plants. Their principal ecological role is as grazers of bacteria. Their activity, so important in nutrient recycling, is proportionally greater than their biomass: in soils, protozoa contribute about 30% to the standing crop biomass but nearly 70% of the total animal respiration.

fungi, the bodies of decomposer micro-organisms and, of course, other animals which become the prey of predatory species.

Many plants offer a range of positive attractions: to pollinators, to seed dispersers, to protectors and other animals involved in symbiotic associations. Some plants add to the complexity by a variety of devices, structural or chemical, to protect themselves against over-exploitation.

In these ways, the animals play many roles in the maintenance of the forest ecosystem. Energy enters the food chain via the primary consumers - the animals that eat plants, fungi or saprophytic micro-organisms. Subsequently, specialist and generalist animal predators fill the role of secondary or tertiary consumers. Other dependent relationships of all sorts also exist: **commensalism** (the interdependent sharing of living space), symbiosis and external or internal parasitism. Many animals, especially insects, alter their diet at different life stages and thereby have progressively changing roles in the ecosystem.

All animals contribute to the recycling of energy and organic compounds through the excretion of waste products while alive and, ultimately, through the decomposition of their remains after death.

SOFT-BODIED INVERTEBRATES

The soft-bodied invertebrates include many obscure and little known groups of animals, together with the more numerous and familiar flatworms (Platyhelminthes), roundworms (Nematoda) and segmented worms (Annelida). Most flatworms are internal parasites of other animals but members of one Class, the turbellarians (Turbellaria) are free-living, generally inhabiting freshwaters or damp habitats on land. The brightly coloured,

A snail (*Cyclophorus* sp., Cyclophoridae) on a treetrunk.

A snail (*Schistoloma* sp., Pupininae); note the red muscular 'foot'.

elongated land planarians encountered in Belalong forest belong to this group.

NEMATODES

The roundworms or nematodes (Nematoda) are unsegmented, elongated, tapered at each end and circular in cross-section, varying in size from minute up to 15 cm long. Taxonomic differences are difficult to discern and the total numbers of species existing worldwide can only be guessed: present conjectures suggest half a million. Nematodes are ubiquitous. Many species are parasitic in the guts, circulatory systems, body cavities or tissues of other animals, or within the tissues of plants; here they can have debilitating or injurious effects. Many more species are free living in water or soil. Nematodes are undoubtedly important in the ecological processes of all terrestrial environments, including tropical rainforests, but have not been studied at Belalong.

SEGMENTED WORMS

The segmented worms (Annelida) of note in Belalong forest are the earthworms and leeches. No study was made of the former, but the latter can hardly be avoided! Leeches have 34 internal body segments, a set of three horny jaws, ten eyes and a muscular suctorial disc at each end of the body. Those that draw most attention at Belalong are the land leeches (Family Hirudidae), whose generic name, *Haemadipsa*, appropriately means "blood drinker". The dedicated naturalist can watch with fascination as an approaching leech loops across the path or drops auda-

WOODLICE (ISOPODA) OF BELALONG FOREST

A survey of the woodlouse fauna in the Belalong forest revealed 20 morpho-species, showing variation in their distribution, pigmentation and locomotory behaviour. Some species occur in leaf litter throughout the forest, from the valley bottoms to the summit of Bukit Belalong. These appear to be generalists, tolerant of changes in local humidity and litter quality. Other species are restricted to rich, stable accumulations of litter that are constantly damp - for example, litter trapped in the axils of salak (*Salacca)* or aping (*Arenga)* palms. These seem to be specialist forms, adapted to more specific microhabitats within the forest.

The species of woodlice found in the Belalong forest can be sorted into four eco-morphological groups: Runners, Creepers, Jumpers and Rollers. Members of the different groups can be distinguished by their general appearance and their escape behaviour. Runners have smooth, elongated bodies and long, strong legs; when disturbed they run away at speed. Creepers have broad, flattened bodies with short legs and a reinforced dorsal exoskeleton. Their body form is adapted to life in the matrix of narrow spaces within leaf litter, rotting wood and rocky microhabitats; when disturbed, they move deeper into the matrix in search of refuge. Jumping woodlice are similar to Runners in appearance and ordinary locomotory behaviour, but they respond to sudden disturbance with high somersaulting jumps. Rollers, like Creepers, have a thick dorsal exoskeleton and short legs, but roll into a ball. Representatives of all four eco-morphological groups can be found in the vicinity of Kuala Belalong Field Studies Centre.

Four eco-morphological types of woodlice: (The scale is in millimetres)

1. A creeper

2. A runner

3. A roller

4. A jumper

Among the millipedes (Diplopoda) the body segments are fused in pairs so that each apparent segment bears two pairs of legs. When a millipede is walking, its legs move in sychronised waves.

The pill millipede (*Oniscomorpha*) rolls up when disturbed.

The large glossy millipede (*Thyropygus.* Harpagophoridae) feeds on vegetable detritus.

228

MILLIPEDES AND CENTIPEDES

Centipedes (Chilopoda), such as this *Scolopendra* possess one pair of legs per segment, and are predatory.

The long-legged centipede (*Scutigera*) is a fast moving predator of smaller vertebrates.

ciously from adjoining vegetation in search of the meal of mammalian blood that it needs so urgently. The unwary will find that the hirudin, injected when biting from the leech's modified salivary glands, is an effective anticoagulant.

At least three species occur at Belalong. These are: the common ground leech, brown above, with a black median dorsal line, paler brown below; the large ground leech, with two submedian black stripes enclosing a pale area down the length of the back, with an indistinct median line; and the painted (or stinging) leech, greenish brown on the upperside, with a yellow marginal stripe along each side, and pale brown underside. The painted leech is a capable climber, often seen on low vegetation. Its bite delivers a mild sting, generally enough to draw attention to its presence.

MOLLUSCS

The phylum Mollusca is represented at Belalong only by snails (Class Gastropoda), non-segmented invertebrates with a body consisting of a head, and a single, muscular 'foot', richly supplied with slime-secreting glands, above which the main body mass is enclosed by the **mantle** and protective shell. The feeding apparatus of a snail involves a rough organ, the **radula**, by which the mainly vegetable diet is broken down.

ARTHROPODS

The arthropods (Arthropoda) form the most numerous and diverse Phylum of the animal kingdom, containing perhaps 85% of all extant animal species. They are characterised by a hard external body covering, generally divided into segments, and jointed limbs. The principal Classes are crustaceans (Crustacea), millipedes (Diplopoda), centipedes (Chilopoda), insects (Insecta) and spiders, mites and allies (Arachnida).

CRUSTACEANS

Most crustaceans (Crustacea) are aquatic, but only the woodlice (Isopoda) are so well adapted to living on land that they never have recourse to water. Nonetheless, woodlice remain vulnerable to desiccation and live mainly in damp, sheltered habitats, especially in the A horizon of the soil (See Chapter 4) and in surface leaf litter. They mainly eat dead plant matter. The young are born alive and, while small, are brooded in a pouch-like enclosure below the female's body (the **marsupium**), where they draw sustenance from glandular secretions. The number of young in the marsupium varies among different species of woodlice, ranging from as few as six to more than sixty. Tropical woodlice generally have smaller broods than those from temperate regions.

INSECTS

Insects (Insecta) are the most abundant Class of arthropods on land and in freshwater. The body of the adult is divided into three parts: the head, generally bearing a pair of antennae and a pair of compound eyes; the mid-part or **thorax**, from which arise three pairs of jointed walking legs; and the hind part, or **abdomen**. In many Orders of insects, the adult form bears wings, also arising from the thorax; in all but the flies (Diptera) there are two pairs of wings, but in some bugs (Hemiptera, suborder Heteroptera) and in beetles (Coleoptera) the forewings are modified to form hard, protective covers for the membraneous hind wings, which provide the power and lift for flight.

Insects develop from eggs, although in some species they may be retained within the body of the female so that live young are laid. Among the primitive insects (including the Orders Ephemeroptera, Odonata, Orthoptera, Hemiptera, Phasmida and Termites), the egg hatches to a juvenile form or **larva** which possesses the 3-part body form of the adult, including legs but not wings. The larva grows in progressive stages, periodically shedding its hard outer skin by a process known as moulting or **ecdysis**. At each moult, the developing larva emerging from its old skin looks a little bit more like the final, adult form. In the latter stages of larval growth, wing buds may be discernible, but only adults have func-tional wings. Among the higher insects (including Neuroptera, Lepidoptera, Trichoptera, Diptera and Hymenoptera), there are distinct life stages after the egg. First is the larva, quite unlike the adult in form, generally maggot-like, with or without short legs. The larva is active and feeds voraciously. Its growth again proceeds by a series of moults, but culminates in the production of a **pupa**, a non-mobile form, often sheltered within a protective covering. Within the pupa, a radical restructuring of the body organs occurs, a process known as **metamorphosis**. The adult that finally emerges is the active reproductive stage, occupying a niche totally different from that of the larva.

ODONATES

The odonates (Odonata), an ancient Order of insects known as fossils dating back some 300 million years, comprise about 5,000 species worldwide, divided into two suborders, the Anisoptera (dragonflies) and the Zygoptera (damselflies). The two suborders are distinguished as follows: Anisoptera hold their wings outstretched when at rest; in most species the eyes are very large and actually touch each other on top of the head; the forewings and hindwings are differently shaped. The Zygoptera are delicate, slender-bodied species which at rest hold their wings closed over the body or only partly

231

A male *Rhinocypha biseriata* guarding his female while she lays her eggs inside a hole in a log.

About 300 species of Odonata occur in Borneo, of which 27 species (7 Anisoptera and 20 Zygoptera) have so far been recorded at Belalong. While some species occur on the river and larger streams, many fly in the forest, sometimes in the canopy and are often crepuscular. Forest dwelling species are furtive and inconspicuous. They may breed in water-filled treeholes and bamboo internodes, as well as in small pools or rivulets.

The best sampled and most conspicuous group, found almost entirely by the river at Belalong, is the damselfly superfamily Calopterigoidea, including 12 species in the three Families Calopterigidae, Chlorocyphidae and Euphaeidae. These calopterigoids are mainly adapted to well oxygenated, fast running water, but the larvae of some species found in slower flowing backwaters of the stream are unusual among the Odonata in having abdominal gills which presumably improve their respiratory efficiency.

Commonest is *Neurobasis chinensis* (Calopterigidae), whose brilliant green males patrol along the edges and over the river wherever the current is reasonably fast. Its larvae have been found clinging to stones in shallow riffles.

Within the genera *Vestalis* (Calopterigidae), *Rhinocypha* and *Euphaea* (Euphaeidae), all species are very similar to one another. Ecological segregation is apparent in the slightly different microhabitats chosen by territorial males and ovipositing females. Female chlorocyphids and euphaeids insert their eggs in dead wood, guarded while they do so by the male. Territories are always in the vicinity of fallen logs and branches but the different species choose areas of different current velocity.

A male *Rhinocypha aurofulgens.*

spread; their eyes are well separated, placed at the sides of the head; and the forewings and hindwings are similarly shaped, although sometimes differently coloured. The aquatic larvae also show differences. Only damselfly larvae have external palmate 'tails', which are used for respiration. In the larvae of Anisoptera, the gills are concealed within the rectum.

Their large eyes, coupled with fast, manoeuvrable flight equip the dragonflies and damselflies to excel as aerial hunters, preying mainly on other insects. As larvae, they are also predators, but strictly aquatic. Eggs are laid in all sorts of freshwaters in the forest, depending on specific adaptations. The mating pair often fly attached and in tandem during the process. The larvae spend many weeks, even years in water, moulting periodically as they grow. The wings develop progressively with each growth stage, but do not become functional until the larva finally emerges and undergoes its last moult from which the adult emerges.

233

Bornean odonates, showing the difference in appearance of a dragonfly *Sieboldius japponicus* (Anisoptera) above and a damselfly *Euphaea subcostalis* (Zygoptera) below.

TERMITES

Termites (Order Isoptera) are predominantly tropical in distribution. Species diversity declines from a peak in tropical rainforests to zero beyond latitude 50°N, where minimum temperatures do not allow them to survive. One of the highest records of richness occurs in lowland Mixed Dipterocarp Forests in Borneo, where 59 species have been collected from a locality in Sarawak.

Termites live in colonies and the highly organised social structure may account for their success. At the heart of each termite colony is one (occasion-

PROCESSIONAL TERMITES

Processional termites of the genus *Hospitalitermes* (Macrotermitidae, subfamily Nasutitermitinae) are conspicuous in the forest. Their nest sites may be within the trunks of standing trees or around the stumps of fallen trees and free-standing on the forest floor. Soldiers are constantly present at the nest entrances.

The processional trails leave the nest in the afternoon or evening and return the next morning, foraging taking place through the night. Food balls from the foraging site are taken back to the nest, and contain a mix of wood constituents, bryophytes, blue-green algae and fungal hyphae, lichens and their spores.

Four colonies were studied in 1991: three within Plot 01 and a fourth, just outside the plot to the northwest. For 65 days, these four nests were examined each morning between 0800 - 0900 hours. Trails were marked by laying coloured wool along the route taken by the termites from the nest entrance to the feeding site, or to the point where the trail ascended to the canopy. The trails were then surveyed, using tape and compass. On 26 days, the formation of outgoing trails from nest 1 was observed.

The termites did not emerge to forage every night. The number of nights spent foraging varied between the nests, from 46% to 72% of the number of days they were studied.

Nest 1 was watched most closely. No individual scouts were seen as the termites started their foraging trails. Frequently, many trails left the nest at the same time, retreating and advancing independently. After up to 6 hours spent doing this, one (or occasionally more) trails would become consolidated and surplus trails would retreat. It remains a mystery how the final foraging trails were chosen and others rejected.

The trees that the trails finally ascended varied in diameter from 8 to 148 cm. There was no relationship between tree diameter and the number of times it was visited, perhaps denoting that the final canopy feeding area was not confined to the crown of the tree climbed.

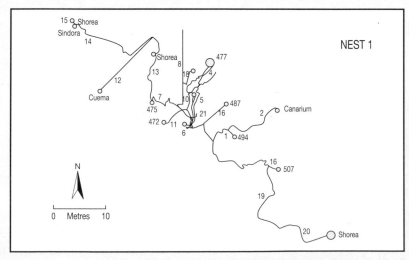

Plot of trails of *Hospitalitermes* from nest 1.

From these four nests, in 85 instances, the tree that was climbed could be identified to Family or genus. In 39 cases, involving only four individual trees, this was meranti (*Shorea*); next most frequent was 11 visits, to two pelawan (*Tristania*) trees, followed by six visits to three ubah (*Eugenia*) and six to two *Cratoxylon*. For trees within Plot 01, these figures did not relate to relative abundance: meranti accounted for over 10% of all trees in the plot, and therefore was under-represented in the termites' choice, whereas pelawan accounted for only 0.3% and was over-represented.

Many trees were re-visited, and on these subsequent occasions the route invariably followed a previous trail. The number of times a trail was used or re-used varied from 13 times (nest 1, trail 10, going to tree 477), to only once (nest 1, trail 11, going to tree 472); mean of all trails, 2. Parts of trails were reused many times, with branch trails to different trees (see plot of trails of nest 1). The part of a trail being re-used was followed exactly by the termites, despite intervals up to two months between use.

The length of the trails from the nest to the point at which the termites ascended into the canopy was very variable: the longest was 65 m and the shortest 1.6 m. The mean trail length was 27 m.

The distribution of the nests was not uniform. Nests 1 & 4 were not near any other nests while nests 2 & 3 were only about 30 m apart. The trails of these two nests interdigitated to some extent, and some trails from each nest led to the same trees (trees 115 & 151), though simultaneous foraging up these trees from both nests did not occur.

Based on the sample of Plot 01 (3 nests), Plot 02 (one nest) and 1 ha plot on the West Ridge (no nests), the average nest density of *Hospitalitermes* at Belalong is approximately 1.3 per ha.

Mounds of *Dicuspiditermes nemorosus*, built of faecal material, are usually at the base of a palm or buttress root.

235

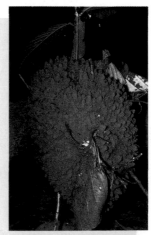

Nest of *Lacessititermes*, one of the rarest in Belalong forest. This nasute termite feeds on rotten wood.

The nest of *Microcerotermes dubius*, distinguished by numerous downward-pointing spikes, which help to shed rain.

TERMITES AT BELALONG

Some termites build their nests in the soil but the greatest diversity of nesting sites occurs above ground. Nests may be attached to tree trunks, in the buttresses of large trees, inside old tree stumps and even hanging from climbers or palm leaves. **Epigeal** mounds (on the soil surface) and **arboreal** nests can exceed 75 per ha.

Odontotermes spp., feed on dead wood but have subterranean nests and are members of the fungus-cultivating Macrotermitine subfamily. These are perhaps the most numerous termites found in the soil (more than 400 per sq. m), responsible for about two-thirds of all the consumption of organic matter by termites in the forest.

Also common is the leaf-litter feeding termite, *Longipeditermes*, (Termitidae, subfamily Nasutitermitinae). The distinctive feature of all members of this subfamily is a long snout or **nasus** at the front of the head, through which a toxic chemical can be ejected at attackers. This organ has made the nasute termites very successful, allowing them to forage in the open. *Longipeditermes* are black in colour, an adaptation to surface foraging during the day, with soldiers distinctly dimorphic in size. They have about eight colonies per ha and, when foraging, they form short columns which fan out across the forest floor when feeding, occupying an area of about 10 sq. m.

Leaf and wood fragments form the diet of many termite species that feed on humus-rich soil, of which the mound-building termite *Dicuspiditermes nemorosus* is most abundant. Although the mounds are obvious, the termites are rarely seen, because the workers forage for food underground. The nest is defended by 'snapping' soldiers which have asymmetrical mandibles. The right mandible is flat and can be drawn across the left mandible and held in place by a central twist in the left mandible. When released, the right mandible springs outward to deliver a heavy blow capable of incapacitating an invading ant or flicking it away.

Microcerotermes dubius occurs in relatively low abundance, with one or two colonies per ha. It can have a significant influence beyond its numbers. This species attacks live trees, boring into the woody tissue and producing extensive galleries in the trunk eventually causing the tree to die. Covered runways radiate out from the original nest along branches allowing the termites access to adjacent trees and the subsequent formation of new nests.

Trees of different sizes may be affected including understorey and canopy species. If a sufficient number of trees are killed a canopy gap may form, which can be a significant factor in forest dynamics.

ally more) fertile female, the 'queen', accompanied throughout her life by a fertile male ('king'), and capable of producing hundreds, and in certain species, thousands of eggs per day. The larvae have the potential to develop into adults of three **castes**: workers, soldiers or reproductives. The workers are responsible for construction and maintenance of the nest, gathering food and tending the eggs and larvae, while the soldiers' role is to defend the colony if attacked. The workers feed the queen and king, the larvae and also the soldiers, whose mouth-parts are so highly modified for defensive purposes

The spherical nests of the nasute termite *Bulbitermes* are often attached to a vine or supported on a sapling.

237

that they are unable to feed themselves. Only the reproductive caste, known as **alates**, develop wings. At certain times of the year, usually after seasonal rains, the alates swarm, flying from the nest to seek a partner of the opposite sex. If successful, the new pair will shed their wings and seek a suitable nest site where they can mate, produce eggs and thus found a new colony.

THE ROLE OF TERMITES IN THE FOREST

Most termites feed on dead plant material; with fewer species in the forest attacking living plant tissue. The Rhinotermitidae consume rotting dead wood and usually nest at their feeding site inside logs and branches. A major constituent of all termite diets is therefore **cellulose**, a form of carbohydrate which is the main structural and strengthening component of plant tissue. Termites are unable to digest cellulose directly, but within the guts of many species there are symbiotic micro-organisms capable of breaking down cellulose and thus making it available as a nutrient to their termite hosts. Exceptions are members of the important termite subfamily Macrotermitinae, which lack these micro-organisms. Instead, within their nests, they cultivate the fungus *Termitomyces* on combs that the workers construct from their faeces. On the combs, the fungus breaks down cellulose and concentrates nitrogenous and other nutrients which the workers then re-ingest. With this efficient system, the Macrotermitinae can consume fresher plant litter than other termites which rely on organic matter that has been partially decayed by free-living fungi.

In Belalong forest, it is likely that termite numbers exceed 15 million per hectare. As a result of their vast numbers, termites are important members of the rainforest community, and their activities have a significant impact on the ecosystem. Three major factors make termites so important. Firstly, they consume large quantities of dead organic matter, thus directly influencing nutrient and carbon cycling in the forest. Indirectly, comminution of plant material enhances overall decomposition by improving the conditions for micro-organisms to act. Secondly, termites alter the physical structure of the environment by translocating organic material from feeding

INSECT NOISES

ENSIFERAN
STRIDULATION

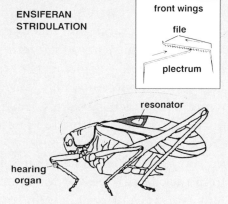

front wings

file

plectrum

resonator

hearing
organ

The sound-producing mechanism of
crickets and katydids.

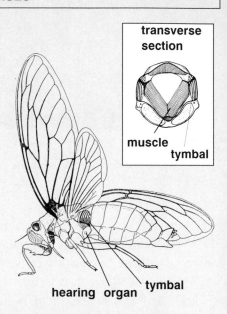

transverse
section

muscle

tymbal

hearing organ   tymbal

Sound-producing mechanism of cicadas.

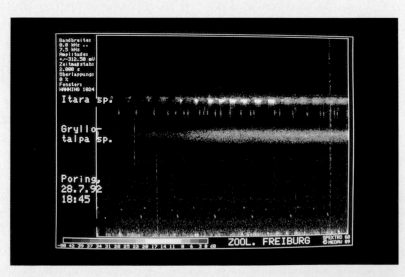

Two crickets forming the principal components of the late dusk chorus: a mole cricket
(*Gryllotalpa*) generates the lower frequency band between 3.7 and 3.95.1 kHz, and the eneopterine
cricket (*Itara*), singing at a higher frequency of 5 kHz (pulse intervals 76 ms, chirp-length around 1 s,
chirp intervals around 1.6 s). After several chirps, additional individuals of *Itara* fall in,
forming a chorus, which results in a blurring of chirp structure.

In the daily cycle of changing sounds in Belalong, many noises are produced by insects, their chief purposes to attract potential mates and/or advertise territory.

Orthoptera: Many Orthoptera produce noises, using a great variety of sound-producing mechanisms. At Belalong, it is the group known as long-horned grasshoppers (Ensifera) that produce the majority of buzzes and chirps to be heard in the forest at night. Among these, crickets (Gryllidae) and katydids (Tettigoniidae) employ a mechanism at the underside of the forewings, consisting of a scraping organ (**plectrum**) which is rubbed against a file-like row of cuticular teeth during inward movements of the wings. Loud, repetitive signals with a narrow-band carrier frequency between 4 and 9 kHz, are generated by the rhythmic wing movements of male crickets. Wing movements produce pulses of sound which can be mixed to produce more complex sounds, called 'chirps'. Carrier frequency, pulse rate and chirp are species-specific, and are important stimuli for the innate behavioural responses of searching conspecific females.

The katydids employ the same sound producing mechanism but, in general, their songs consist of a broader range of frequencies, reaching up to the ultrasonic. At Belalong, however, species of *Tympanophyllum* producing narrow carrier frequencies have been observed; these belong to the leaf-mimicking tettigoniid subfamily Pseudophyllinae.

Phasmida: At least six genera are known to have sound-producing organs; in all cases the noise appears to be used only for defence. Three of these genera occur in Borneo, and one species, *Haaniella echinata*, is common in the Belalong forest. *Haaniella* and *Heteropteryx* (subfamily Heteropteryginae) both have short wings which are used to produce a noise (which sounds like a combination of rustling and clicking) by rubbing the wings together. This stridulation is produced in response to attack and is often combined with raising the abdomen, and stabbing or pinching movements of the powerfully spined hind legs. Two species of leaf insects (*Phyllium*) recorded from Borneo produce sounds by rubbing together the thickened third segments of their antennae.

Cicadidae: The calls of cicadas are among the loudest noises of the forest, a variety of buzzing, whining or trumpeting sounds, each distinctive to one species. The sound is produced by **tymbals** situated at both sides of the first abdominal segments. The stiff cuticular tymbal membrane is drawn inward by a strong muscle and flips back by its own elasticity, thus producing a click. The songs consist of a complex sequence of clicks arranged in a species-specific time sequence, with a characteristic spectrum of higher harmonics. It is amplified by an airsac which can occupy a large part of the abdomen.

Lepidoptera: Several butterflies and moths also produce sounds, although these are less strident. The mechanisms differ from one group to another. For instance, some hawk moths (Sphingidae) pass air through the mouth region to produce a squeak; an example of a 'squeaker' in the Brunei fauna is the Death's head hawk-moth (*Acherontia lachesis*). Males of some other hawk moths (e.g. *Psilogramma menephron*) produce sound by rubbing patches of stiff scales at the apex of the abdomen and on the genitalia to produce a hissing noise. Other Lepidoptera produce sound by rubbing roughened surfaces on opposite pairs of legs, leg against wing or wing against wing, or by tapping or vibrating specialised structures of the external skeleton (tymbal organs). In some cases, these noises fulfil the general functions of communication with mates or territorial rivals but, among night-flying moths, the sounds produced are of high frequency and evidently designed for defensive purposes, to confuse predatory bats by jamming their sonar (echo-detection) system or to tell the bat that the moth is distasteful, poisonous and best avoided.

239

FOREST SOUNDS

The daily cycle of cicada calls dominate the sounds of Belalong forest. Calling begins in the middle of the day, increasing progressively towards dusk. The loudest caller of all has been nick-named the 'six o'clock' cicada, because it normally sounds off around the hour of dusk. After preliminary clicks and grunts, one will lead with its sonorous, trumpeting call, to be followed by others as the chorus moves up or down the valley. Changes in light intensity and in humidity of the air evidently affect the timing of onset. In the wet weather of October/November (1991), on heavily overcast and rainy afternoons, individuals called as early as 1630 hours and the chorus could develop locally from 1640 hours - often ceasing in subsequent rain; but resuming around the expected 1800 hours. As the day finally darkens into night, the cicadas fall silent, and other vocalists take up the task.

Acacus sarawacus - a non-winged member of the Necrosciinae, a widespread stick insect in all parts of northern Borneo.

sites, and building nests and galleries, while their subterranean tunnels, affect rates of water infiltration. Thirdly,

being so numerous, termites are an important food resource for other animals. Ants, among the invertebrates, and many vertebrates, such as the pangolin, Malay civet and sun bear, are termite predators. Some species of frogs and snakes are termite and ant specialists, while others, including lizards and squirrels, will feed opportunistically on termites wherever large numbers concentrate, for example, at feeding sites, foraging columns and nest entrances. When alates emerge to swarm, they are eagerly hunted by insectivorous bats.

STICK INSECTS

The stick insects (Order Phasmida) are predominantly tropical in distribution, especially in forest environments. There are over 2,900 named species, worldwide, of which some 300 are recorded from Borneo. They feed on soft plant tissue, typically shoots and leaves, and most are nocturnal.

By day, rely for concealment largely on stillness and the cryptic colours and outline of their elongated, twig-like bodies. A few are spiny, and some emit strong smelling, irritating liquids when disturbed. Nonetheless, they frequently fall prey to insectivorous predators.

Members of the subfamily Lonchodinae drop their eggs to the ground and, as a result, tend to live near the ground and are seen more

Dares validispinus - Stick insects of this ground-dwelling genus occur in all parts of Borneo.

Carausius everetti - No formal description of the male shown here has yet been published.

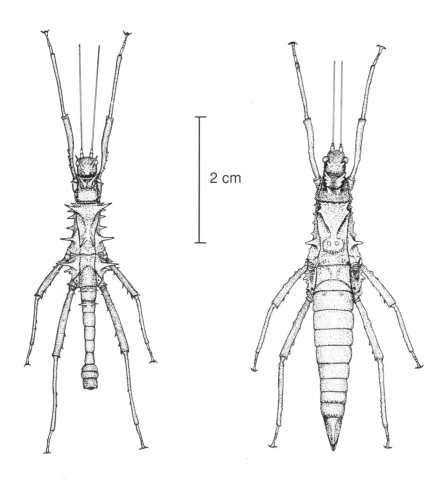

2 cm

The stick insect (*Hoploclonia cuspidata*), male and female, collected at Belalong, rediscovered for the first time since the original description of the species in 1906.

STICK INSECTS AT BELALONG

During 12 nights, adults of 30 species were collected; this included representatives of five of the nine subfamilies which occur in Borneo. With the exception of members of *Acacus, Dares, Haaniella* and *Lonchodes* (four genera which seem to be found everywhere in Borneo), most species were represented by a single example. Of 26 species identified, one is new (*Lonchodes harmani*) and eight are species for which either the male or the female is unknown.

The subfamily Necrosciinae includes most of the winged phasmids amounting to about half of all species known to occur in Borneo. Many, perhaps most, seem to live in the forest canopy and as a result a few are commonly found. Many species glue their eggs to the trees or push their eggs into cracks in the trees, and do not need to descend to ground level.

The range of sizes was large among the collection: a male *Presbistus fulvipennis*, at 3 cm long, is one of the smallest in Borneo, and a female *Pharnacia saggita*, at 28 cm long, is the second longest phasmid ever recorded from Borneo, much longer than previous records of this species, and one of the longest insects in the world!

often. The two most numerous genera of this subfamily in Borneo are *Lonchodes* and *Carausius*.

Members of the subfamily Heteropteryginae lay their eggs in the soil and many, perhaps all, hide on the ground during the day. They are quite heavily built, more like pieces of tree bark rather than sticks. Three genera, *Dares*, *Hoploclonia* and *Haaniella* were found.

A mantis of normal shape, showing its grasping forelegs and widely set eyes.

Cryptic colouration camouflages this mantis most effectively on a dead leaf.

GRASSHOPPERS AND MANTISES

The grasshoppers and crickets (Orthoptera) have biting mouthparts and are primary consumers in the forest. Most are winged, and in some, the wings take strange shapes, part of elaborate modifications that disguise the form of the animal – often as a leaf.

The mantises (Mantodea) are medium to large-sized predaceous insects,

SEXUAL CANNIBALISM

Sexual cannibalism is the predation, by one sex or another (but ordinarily by the female), of a mate before, during or after mating. This behaviour is common among mantises. Every male mantis will approach a prospective mate slowly and cautiously, but nonetheless about one in three will fall prey to her. Yet, even when the head and thorax of a male are consumed, mating can successfully be completed. The sperm is then stored internally, within the female, allowing fertilization to occur later, at the right moment. The evident advantage to the species is that the mated female receives an ideal package of extra food at the right time to nourish the eggs developing within her!

The orchid mantis (*Hymenopus mantis*) mimics a flower.

Many grasshoppers and crickets (for example, this pseudophylline bush-cricket, Family Tettigoniidae), have independently evolved leaf-like shapes and colouring to conceal them from diurnal predators such as birds.

with an elongate **prothorax** and spiny, grasping front legs which they dart out to catch their prey. Many are cryptically coloured, elaborately disguised.

BUGS

The bugs (Order Hemiptera) are a widespread and successful group of insects, with about 82,000 named species, worldwide. The oddly shaped lantern bugs (Fulgoridae) are often seen at Belalong (See Chapter 5). Bugs are characterised by mouth parts adapted to piercing and sucking. Most feed on plant fluids but some are predators of other invertebrates and a few are bloodsuckers. As a preliminary to feeding, many bugs inject saliva containing enzymes that dissolve part of the tissues of the food organism and, in the predatory species, also disable it. This preliminary injection can be irritating or painful for humans. Their feeding habits can also transmit pathogens, especially viruses, from one plant (or animal) host to another. Many plant-sucking bugs produce conspicuous external exudates, such as foam, or waxy materials which serve as protection, disguise or concealment (See pp.242/243). Some secrete honeydew which is harvested by ants or other insects. Important symbiotic relations are established between the provider bug and the ants that make use of its secretion.

The cicadas (Cicadidae) are large bugs with sucking mouth-parts by which they are adapted to feed off plant juices. A cicada spends most of its life (often several years) underground, as a wingless larva sucking the sap of roots, periodically moulting its skin as its size increases. Ultimately the larva extends its underground tunnel above

Cicadas

The emergence tube of a larval cicada can be more than 10 cm tall.

The empty last larval skin of a cicada, split along the midline, remains clinging to a tree trunk.

The adult cicada (such as this *Dundubia* sp.) is brightly coloured, with well developed wings.

ANTS OF BELALONG

A comprehensive collection made at understorey and ground level 'using protein and carbohydrate baits, litter sorting and extraction, hand collection from vegetation and opportunistic collection from rotten wood, fallen trees and ant plants, yielded approximately 200 morphospecies, of 51 genera. The fauna living in the leaf litter and rotting wood seems to be the richest in species. Litter extraction has shown that ants form 70 - 80% of arthropod individuals in samples. This is consistent with other investigations of invertebrate biodiversity of rainforests.

The giant ant (*Camponotus gigas*) a ground-dwelling, specialist fungus feeder, aggressively defends its territorial area; here, two ants engage in combat.

DIACAMMA

The large, ground-dwelling ponerine ant *Diacamma intricatum* embellishes its nest entrance at the bases of small saplings with a circular to subcircular ring of interwoven twigs, in the centre of which is found the entrance to the colony. These entrances make location of the colony very easy.

The large ponerine ant *Diacamma intricatum* .

The behaviour of this ant in interaction with other species appears to be complete submissiveness: it usually avoids other species of ants at baits, and is only persistent and successful where they are not present. It is a solitary forager, and may be robbed of food by other ants, particularly *Odontoponera transversa*, another ponerine of similar size.

The entrance to a nest of *Diacamma* at the base of a small sapling.

In a 70 m x 80 m gridsquare of 10 m x 10 m squares in Belalong forest, at 275 m altitude, there were 121 nests. Statistical analysis of spatial patterning showed that the nest entrances were significantly uniformly distributed, as opposed to aggregated or randomly dispersed. Although overt aggression between colonies has not been seen, this dispersion of nest entrances indicates that there may be some form of intraspecific competition occurring between colonies of *Diacamma intricatum*. From 28 nests, all ants were smoked out and counted. Nest entrance height proved to be significantly related to colony size, as was nest entrance diameter. Nearer nest pairs tended to have smaller nest entrance heights than further nest pairs, although there was no relation between nest distance and height differences in the nest entrance size.

Some mahang, *Macaranga* species at Belalong are associated with ants of the genus *Crematogaster*, which nest inside the hollow stems. When the plant is colonised by a *Crematogaster* queen,she bites

Macaranga beccariana stem in section showing ant brood.

a hole in the stem and travels to its base where she produces her brood of workers.

Workers also make many small holes along the stem which serve as nest entrances and exits. The ants never leave the plant and apparently derive their sustenance mainly from food bodies (**Beccarian bodies**), small balls of nutrient rich lipoprotein, produced by the plant, characteristically located on the undersurfaces of young leaves and, in some species, also under recurved stipules. The young leaves of *Macaranga* also have at their margins glandular structures which may secrete nectar and are often attended by the ants.

It is generally accepted that the ants protect the plant from herbivorous insects and may also prevent vines from growing on it. The relative degree of ant attendance and the effectiveness of ants in preventing herbivory was tested in four species by Yong Nget Yung and Penroose Saleha.

Penroose examined the relationship between ant density and degree of leaf damage in *Macaranga trachyphylla, M.*

Ants collecting Beccarian bodies from young leaves of *Macaranga beccariana*.

winkleri, M. beccariana and *M. hosei*. She found that in *trachyphylla* and *winkleri*, there was an inverse logarithmic relationship between ant density and degree of leaf damage. In other words, the higher the ant density the less the leaf damage. However, no such relationship was found

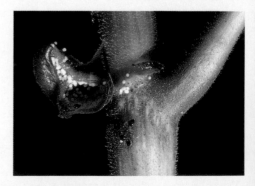

Beccarian bodies on the stipules of *Macaranga trachyphylla* (stipule folded back).

	trachyphylla	beccariana	hosei	winkleri
Ants per leaf (av.)	60.4	79.6	15.8	25.3
Damage in plants with few ants (%)	10.5	4.4	2.0	1.3
Food bodies under stipules	YES	YES	NO	NO
Increasing damage at low ant numbers	YES	YES	NO	NO

in *hosei* and *beccariana*, in which levels of herbivory were generally low compared with the other two species. *M. trachyphylla* and *winkleri* differ from *hosei* and *beccariana* in that they produce Beccarian bodies under the stipules (recurved into a doughnut shape in *trachyphylla*) as well as on young leaves, which may be needed to sustain larger colonies of ants for the same sized plant.

Almost no herbivores were found on *hosei* or *beccariana*, and it is probable that they are much less generally palatable to herbivores than the other two species. The question why *beccariana* continues to manufacture the food bodies which ensure they are regularly inhabited by ants was tested by Yong, who experimentally removed all ants from *trachyphylla* and *beccariana* plants by injecting their stems with a non-persistant insecticide, and moni-

tored herbivore damage over a period of three months compared with control plants of both species. She found that experimental *trachyphylla* plants from which the ants had been removed were attacked by a wide range of herbivores, including adult and larval Coleoptera, a wide range of Homoptera, several Lepidoptera larvae, especially Lasiocampidae, Nymphalidae and leaf rolling Thyrididae, as well as leaf-mining microlepidoptera, and various Orthoptera.

By contrast, on experimental *beccariana*, few of these were recorded and little leaf damage occurred apart from the formation of galls by cynipid wasps which, in certain experimental plants, was spectacular. The protection of the plant from these wasps may be sufficient to account for the selective value of symbiosis.

A caterpillar of the butterfly *Tanaecia* sp. (Nymphalidae) on *Macaranga trachyphylla*.

If ants are removed from *Macaranga beccariana*, the plants are attacked by gall-forming wasps.

the ground, building a hollow column of soil through which it emerges. It then climbs the stem of a small tree or shrub and takes firm hold with its clawed feet. Here the brown larval skin splits open for a final time and the glittering, colourful winged adult emerges.

ANTS, WASPS AND BEES

The ants, wasps and bees (Hymenoptera) are not only very diverse but in many cases are also colonial, and therefore contribute more individuals than any other Order of insects in tropical rainforests. They show great variation in size, from 0.1 mm length in parasitic forms to 50 mm among large wasps. Mouthparts are of the chewing type, minute but in many cases modified for lapping or sucking. Wings may be absent, reduced, or well developed for powerful flight, two pairs, transparent and similar in form.

The hymenopterans have very varied diets, including plant tissues and secretions, living and dead animal matter; many species are predators or parasites of other insect larvae (including other hymenopterans, as among the fig wasps, p.136); some of the smallest are even **hyperparasites**, being parasitic Hymenoptera within the body of the primary host.

The ants (Formicidae) form colonies, in which there is usually one (or more) egg-laying female (a 'queen')

and many smaller, non-reproductive 'workers'. As among termites, only the reproductive forms are winged. In an established colony, large numbers of winged males and females are periodically produced, leaving the nest in swarms and mating in flight. After mating, the males die and the female seeks a suitable nest site to found a new colony.

Ants have very varied diets: some are predators, some specialist feeders on fungi or plant material; several species associate with plant-sucking bugs that secrete honeydew.

Some plants are structurally modified to provide living space for ants (See Chapter 10). Some such as mahang (*Macaranga* sp.) also produce exudates attractive to ants. In these cases, there

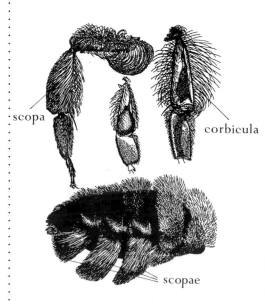

Pollen brush on a bee's leg.

Human perspiration provides minerals attractive to bees: giant honeybees are quick to gather on Tom Mitchell, May 1992.

are assumed to be advantages for both members of the symbiosis.

BEES

Bees are of special interest because it was in tropical habitats of the early Cretaceous era (120-140 million years ago) that the first bees evolved alongside the flowering plants.

Bees are distinguished from wasps by adaptations for gathering pollen as a food source and by the possession of specialised mouthparts including a tubular 'tongue' (**glossa**). Pollen is most often carried by means of modified hairs on the legs or body, but may be swallowed.

Worldwide, there are some 20,000 named species of bees, with about the same number again likely to exist as yet undescribed. Species diversity is not markedly higher at tropical than at temperate latitudes, but the South East

Asian fauna is rich. Bees may be solitary or colonial to varying degrees. The tropics are the centre of the most highly social colonial bees, which have evolved in two lines: the stingless bees and the honey bees. These two groups are numerically predominant in the Belalong forest. Among these bees, each colony normally has one fertile queen; other females are sterile workers.

Bees exploit a range of resources as food or nest material. Most important are pollen, nectar and oils and fragrances from flowers; some species also use gums and resins, or rotten wood, bark, seeds, leaves and other plant parts, sap and fruit juices, animal faeces or urine, carrion, honeydew excreted by bugs, soil and salts and water. Their nesting habits can be categorised as 'diggers', excavating nests in soil, termite nests or elsewhere; 'lodgers', utilising pre-formed cavities, or 'masons', building unenclosed nests of materials found elsewhere and/or secreted by bodily glands (e.g. wax). These habits are not always fixed: honey bees are normally lodgers but may build their combs in the open, as do the giant honey bees (*Apis dorsata*). There are bees parasitic on other, often closely related species: in some cases, one species usurps nests built by other species; others are 'cuckoos', depending on workers of the host species to feed their larvae and some actually kill the larvae of the host.

Bees navigate principally by visual clues and can orientate by reference to

249

BEES AT BELALONG

At Belalong, 22 species of kelulut, the stingless honey-making bees (Meliponinae) were found, out of 29 known in all Borneo, ranging in size from the minute *Pariotrigona pendleburyi* and *Trigona (Heterotrigona) fuscobalteata* (2.5 mm) to the relatively large *Trigona (Heterotrigona) thoracica* and *T. (Homotrigona) fimbriata* (8 mm). Three species known only from Borneo, *T. melanocephala, T. hobbyi* and *T. haematoptera*, are relatively common in the Belalong forest.

There are also four species of honeybees at Belalong. Most common are the giant honeybees *(Apis dorsata)* and the Malesian honeybee *(Apis koschevnikovi)*, with the small *Apis andreniformis [= A. nigrocincta*?], a bee about 8 mm long, and *Apis cerana* seemingly less common. The few other prominent bees observed at Belalong were the nocturnal carpenter bee (*Xylocopa myops*); *Amegilla* sp., a large bee having a tongue among the longest of any bee; and some large megachilids. The complement of stingless bees and honeybees suggests that the bee fauna is intact.

Bees' nests numbered about three per ha. Giant honeybees build open combs, commonly suspended from branches of mengaris (*Koompassia excelsa*)(See p. 132). Virtually all other bees (except those of *Lepidotrigona)* nest in or under the bases of large trees, 90 - 180 cm dbh. Nests of stingless bees were mostly within a few metres of ground level, and all were associated with living trees. All species, except *Trigona apicalis*, produced a resin and wax entrance tube that projected from a few to a few dozen centimetres. Three species nested in the ground under large trees: *T. collina, T. drescheri,* and *T. melina.* A nest of the last species was in the same tree base as a colony of the giant ant (*Camponotus gigas*). *Pariotrigona pendleburyi* and *Trigona collina* were the most common colonies, amounting to over half of those seen. The former frequently had two nests separated by a few dozen centimetres in the same tree, and those of the latter were frequently found in groups of two to four within root systems. The results of attacks by civets or sun bears were seen at the terrestrial nests of *T. drescheri* and *T. melanocephala*; unmistakable claw marks of bears were seen going up the trunks of five trees, and a cavity in one tree had been chewed open, through 6 cm of living wood, at 3 m above ground, exposing a hole 30 x 12 cm - very likely a former nest of *Apis* or *Trigona*.

The biological diversity of temperate and tropical bee communities is difficult to compare, owing the the predominance of social species in the tropics and their near absence in the temperate zone. For French Guiana and Sumatra, in which the total bee fauna in a given forest is approximately 250 and 125 species respectively, about 25% of the bees are stingless bees and honeybees, and 50% are to some degree social. In Mexico and the United States, for comparison, where there are 1,600 and 3,745 recorded bee species respectively, only 12% and 2% are social. The ecological

the direction of polarisation of sunlight. The giant bee will fly by moonlight at half-moon or fuller, and on some nights will gather in numbers round the lights at KBFSC. The stingless bees lay tracks by releasing minute droplets of odorous liquid. By their famous dance language, returning honey bees and stingless bees inform their nest-mates of the direction and distance to food sources. They possess colour vision, but are sensitive to diversity of the stingless bees and honey-bees, which are by definition perennial colonies, must be great since they are active every day and have the opportunity to interact with far more plant species, other resources and natural enemies.

If the lowland forests near Belalong have the same component of honeybees and stingless bees as West Sumatra (approximately 25%) then the total number of forest bees should be somewhat higher than 100 species.

Workers of the Malesian honey bee (*Apis koschevnikovi*), marked in a study of foraging behaviour at baits.

The resin tube that forms the entrance to a stingless bees' nest is continuously added to and can grow to considerable length, periodically breaking off and being renewed.

Tongue extension of a euglossine bee related to the extremely long-tongued bees, *Amegilla*, found at Belalong.

The nest entrance of a subterranean nest of the stingless bee, *Trigona (Heterotrigona) collina*, sprawling along a rock.

shorter wave lengths than man, so that ultra-violet (very short wave lengths) is seen as a colour, but deep orange-reds are not. Foraging bees attracted to a food source rarely attack rivals, apart from group-foraging stingless bees (*Trigona*), which form enormous colonies and discover resources slowly, and subsequently defend these.

The honeybees probably evolved in a habitat similar to Belalong. Their principal resources are found in the forest canopy. The most common bees at Belalong are the giant honeybees and the smaller Malesian honey bees (*Apis koschevnikovi,*) both permanent residents of the forest. Both are very quick to discover resources in the canopy. The latter species usually makes the find first but, as the giant honeybees recruit to the resource, the smaller Malesian honeybees are displaced. This is usually not by aggression, but by the overwhelming numbers of giant honeybees that quickly find the resource after being directed to the general area by their nest mates.

Although not the only insect pollinators active in rainforest (See Chapter 7), bees are generally the most important. Among many bees, the breeding cycles are synchronised with flowering seasons. In this environment, the persistence of high genotype diversity is dependent on outcrossing. For a plant, rooted in one place, often distant from its few and scattered conspecifics in the rainforest, active transport of the pollen (for which a bee is so admirably adapted) is vitally important.

BEETLES

Beetles (Coleoptera) form the largest Order of insects, comprising some 400, 000 described species worldwide, with about 20,000 in Europe and 4,000 in Britain. Easily characterised by their hardened forewings (**elytra**) and bit-

Largest of the beetles at Belalong are the three-horned atlas beetles (*Chalcosoma*).

A male stalk-eyed fly (*Teleopsis belalongensis*), uses his forelegs to clean the surface of his right eye.

ing mouthparts, they show an astonishing range of form and function. This great diversity is a product of three key factors of coleopteran biology. Their range of sizes, often small, enables them to occupy ecological niches not available to other insects.

Flight, an ability possessed by most beetles, means that they can utilise even the most temporary resources such as dung, fungal fruiting bodies, or flowers. Their generalised biting

BEETLES OF BELALONG

A large dung beetle rolls and manipulates a ball of fresh dung.

About three-quarters of all described species belong to just eight of the 160 or so beetle families: Carabidae (ground beetles), Staphylinidae (rove beetles), Scarabaeidae (scarab beetles), Buprestidae (jewel beetles), Tenebrionidae (darkling beetles), Cerambycidae (longhorn beetles), Chrysomelidae (leaf beetles) and Curculionidae (weevils). These families are also dominant in terms of species numbers in Belalong forest. To date 5,600 beetles have been sorted to an incredible 1,668 species.

Beetle feeding habits have led to them occupying almost every level in the food web. Many arboreal species are plant feeders, chewing leaves (chrysomelids) or boring into and living protected inside the plant tissue (mordellids, longhorns and scolytids). These and other plant feeders will support a range of predators such as the carabid beetles and fast-flying clerid beetles, which amass in favoured places

and swoop down on unsuspecting prey. The litter also provides a rich resource to the many saprophagous species. Gaining their energy from the decaying organic matter of the litter they form an important component of the detritivorous food web of the tropical forest. Particularly dominant in this community are the staphylinid beetles, and the many species of fungus-feeding beetles that live on the ubiquitous fungal flora.

Beetles are involved in a great range of forest processes at Belalong, from the removal and recycling of vertebrate dung by the 80-100 species of dung beetle (Scarabaeidae) to pollination. Pollination is one of the most important, and Belalong flowers often attracted beetles: a spectacular record was an aroid (*Epipremnum falcifolium*) which attracted into its inflorescence dozens of large ruteline scarabs (*Peltonotus malayensis*). It is not known how many species of plant depend upon beetles for pollination. However, following pollination, other beetles become a plant's enemy for, as seeds are formed, beetles such as seed-eating weevils start to attack. The results can appear devastating, with up to 100% of some dipterocarp seeds being attacked by weevil larvae. Attack by seed predators, such as weevils, has probably produced selection pressure for the evolution of mass fruiting as exemplified by South East Asian dipterocarps. Mass fruit production, at irregular intervals, ought to make it difficult for potential seed predators to gear their life cycles to the fruiting season – but somehow these weevils have managed it! In this case, clearly, the size of an organism bears no relationship to its ecological effect.

253

mouthparts permit just about every heterotrophic feeding habit, including the parasitoid habit.

Beetle size varies from the smallest litter-dwelling ptiliid beetles, scarcely over 1 mm long, up to the

---

BARK AND AMBROSIA BEETLES

The bark and ambrosia beetles (Families Scolytidae and Platypodidae) are small beetles adapted for a life in tunnels bored under the bark or in the wood of trees. The adult bark beetle bores a brood gallery in which the eggs are laid. Usually a single pair of adults is involved, but in some species a male may have a harem of two or more females. The larvae excavate further tunnels leading away from the brood gallery, engraving a characteristic pattern below the bark.

More important in the tropics are the ambrosia beetles which feed on symbiotic 'ambrosia' fungi which grow on the walls of their galleries. Many of the scolytid ambrosia beetles are closely inbred. Each family produces only one or a few males, which are dwarfed and flightless. They mate with their sisters within the gallery system, and then die there, whilst the mated females fly off in search of new breeding sites. Fungal spores are carried by the female (sometimes also by the male) from the gallery in which she developed, and released into the brood gallery. Sometimes both male and female are involved in gallery construction, but often only the female. The fungal growth forms the food of adults and larvae.

---

impressive three-horned atlas beetles (*Chalcosoma*). Body shape is also modified extensively, depending upon the habits and microhabitat in which the beetle lives. A bizarre Bornean example is the fiddle-shaped and greatly flattened carabid (*Mormolyce phyllodes*) (See p.74). Most beetles, however, are small and cryptic, being hidden away in litter and rotting logs or in the nooks and crannies of living plants and trees.

FLIES

The two-winged flies (Diptera) are very abundant and species-rich in Asian tropical rainforests. Many flies have sucking mouthparts and are dependent on liquid diets, especially plant sap, nectar and fruit juices, or the body fluids of animals. Important groups include the bloodsucking mosquitoes, midges and sandflies, whose bite is irritating and can transmit disease-causing micro-organisms, such as the plasmodium that causes malaria or the virus responsible for haemorrhagic fever. In these cases, the biting fly is termed the **vector**, and prevention of the disease may depend on control of the insect. Other biting flies include the large and aggressive horse flies (Tabanidae).

The compound eyes of some Diptera are borne on the tips of long, rigid lateral extensions of the head. Stalked eyes are a typical feature of males in a few species of different Families, for example the Tephritidae. In the diopsids (Family Diopsidae), both sexes of all species have eye-stalks. In large diopsid species the approximately 2,500 facets of each compound eye have small receptive angles. These provide a high visual acuity, often well

STALK-EYED FLIES AT BELALONG

Male on the left and female on the right of the new species of stalk-eyed fly (*Teleopsis belalongensis*) to show the difference in eye-stalk length.

In South East Asia, diopsids are found close to creeks and rivers. They are a substantial part of the dipteran fauna along these waters, as long as the vegetation is undisturbed. Their larvae feed on decaying plant material, taking part in rainforest ecology by decomposing organic matter (as do many other dipteran larvae). From Borneo, seven diopsid species have been described but, during two short stays in Belalong forest, we found 12 species, most not yet described. Local diversity in this family is evidently higher than hitherto assumed.

In some diopsid species male and females have eyestalks of about the same length. The two largest species from our Brunei samples belong to this group. In other species, especially in the genus *Teleopsis*, males have much longer eyestalks than females and variability of eyespan is high.

Of the diopsids found at Belalong, the smallest (two species of the *Sphyracephala* group) showed the closest affinity to water. We found them on boulders and logs in the river or close to the river banks. The two largest species *Eurydiopsis argentifera* and *Cyrtodiopsis quinqueguttata* were sometimes found distant from the river, several hundred metres

up the slopes. The *Teleopsis* species kept to the river banks or fairly close to smaller creeks uphill. Among the new Bruneian diopsid species *Teleopsis belalongensis* holds a record: the eyespan of large males may reach 20 mm, compared with a body length of only 8 mm. This large eyespan makes eye cleaning a difficult task.

In some sexually dimorphic species, females outnumber males. Typically the flies gather at sunset, usually on an aerial rootlet or a dry vein of a rotten leaf. In most cases a large male is the first to settle on a sleeping site, followed by smaller males and females. Given a choice, females favour a sleeping site already occupied by a large male. Lesser males are often driven away by a large male. Males of equal size frequently engage in highly ritualised fights to win a harem. While this behaviour was thoroughly studied in the Malay species *Cyrtodiopsis whitei*, first observations on the behaviour of two of the Bruneian species, *Teleopsis pallifacies* and *Teleopsis belalongensis* also show competitive behaviour of males at sleeping sites. Allometric data of the two Bruneian *Teleopsis* species and of the Malay species *Cyrtodiopsis whitei* illustrates also a close concordance between Bruneian and Peninsular species.

TEPHRITID FLIES

On Belalong West Ridge we encountered a stalk-eyed member of the tephritid family, *Themara hirtipes*. In tephritids, the female has a normal fly's head configuration; eye-stalks are exclusive to the male. Yet, as among diopsids, the male eyespan is strongly correlated with body length. The width of the visual field of tephritid males is about the same as that of diopsid males.

We observed a population of more than 50 animals for ten days in the field. The flies usually arrived at the log in the morning, stayed there during daytime and left for an unknown destination in the late afternoon. About 50 were captured, measured, marked and released again. Some marked males returned on ten successive days and fought for territories on the log or

sometimes on the ground close to the log.

Sizing up the opponent is the initial behaviour in male-male encounters. The smaller of the two usually turns away. Males of about equal size make contact with their heads and eyestalks and try to push each other off the premises. Such contests may last for many minutes and are sometimes repeatedly resumed by the same pair of males. The winner stays in the territory, the loser runs or flies away. Females that pass by are courted. Successful courtship leads to copulation, which lasts 20 minutes on average. Shortly thereafter, the female begins to deposit eggs, searching with her mouthparts and the abdomen for insect-made holes in the log. Normally after copulation and during egg deposition the male guards the female; this may last for an hour. While mate guarding, even a small male is very pertinacious and successfully fights off much larger intruders. We even observed a small male alternately fighting with two simultaneous intruders. Yet another female passing the territory will cause most males to turn their interest from the egg-laying female to the newcomer.

A pair of male tephritids (*Themara hirtipes*) square up to each other. The coloured dots were applied for identification.

The female tephritid *(Themara hirtipes)* is a very normal-looking fly.

The Mantispidae (Order Neuroptera) are hunters, possessing mantis-like forelegs adapted to catch and grasp their insect prey.

below one degree in the frontal direction. Comparable high visual acuity is mostly found among much larger in-sects, e.g., honey bees and dragonflies. The eyestalks of diopsids provide several selective advantages by improving visual capacities. The visual field of each compound eye exceeds the perimeter of its respective hemisphere, so that both eyes together allow panoramic vision, and additionally survey binocularly two-thirds of the entire sphere, leaving monocular vision to only the lateral parts. Eyestalks also allow their owner to look out from hiding places and, most importantly, a wide eye separation allows a far ranging binocular estimate of an object's size. This last ability is crucial for rec-

DIPTERA AND WATER

Many Diptera are aquatic in the larval stage of their lives. Members of several Families are associated with the water-air interface, where their larvae may form a large proportion of the insect biomass.

Where water trickles down rock faces and stream banks in a thin film, adult flies are often the dominant or at least the most conspicuous insects. Such habitats in tropical forests may be of great importance to a wide range of flies with semi-aquatic larvae.

Some families, notably soldier flies (Stratiomyidae), are useful indicators of the quality of wetland habitats in Europe. They may prove similarly useful in tropical regions as indicators in these localised, but nevertheless important, thin-film habitats where they may reflect changes such as drying out caused by natural tree-fall and man-made clearances.

Seepages and ephemeral streams, such as this one near Sungai Babi, are important breeding habitats for flies (Diptera).

A Common nawab (*Polyura athamas*, Nymphalidae).

ognising and sizing up conspecifics. In species with sexually dimorphic eyestalk lengths the male's eyespan is strongly correlated with body size: 25% increase of bodylength corresponds to 75% increase of eyespan. Thus eyespan signals a male's strength in a much exaggerated way. This facilitates male competition and female choice. With the sensory advantages of eyes on long stalks a male is better equipped to size up a competitor's strength yet simultaneously the eyespan is an enhanced signal of the male's own strength.

LEPIDOPTERA

Members of the Order Lepidoptera are called butterflies or moths, but the distinction is based on a mix of features. The moths, comprising the large 'macro' moths and many thousands of species of 'micro' (little) moths (**microlepidoptera**), are in fact not a natural group. Most moths are nocturnal, and most butterflies diurnal; yet there are moths which fly in bright sunshine and a few butterflies which fly only at dusk and dawn. Most moths at rest fold their wings into a roof-like shape, with the fore-wings covering the hind-wings; some spread them flat and very few close their wings over their backs on settling, as butterflies do. Many moths have the fore- and hind-wings linked by a bristle-and-catch arrangement which enables the wings to move in unison, whereas butterflies can in general move their wings independently. There are species of moths in which the female is wingless. The major difference is in the antennae. Those of butterflies are usually club-shaped, or at least thickened towards the end. This is never the case among moths, in which there is however considerable diversity. Some

MOTHS AT BELALONG

Collections of small moths made in Belalong forest show a spectacular degree of species diversity: 1230 individuals collected represented 571 species. The Belalong community is distinctive, sharing only 27 species with a similar collection made in the montane forest of the Crocker Range, Sabah, and only 37 with a collection taken on the boundary between *Rhizophora* (mangal) forest and open secondary veg-etation at Muara. There were also differ-ences between the Belalong collections from opposite sides of the valley, about 1 km apart. While there was uniformity in a strongly flighted group of moths (Pyraloidea) this was not so for other, poorly dispersive groups, the Microlepidoptera. Projections from these samples suggest a total diversity of at least 3,750 moth species in the whole forest.

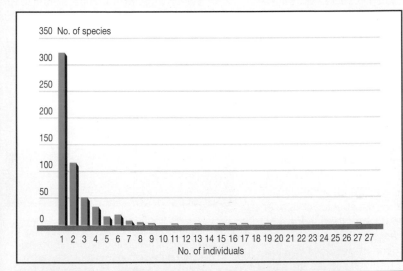

The number of species represented by different numbers of individuals in the entire (pooled) sample of Microlepidoptera from Kuala Belalong.

A large group of pierids (*Eurema*, 3 spp, *Appias*, 2 spp, *Ixias pyrene*, *Cepora* 2 spp), a papilionid, (*Graphium evemon*) and several lycaenids (*Prosotas*, *Nacaduba*, *Anthene*, *Castalius*).

324 species of butterfly have been recorded from the lowland forest within 1 km of the Field Studies Centre. Of these Families, chiefly swallowtails (Papilionidae), whites and yellows (Pieridae) and nymphalids (Nymphalidae) are much better represented than are the blues and hairstreaks (Lycaenidae) or Skippers (Hesperiidae). Extrapolations suggest that the actual number of species present in this area may be 450-650, compared with a total Bornean fauna of 950 species.

Typically, a day's count yielded 60 to 100 species, but only 54 species could be considered common (greater than 50 records overall), 112 were moderately common, at least sporadically (between 10 and 50 records) and the remaining 158 species were rare (less than 10 records, often only a single specimen). Common species usually fluctuated substantially in abundance but there was little evidence for regular seasonal trends either in the phenology of individual species or in overall species diversity and abundance.

Newly emerged males of many butterflies, including most species of swallowtails, and whites and yellows are attracted to damp sand, seepages and excreta. These places are rich sources of salts needed for sustained flight activity. Butterflies attracted to the sewage outlet at KBFSC were easy to sample quantitatively, as were those attracted to rotting fruit. There was a significant seasonal change in numbers and relative abundance of species.

Within the area sampled, about 13% of species for which there are reliable

The pierid *Leptosia nina* is a weak-flying butterfly widely distributed in South East Asia. This individual, a male, is feeding on a bird dropping probably to obtain salts.

A Bornean faun (*Faunis stomphax*, Nymphalidae) which feeds on palms and inhabits the understorey.

260

records were apparently restricted in their distribution. For example, although it is a large, strong-flying butterfly, *Charaxes durnfordi* was found only along the summit of the East Ridge. Several lycaenids were confined to small areas of a few hundred square metres, presumably in the vicinity of their larval food plants. *Flos morphina*, normally considered to be very rare, was always present at one spot on the East Ridge but nowhere else. The Red harlequin (*Paralaxita telesia*), although a common butterfly elsewhere, was found only in a limited area on the West Ridge trail.

Many more species were restricted to particular microhabitats, such as the river banks and open areas, the forest understorey, the subcanopy and the canopy. Within the forest there is a vertical stratification of species distributions, which changes as the day progresses with all species moving lower after about 1100 hours as relative humidity in the canopy falls. Microdistributional patterns were complex and a major source of unevenness in sampling the butterfly community. For example, many or most of the species at seepages are essentially canopy dwellers, and only the young males come to drink salt. The distribution of males and females is often very different. Females of many species with canopy dwelling males spend much of their time fluttering through the undergrowth searching for plants on which to lay their eggs.

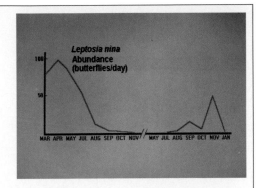

Leptosia nina abundance (butterflies/day).

261

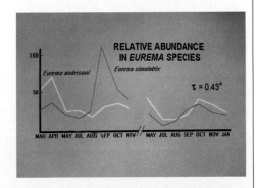

Relative abundance in *Eurema* species.

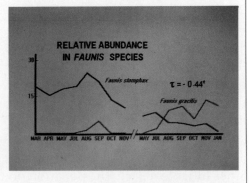

Relative abundance in *Faunis* species.

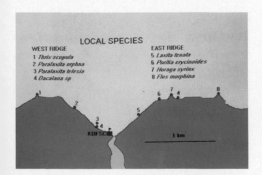

Some local distributions of butterflies.

moths have antennae which are thread-like; the antennae of others are feathery, or have tiny spoon-shaped attachments, or are spurred. Often the antennae of the male of a species are complex, whereas those of the female are simple, but there are species in which this is reversed.

LIFE CYCLES

All Lepidoptera usually lay their eggs on or near to the food of the larva - in most cases a plant, though other organic materials are chosen by some species. Eggs are often deposited on the underside of the leaves of the food plant. When the larva (generally called a caterpillar) hatches, it frequently eats the eggshell before beginning on the plant. As it continues to eat and grow, it must moult its skin four to seven times. Often the shed skin is eaten by the larva. This change of skin, known as ecdysis, is a dangerous and vulnerable time. The process begins by the larva spinning a layer of silk on a chosen spot, to which it firmly anchors its hinder legs. The skin then splits, and the larva slowly emerges. If it has long hairs it will flex the body and comb them against each other to straighten them out. When pupation takes place, among most butterflies, the pupa is naked and suspended from a twig or other suitable object. The pupation of moths is more varied; some spin cocoons in which to pupate and hairy

caterpillars include their hairs in their cocoons; other groups glue the leaves of their food plant or a nearby plant into a shelter, inside which they pupate. Many moth larvae burrow into the earth and hollow out a chamber for pupation. Sometimes dry leaves and other material, such as bark and lichen, are incorporated into the cocoon, so camouflaging it against the surroundings! After a period ranging from one or two weeks to several months the adult insect emerges.

ARACHNIDA

Members of this Class of arthropods possess four pairs of walking legs, a pair of jaws and a pair of palps. The body can be undivided or (as in spiders, tailless and tailed whip-scorpions and wind scorpions) it can be divided into two parts, anterior and posterior. They do not have a distinct larval stage in the life cycle, so that the young resemble the adults but lack the capacity to reproduce. Most are terrestrial, although a few are specialised for aquatic habitats.

The spiders (Araneae) and the ticks and mites (Acari) are important components of the biodiversity of the Belalong forest; scorpions (Scorpiones), false-scorpions (Pseudoscorpiones), harvestmen (Opiliones) and both tailed and tailless whip-scorpions (Uropygi and Amblypygi) may also be encountered.

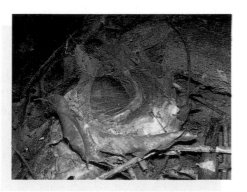

Silk-lined entrance of a theraphosid spider's burrow .

A female spiny spider *Gasteracantha arcuata* at the centre of her web.

A huntsman spider (Heteropodidae).

An ant-mimicking jumping spider (Salticidae) with its ant prey.

The brilliant markings of the orb-web spinning spider *Nephila* are conspicuous in the sunlight.

SPIDERS OF BELALONG FOREST

During 1991-92 approximately 370 morphospecies were collected, representing 32 Families. Spiders were usually to be found in low densities, although occasionally large numbers of small orb-web spinners of the genus *Cyclosa* could be found at the sites of tree falls. The diversity, however, was high. Many of the species taken were represented by a single specimen and many more by a very small number of specimens. One of the exceptions was a leaf-dwelling corrinid spider of the genus *Paccius* which was found on low vegetation throughout the forest.

The most numerous, and in many ways the most noticeable spiders are the jumping spiders (Family Salticidae), represented at Belalong by 85 morphospecies. Many of these were found in sunny areas in the vicinity of the Field Centre. Some are beautifully marked with patterns of irridescent and metallic hairs while others, particularly the genus *Myrmarachne*, mimic species of ants in appearance and behaviour with such accuracy that even the trained observer can be deceived. Another mimic found at Belalong is *Orsima ichneumon*, a species of salticid in which the tip of the abdomen and the spinnerets resemble the head of an insect. The behaviour of this species adds to its insect-like appearance. Also to be seen on occasion at KBFSC was *Portia fimbriata*, one of a small group of the salticids which spin

webs to enable them to prey on other spiders. This species is covered with small tufts of hair which with its characteristic stance, makes it look like a harmless piece of debris.

Present in and around the Field Centre are large orb-web spinning spiders of the Families Araneidae and Tetragnathidae. The most common of these, *Nephilengys malabarensis*, with its very striking orange sternum, occurred in large numbers under all the houses. *Nephila pilipes* could also be seen, although in lower numbers, in their great golden orb webs. These probably occur in greater numbers high in the canopy. The spiny-backed spiders of the araneid subfamily Gasteracanthinae were more often seen in the forest with their fragile webs spun across the trails. The most commonly encountered of these was the bright yellow and blue-black *Actinacantha globulata*; however, also present in the secondary vegetation around the camp was *Gasteracantha arcuata*, with its remarkable long curved abdominal spines. Many *Gasteracantha* species, as well as *Nephila* and *Argiope* species, have tiny males which can often be seen in small numbers living round the edge of the female's web. These are sometimes mistaken for kleptoparasitic theridiid spiders of the genus *Argyrodes*. The Family Theridiidae, the comb-footed spiders, were

SPIDERS

Spiders (Araneae) are predatory arachnids distinguished by possessing bodies clearly divided by a narrow waist (**pedicel**); the anterior part is the **cephalothorax** and the posterior, the abdomen. They have specialised abdominal glands which produce silk through **spinnerets** for various purposes, including the intricate webs with which their prey may be trapped. Some spiders hang their egg sacs in the webs, while the females of many cursorial species construct egg sacs which they in fact the second most abundant Family, with 60 morphospecies, most being taken from low vegetation when sweep netting.

In the litter layer of the forest the family dominating the collections was the Oonopidae with 28 species. The Family Tetrablemmidae with four species (mostly *Paculla*) was also found in some numbers. Both these families comprise small to tiny spiders which are often heavily armoured and have reduced numbers of eyes. This habitat also yielded six species of zodariids and eight heteropodid huntsman species. In brighter, more open areas such as gravel beaches by the river, the summit of Bukit Belalong and the helipads, the huntsman spiders are replaced by wolf spiders of the Family Lycosidae. It is not clear how these spiders colonise such small, isolated islands of habitat, as none were taken in the collection from the forest itself.

The presence of large 'bird-eating' spiders (Theraphosidae), often wrongly called tarantulas, was shown by the silk-lined entrances to their burrows. These were not uncommon in banks and slopes throughout the forest. One of these was excavated and found to contain a female *Phormingochilus*. Male theraphosids, and most of the large huntsman spiders are best found at night, when their eyes reflect a green light in the beam of a torch. Males may be found in pitfall traps, as was a tiny diplurid, probably an unknown species of the genus *Masteria*.

carry about until the young hatch. In some species, the female continues to carry the young for some time. The palps of the male carry copulatory organs.

Spiders are diverse and abundant in the forest, active by night, occupying varied niches, from streams to the tree-tops.

ACARI

The ticks and mites (Acari) are generally hard-bodied, rounded or flattened, without a pedicel. The ticks (suborder Metastigmata or Ixodiodea) have mouthparts specialised for piercing and sucking and are all external parasites, feeding on blood or other body fluids. The mites are generally smaller and are very diverse in their habitats. The mites include internal and external parasites of invertebrates and vertebrates, scavengers of dead organic matter and predators of smaller, living decomposers and micro-organisms. Small mites are exceedingly numerous in many habitats, including the spaces between the barbs of birds' feathers, under the scales of reptiles or among the fur of mammals. There are aquatic and terrestrial species. Mites are especially abundant in the soil where they are key members of the decomposition process that recycles nutrients within the forest ecosystem.

Mites and ticks can act as vectors of the arthropod-borne diseases prevalent in these forests, such as scrub typhus. Blood-sucking mites feed only transiently on human hosts, but ticks become partially embedded in the skin, causing local irritation and severe itching. While this is annoying, the potential further consequences of tick-bite should not be overlooked, especially if an inflammation develops around the site of the bite.

265

SOIL INVERTEBRATES

As we have noted, invertebrates of the soil and ground litter layer are vital members of nutrient cycling and decomposition processes. Some feed directly on organic detritus and other dead matter; others consume decomposer micro-organisms or saprophytic fungi.

Soil dwelling nematodes are known to be very numerous, but poorly studied, and several important and diverse groups of arthropods of small size, including the mites (Acari) and springtails (Collembola), are difficult to collect and remain uninvestigated at Belalong.

Likely numbers of soil invertebrates can be inferred from collections made in nearby rainforests. In Mixed Dipterocarp Forest in Gunung Mulu National Park, Sarawak, the estimated density and biomass of the important larger invertebrates has been estimated as about 19 million individuals per ha. Added to this number are myriads of minute arthropods, mostly mites and soil-dwelling nematodes.

Nematode density at Pasoh, Negeri Sembilan, was some 56,000 per sq m, equivalent to 560 million per ha, and mites at Mulu National Park, Sarawak, equivalent to 950 million per ha. These mind-boggling numbers are evidently normal for tropical rainforests, but in some cases are actually low by comparison with fertile temperate soils.

ARBOREAL INVERTEBRATES

Among an estimated total of 42.3 million arthropods per sq m in a rainforest in Seram, Indonesia, the relative representation in the soil and in the plants above has been computed by N. E. Stork as follows: soil 56%, litter 14%, ground vegetation 0.2%, tree trunks 1.2% and canopy 28%.

Dr Stork has also made collections from the canopy of Mixed Dipterocarp Forest in Brunei Darussalam. From ten trees in Bukit Ladan Forest Reserve — two species of dipterocarps, *Shorea johorensis* (4 trees) and *Shorea macrophylla* (2), one pelong (*Pentaspadon motleyi*) (2), a chestnut, berangan (*Castanopsis*) (1) and one unidentified — insecticidal fogging brought down 23,874 arthropods. Among this massive collection, 3,059 different species were identified. The full list shows the enormous variety of invertebrate animal life inhabiting the tree tops.

The diversity varied among different taxonomic groups. Among spiders, the collection of 947 represented at least 182 species, so that on average 5.2 individuals of each species were taken. Among beetles, on average each species was represented by 4.7 individuals, a very similar ratio; but among flies, the ratio was 11.5, and among ants 45.8. This mixed assemblage of arthropods is unlikely to represent a single association over a longer time cycle, and it is not certain how much

---

SOIL-DWELLING INVERTEBRATES

Mean numbers and live weights of soil-dwelling invertebrates (excluding nematodes) under Mixed Dipterocarp Forest in Gunung Mulu National Park, Sarawak:

	Abundance (Individuals per sq m)	Biomass (live weight mg per sq m)
1. <u>MACROFAUNA</u>		
Detritivores/root feeders		
Earthworms (Megascolecidae)	25	627
Woodlice (Isopoda)	17	31
Myriapods (Diplopoda, Symphyla)	30	21
Springtails etc. (Diplura)	44	48
Termites (Isoptera)	1148	1818
Beetles (Coleoptera)	63	494
Others	38	370
Total detritivores	1365	3409
Predators		
Spiders (Araneae)	57	171
Centipedes (Chilopoda)	43	370
Ants (Formicidae)	471	527
Others	2	14
Total predators	573	1082
2. <u>MICRO-ARTHROPODS</u>		
Mites (Cryptostigmata & Mesostigmata)	94776	-
Others	1400	-

[Data from N. M. Collins, J. M. Anderson & H. W. Vallack (1984, *Sarawak Mus. Journal*, 30, Special Issue No.2, Gunung Mulu National Park, Sarawak, Part II) and N. M. Collins (1980. *Oecologia* 44, 263-275)].

these assemblages of arthropods would vary or remain broadly unchanged.

The vertical distribution of flying insects by night was studied in Mixed Dipterocarp Forest, elsewhere in Batu Apoi Forest Reserve, by S. L. Sutton using low voltage mercury lamps set at heights of 1 m, 10 m, 20 m and about

The fogging machine is hauled into the forest canopy when the air is still and disperses a cloud of quick-acting, short-term knockdown insecticide.

30 m above ground. The results suggest differences between insect orders in partitioning the vertical profile, but overall the richest fauna is that of the upper canopy, with another peak in numbers near the ground.

These methods of mass collection provide rich samples of species biodiversity in the rainforest at one time and place. They can be repeated to give longer series which may then show how the member species partition the environment in time, on a short or long term scale. For instance, many insects follow a diurnal cycle, becoming active only for short periods of the day. The timing of activity may match an external event or be internally governed. A key factor may be cyclic patterns in the plant community: thus, the nocturnal flight of moths matches the opening of night-blooming flowers such as durian blossom.

A striking audible periodicity at Belalong is the daily cycle of cicada

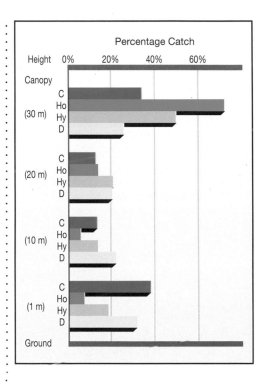

Results of light trapping in Mixed Dipterocarp Forest of Batu Apoi Forest Reserve, at different heights above the ground, showing percentage catch at each level for beetles (C=Coleoptera), bugs (Ho=Homoptera), bees, wasps and flying ants (Hy=Hymenoptera) and flies (D=Diptera) in Mixed Dipterocarp Forest. Data from S L Sutton (1983).
Tropical Rainforest Ecology and Management, special publications of the British Ecological Society No. 2 pp.77-91].

calls. Another, for the unfortunate, may be the staggered feeding hours of different species of mosquitoes! Both are instances of time-partitioning of the environmental resource by related animals. There are also longer cycles, sometimes related to seasonal breeding. These too, on this extended scale, may reflect variations in external factors (such as the seasonal pattern of rainfall, or the leafing cycle of a food plant)

INVERTEBRATES OF THE FOREST CANOPY

Numbers of individuals and minimum numbers of species of principal groups of arthropods collected from ten tree canopies in the Brunei Darussalam rainforest by knock-down insecticide by N. E. Stork. Groups marked (?) could not be identified to species.

Group	Individuals	Species
Woodlice (Isopoda)	84	?
Myriapods (Myriapoda)	1	1
Springtails (Collembola)	740	22
Silverfish (Thysanura)	26	?
Mayflies (Ephemeroptera)	15	8
Dragonflies (Odonata)	4	4
Crickets (Orthoptera)	466	65
Roaches (Blattodea)	451	40
Earwigs (Dermaptera)	48	5
Stick insects (Phasmida)	26	11
Mantises (Mantodea)	10	5
Bark lice (Psocoptera)	896	?
Bugs (Hemiptera)	2656	269
Thrips (Thysanoptera)	851	130
Lacewings (Neuroptera)	21	7
Butterflies & moths (Lepidoptera)	626	50
Caddis flies (Trichoptera)	1	1
Flies, mosquitos, etc. (Diptera)	5106	444
Beetles (Coleoptera)	4043	859
Ants (Formicidae)	4489	98
Wasps, bees (other Hymenoptera)	2155	847
Mites (Acari)	151	?
Pseudoscorpions, etc. (Pseudoscorpiones & Opiliones)	59	>11
Spiders (Araneae)	947	182
TOTALS	23874	>3059

[Data from N. E. Stork (1991. The composition of the arthropod fauna of Bornean lowland rainforest trees. *Journal of Tropical Ecology* 7, 161 - 180)].

or, once again, be staggered to allow closely related species to share a resource without competing. Time-sharing in this way is one aspect of the niche (See Chapter 6).

BETA DIVERSITY

We have already seen how the species composition of trees varies between

BETA DIVERSITY: MOTHS

Collections of 'micro' moths were made at two sites, on the sides of the valley of the Belalong above KBFSC (See Chapter 5). Both were on steep slopes, under closed-canopy primary lowland Mixed Dipterocarp Forest. Site KB1 was on the western side of the valley and site KB2 diagonally opposite on the eastern slope about 1,000 m from site 1. Both were at about 125 m altitude. Moths were attracted to a white sheet, illuminated by a 125 watt mercury-vapour lamp suspended 1 m from the sheet surface. Collecting began at dusk and usually ceased by about 2300 hrs when flight activity had become minimal. Collections were made from site KB1 on 4, 6-8 and 10-11 July 1991 (6 nights) and from site KB2 on 13-16 July (4 nights). Nightly samples were kept separate and specimens from each labelled with the precise night of collection.

Only seven species were represented by 10 or more individuals, the most abundant having 27. Values of α for the total sample at each of the two Kuala Belalong sites, 355 and 413, respectively, are very high. So too, is α for Pyraloidea only: mean α in the UK for Pyraloidea is 2.9; at Genting, Peninsular Malaysia, it is 91, and at Kuala Belalong it is 203.

Comparison of these collections shows that species shared, to within 15% of the figure expected, were from a common population. Examined separately, however, the Pyraloidea match the expected figure almost precisely, whereas the other microlepidoptera diverge by 32%.

Since most moth caterpillars feed on the leaves of plants and are to a greater or lesser extent host-specific, moth diversity in a habitat reflects surrounding botanical diversity. The high diversity of Mixed Dipterocarp Forest in the Belalong valley is matched by high moth diversity. The mosaic nature of the forest is matched by the moths but tempered by their ability to disperse by flight and thereby 'smooth out' the heterogeneity of the habitat. While the Pyraloidea at the two sites appeared to be drawn from the same population, the other microlepidoptera did not. Many species in the latter group have limited dispersal powers. The mosaic nature of tropical forest may mean that populations of small microlepidoptera are more localised than are the more strongly dispersive pyraloids.

'Micro' moths light-trapped at Belalong

Site	All	Pyraloidea	Other 'micros'
Numbers of individuals			
KB1	749	377	372
KB2	481	315	166
KB1 + 2	1230	692	538
Numbers of species			
KB1	403	209	194
KB2	319	195	124
KB1 + 2	571	301	270
Diversity α			
KB1	355±46	193±35	164±30
KB2	413±74	218±46	222±77
KB1 + 2	414±39	203±25	216±32

During fogging, insects falling from the canopy are collected in an array of conical traps.

Nick Mawdsley and Impin Lasa constructed malaise traps to be hauled into the canopy of kapur trees.

A malaise trap high in the forest canopy.

different plots, and how species of butterflies and other insects are distributed patchily within the forest. This variation in species composition in samples at different places (and different times), the species turnover (also called Beta-diversity) is a consequence of species distributions being limited due to two main causes.

First of these are spatial changes in the environment. Plants and animals have fairly exacting environmental and resource requirements for their continued survival, so that species adapted to the cool temperatures of high altitudes, for example, may not survive in the heat of lower altitudes, and herbivorous leaf beetles can only survive where their particular food plants are found. Temperature and altitude are only two of many environmental conditions (in addition to a multitude of resources such as food and breeding sites) that are required for the continued survival of a species in a given place. If the conditions and resources change, then so will the species that can utilise them.

The second main cause of Beta diversity is the existence of barriers to dispersal. A species may potentially exist in a given place, but is not found there because it cannot disperse to that place. This is most characteristic of species found on isolated mountain tops, islands and areas separated by

---

INVESTIGATING BETA DIVERSITY

The magnitude and determinants of species turnover are crucial to our understanding of biological diversity. High levels mean that in a region (such as the island of Borneo) there will be many changes in the fauna from place to place; that is, different places will share only a small proportion of their species, and so the total number of species in the region will also be high. At Kuala Belalong beetles were systematically collected, using canopy fogging plus malaise and flight interception traps at ground and canopy level. The samples at different places allow the effects of altitude, distance and tree species composition on beetle species turnover to be assessed, and analysis will help entomologists understand what the biological and ecological features are of those groups that show high levels of species turnover. Those groups that show high species turnover are likely to contain species more susceptible to extinction from loss of habitat, and so an understanding of species turnover will greatly help efforts towards the conservation of biodiversity.

To investigate the pattern of species turnover between environmentally similar sites, six kapur (*Dryobalanops beccarii*) trees were chosen, all growing at c. 1,000 feet elevation, separated by increasing distances of 550m, 1,250 m, 2,000 m and 3,000 m, i.e., 6.05 km overall linear distance. Using a line-thrower, pulleys were put on high limbs of the tree crowns, and aluminium frames carrying Malaise / interception traps were hauled into the canopies. Individual canopies yielded 168 - 643 beetles per trap; ground traps collected up to 10 times as many.

After trapping, each of the six canopies was fogged with a knock-down pyrethrum between 2 - 21 August. Fogs were carried out between 0800 - 0900 hours, the stillest time of the day at Belalong. Despite this, at two sites, wind prevented the fog from reaching the canopy top. At each site, an array of 30 trays was set up to catch the falling arthropods. One other *D. beccarii* tree was also fogged, in Andalau Forest Reserve, some 100+ km distant.

273

---

mountain ranges, where the preferred habitat of a species is isolated by a barrier of unfavourable habitat across which the species cannot disperse. Over evolutionary time, barriers that separate populations of the same species can result in the formation of new, isolated species.

As the distance between sites is increased, the heterogeneity between sites will also increase. A prediction is that sites separated by a greater distance will have a greater beta diversity, and new species will be accumulated at a faster rate. Comparisons of tree species composition of separated forest plots has been given, from Ashton's work in Brunei and from different forest strata at Belalong. Comparisons of moth captures by Gaden Robinson, using light traps on each side of the Belalong valley, showed differences between the less mobile microlepidoptera and the pyraloid moths. Nick Mawdsley's work at Belalong investigated Beta-diversity among bettles, in particular, over altitudinal gradients and in kapur (*Dryobalanops beccarii*) canopies over an extended transect at the same elevation.

Green-crested lizard (*Bronchocela cristatellus*).

CHAPTER 12

VERTEBRATE ANIMALS OF THE FOREST

The vertebrates are much larger than most invertebrates. Because their diversity is less and overall numbers smaller, they are more easily known. Worldwide, it is estimated that few mammals or birds remain to be discovered (See Table on p. 76). Reptiles and amphibians attract less popular attention and, as a result, there are probably more undescribed forms to be found. The faunas of Brunei Darussalam, however, are reasonably well documented, although there remains much to be discovered about the distribution and biology of species.

Of the recognised forest formations (See Chapter 6), mangal supports a few specialised vertebrates, but their distributions do not correspond to the mangrove tree zonation. Within terrestrial forest types, the distribution of vertebrate animal communities does not closely match the forester's formations. Forest faunas of all land vertebrates are, however, altitudinally zoned, the richest communities being those of the lowlands and valley bottoms. Typically, diversity is reduced by the progressive loss of species with increasing elevation (sometimes by replacement with a mid-altitude equivalent) up to a transition line around 900 m, above which a montane community appears. The highest peaks may be home to additional summit specialists.

AMPHIBIANS

In the course of evolution, amphibians (Class Amphibia) were the earliest vertebrates to emerge from water to colonise the land. They still remain associated with freshwater, or at least with damp environments. None live in totally arid deserts, in the sea or in the polar regions. Today over 3,000 species of amphibians are known, divided into three very distinct Orders of which two, the Apoda and Anura, are represented in Brunei Darussalam.

CAECILIANS

Occurring in South America, tropical Africa and Asia, the caecilians (Order Apoda) have long, worm-like bodies with short tails and no limbs or limb-girdles.

The skin is externally segmented, giving the animal the appearance of a dark earthworm, sometimes with a pale lateral stripe. The eyes are covered with skin, an adaptation to a burrowing mode of life. The left half of the lungs is degenerate (as in snakes). Caecilians can measure up to 135 cm long. When caught, caecilians exude mucus from their skin, making them extremely slippery. They live in damp soil and feed on invertebrate prey.

FROGS AND TOADS

There is no scientific basis for the distinction made, in the English language, between frogs and toads; for general reference, we call them all 'frogs'. These are the tailless amphibians (Anura), evolutionarily the most advanced. They occur over most of the globe, on land and in freshwater habitats. Adults are tailless, with a short body, nine spinal vertebrae terminating in a sword-shaped bony **urostyle**, a light, wide skull and, in most, tiny teeth in the roof of the mouth and in the upper jaw. The lower jaw is toothless.

Frogs produce large-yolked eggs, generally laid in water or wet places. The young hatch as larvae, commonly called **tadpoles**. At first, these possess a tail and are without limbs, entirely adapted to life in water, respiring by means of feathery external gills. During their subsequent growth, these larvae undergo changes so dramatic that the process is termed **metamorphosis**. The external gills become covered by a fold of skin and are replaced by internal gills which later disappear when the lungs are formed. During this process the limbs grow from bud-like origins and the tail progressively degenerates.

In adults, the fore limbs are short and have four digits, while the hind limbs are longer and have five digits. The skin is naked and without scales. In most species the skin needs to be permanently moist; it may be smooth, warty or ridged and in several species bears prominent poison glands. The skin is very permeable and may be a significant route of respiratory gaseous exchange, in or out of water. From time to time the outer layer - the **epidermis** - is shed in strips.

In addition to exchanging oxygen and carbon dioxide through the skin, frogs breathe air by means of a pair of lungs. For these amphibians, the voice is an important means of communication. The vocal organs are associated with the respiratory tract, but the calls may be enhanced by inflatable sacs within the mouth region or on each side of it. Many have well-developed senses of smell and sight. Their eyes are covered with movable lids and often stand out prominently above the head, providing binocular vision. This position also enables the frog to submerge itself almost completely in water, leaving only its eyes and nostrils above the surface. The hearing organs of adults include a middle ear and an external eardrum. These are lacking in the larvae which have only sensory receptors, similar to the lateral line receptors of fishes, on the surface of their skin.

Most frogs are adapted for locomotion on land and in water. On the ground they leap or walk. Many have expanded pads at the tips of their toes enabling them to climb plants and cling

Two Yellow-black caecilians (*Caudacaecilia nigroflava*) were taken in 1991/92, one from a pit dug for soil-erosion studies, another from the edge of a stream.

to leaves. In water, they swim by coordinated thrusts of their hind limbs, keeping their fore limbs close to the chest. They also climb into shrubs and trees to exploit the arboreal habitat. Most feed on living prey, typically insects and insect larvae; larger forms may take vertebrates. The tadpoles have many different diets, generally feeding on macrophytes, algae or planktonic matter, sometimes on carrion within the water column, on the surface or on the bottom.

In the Belalong forest, 51 species of amphibians have been recorded, of the following Families: caecilians (Ichthyophiidae) 2 species; litter frogs (Pelobatidae) 6 species; toads (Bufonidae) 11 species; narrow-mouthed frogs (Microhylidae) 6 species; true frogs (Ranidae) 15 species; tree- and bush-frogs (Rhacophoridae) 12 species. This species diversity is rich by comparison with amphibian communities of rain-forest habitats in Sarawak sampled by R F Inger and colleagues, which produced species lists in the range 26-53.

AMPHIBIAN STUDIES

The area chosen for intensive study by Indraneil Das was some 6 ha in extent, including riparian and non-riparian forest, meandering streams, flat seepage zones, areas of tree-fall and the KBFSC clearing. Forty-six species of amphibians were recorded here.

Many frogs and toads were located by their call, and after some time,

Metamorphosis results in little frogs coming on to land with legs (that gradually become more powerful) and a tail (which is slowly absorbed), shown here by a young Large-eyed litter frog (*Leptobrachium montanum*).

The tiny, Cricket litter frog (*Nesobia mjobergi*), 15-18 mm long, is found on low vegetation along streams. It has a loud call and the males chorus together by night.

The Long-fingered slender toad (*Ansonia longidigita*), has a dry 'warty' skin and was most frequently found on low vegetation overhanging streams.

The Giant river toad (*Bufo juxtasper*), up to 215 mm in length, is often encountered along the banks of the larger streams and rivers.

Drift fences with pitfalls trap amphibians and reptiles moving on the forest floor.

many could be identified by their breeding songs. Hand-collecting along transects was the commonest method of capture, often after dazzling them with a powerful flashlight. Pitfall traps, in association with drift fences (buckets buried flush down into the soil, with rigid plastic sheets running towards them) were also utilised, as were hand nets for stream-dwelling frogs and tadpoles.

Blyth's frog (*Rana blythi*) is a giant (up to 175 mm in length). The lower jaw bears a pair of bony, tooth-like projections, especially prominent in males. Blyth's frogs live along stream banks. They do not call and their diet includes crabs, other frogs and even small rodents.

Kuhl's creek frog (*Rana kuhli*) is a medium sized frog with a finely crinkled skin calling from the side of a stream. The vibrations from its vocal sac produce ripple patterns in the water.

A polymorph of the Smooth guardian frog (*Rana palavanensis*) showing the bright yellow vertebral stripe.

The Bornean horned frog (*Megophrys nasuta*) is a leaf-mimic, staying motionless on the forest floor, preying on large insects and snails. It utters a metallic honk.

The name of the Poisonous rock frog (*Rana hosei*) is derived from its toxic skin secretions.

The Black-spotted rock frog (*Staurois natator*) is most commonly seen in the spray zones of waterfalls.

Tree and bush frogs (Rhacophoridae) are the most diverse group of forest amphibians. They lead a largely arboreal life, descending from the canopy only to breed. The Emerald tree frog (*Rhacophorus kajau*) spawns on tree branches overhanging pools and streams, 0.5 to 2.5 m above water, seasonally producing two clutches, each composed of 8-12 eggs. These develop in a foam nest and emerging tadpoles drop directly into the water below. The bush frogs (*Philautus* spp.)produce still fewer eggs that are relatively large and contain sufficient food for the developing embryo; among these frogs, the tadpole stage is completed within the relative safety of the egg capsule, inside which metamorphosis occurs. Most stunning of the canopy dwellers must be the celebrated Wallace's flying frog (*Rhacophorus nigropalmatus*), with a garish-green back, bright yellow eyes and yellow and black webbing between the elongated fingers and toes. The webbed feet, expanded during the jump, are presumed to give some degree of uplift, carrying the frog long distances among the tree-tops.

Wallace's flying frog (*Rhacophorus nigropalmatus*) is capable of spectacular leaps from tree to tree. This species breeds in small, adventitious pools, such as pig-wallows or, at Belalong, in pits dug for soil-erosion studies.

The Painted tree frog (*Nyctixalus pictus*) is perhaps the most beautiful of the rhacophorids. Like others, it is arboreal and nocturnal. Females are slightly larger than males and lay their eggs in water-filled tree holes.

The Four-lined tree frog (*Polypedates leucomystax*) is found in towns and villages and in the forest edges. This is the frog which comes into bathrooms.

The Four-lined tree frog makes nests of foam whipped by the hind legs and attached to vegetation overhanging water. When the foam denatures, the tadpoles drop directly into the water where their development is completed.

Tadpoles of the Emerald tree frog develop inside the egg capsules, which ultimately drop into the water below.

The Emerald tree frog (*Rhacophorus kajau*) lays about 10 eggs, attached to leaves overhanging water.

283

Harlequin tree frogs (*Rhacophorus pardalis*), up to 71 mm in length, are usually heard calling from the canopy. Only when ready to breed do they descend, to be found at night sitting on leaves.

AMPHIBIAN DIVERSITY

The amphibian community of Belalong forest can be divided ecologically into aquatic or riparian (24 species, 46% of the fauna), terrestrial and/or fossorial (14 species, 27%) or arboreal (14 species, 27%). The riparian community has the largest species of both frogs and toads: Blyth's frog (*Rana blythi*), which reaches a snout-vent length of 17.5 cm and the Giant river toad (*Bufo asper*), to 21.5 cm snout-vent length. True toads (genus *Bufo*) are scarce in the non-riparian zone: only one species, the Double-ridged toad, occurs in forested areas far from the river. Their place is probably usurped by the litter frogs, which lead a toad-like existence on the dry forest floor.

All anurans are nocturnal, except Smooth guardian frogs which are active by day and by night. Presumably the forest leaf-litter is generally too dry by day to permit activity by amphibians. The rhacophorids are arboreal when not breeding. One species of an otherwise largely terrestrial/fossorial family (Microhylidae), the Tree-hole frog (*Metaphrynella sundana*), occupies holes in trees where water has collected. Here they live and breed, one to many metres above the forest floor. The single call note of this frog, reverberating hollowly overhead from all directions, is one of the most persistent night sounds on the hillsides at Belalong.

Bizarre morphological features and

unusual life-history tactics have made many frogs and toads famous, and the Belalong forest has its share of such species. The Bornean horned frog (*Megophrys nasuta*) mimics a dried leaf on the forest floor, with pointed flaps of skin above the eyes and leaf vein-like structures on its back. The Smooth guardian frog (*Rana palavanensis*) is polymorphic in coloration. Some individuals have a bright yellow vertebral stripe, which is lacking in others. The presence or absence of this stripe may lower the hunting efficiency of predators by confusing the search image used in finding these frogs. The Red-sided sticky frog (*Kalophrynus pleurostigma*) exudes a sticky secretion from glands on its back that is thought to repel soldier ants, while the Saffron-bellied frog (*Chaperina fusca*) on being caught leaves a deep yellow stain which is suspected to be noxious to its enemies. Blyth's frog (*Rana blythi*) makes a low moated castle of stream-bed pebbles for its nest, in the centre of which its eggs are deposited. Male Smooth guardian frogs (*Rana palavanensis*) guard the eggs after they have been laid by the females on the forest floor until they hatch, and then carry the tadpoles on their backs to the water.

REPTILES

Reptiles are divided into four Orders comprising about 6,000 living species. They occur all over the world, except in the coldest areas, and include arboreal, terrestrial, subterranean, amphibian and aquatic species. Reptiles are diverse and abundant in tropical regions. In the tropical rainforest they exploit the full range of habitats from the tree-tops to the soil, and waters of streams and rivers.

The reptilian skin is dry and generally rough, scaly or horny. Among snakes and lizards the outer layer (the epidermis) is shed at intervals; growing young shed their skin more often than adults. To shed the skin completely, fluid must penetrate between the old epidermis and the new; reptiles therefore look for a damp spot. Typically, they rub off the detached outer layer against a rough substrate, or by crawling through narrow spaces, using snout or limbs to help the process.

Reptiles have a body temperature which is variable although, by behavioural means, many can maintain it higher than the environmental temperature. Basking behaviour to absorb heat from the sun is important among diurnal species.

Male reptiles have a protrusile copulatory organ used to transfer the sperm cells during mating, paired among lizards and snakes, single among tortoises, turtles and crocodiles. Mating is usually preceded by a courtship ceremony or by duels between the males, generally intricate rituals ending in the retreat of the weaker party. Rival snakes, for instance, coil their bodies around each other and push and pull; if they bite, venomous snakes do not discharge their poison. Reptiles

---

REPTILE DIVERSITY AT BELALONG

The reptiles of Belalong forest include ten Families: Testudines: hardshell turtles (Bataguridae); softshell turtles (Trionychidae). Squamata (Sauria): geckos (Gekkonidae); agamas (Agamidae); skinks (Scincidae); monitors (Varanidae). Serpentes: pythons and boas (Boidae); 'typical' snakes (Colubridae); cobras and coral snakes (Elapidae); vipers and pit-vipers (Viperidae).

This fauna appears to be composed of a riparian and a non-riparian community: there are 10 riparian lizards, 9 riparian snakes, 11 non-riparian lizards - two, the Blue-bellied litter skink (*Sphenomorphus cyanolaemus*) and Peters' bent-toed gecko (*Gonydactylus consobrinus*) - also found on riparian sites - and 12 non-riparian snakes. The lizard fauna is composed of a greater number of diurnal species (12) than nocturnal ones (8); the snake fauna has hardly more (11) diurnal species than nocturnal ones (10).

Classified by substrates utilised, 14 lizards are arboreal, while 6 are terrestrial or with limited scansorial capabilities. Among snakes, 8 are arboreal, 9 largely terrestrial and 4 primarily aquatic. All (8) nocturnal lizards are arboreal, while 6 of the 12 species of the diurnal lizards are terrestrial. There are no nocturnal, ground-dwelling lizards. Among the snakes recorded, the diurnal species have 5 terrestrial and 3 arboreal members, the nocturnal/crepuscular ones include 3 terrestrial and 4 aboreal forms.

Aquatic snakes include both diurnal (2 species) and nocturnal (2 species).

285

mark out their territory in different ways: geckos by their calls, some lizards optically, with brightly coloured throat flaps by poses and by movements, and snakes and other lizards chemically, that is by scent applied from femoral pores to raised features in the territory or on paths.

The eggs of reptiles are enclosed in a white shell, either parchment-like (snakes, most lizards and sea turtles) or hard and chalky (geckos, crocodiles and other Testudines). When first laid, the eggs are pliant, and the shell may take several hours to harden. Eggs are laid in clutches, concealed in vegetation or buried in the soil. Even the flying lizards descend to the ground and excavate a shallow cavity in the ground to receive the two to four, elongated eggs. The newly-laid eggs of geckos are sticky and are glued to bark in crevices above ground. Temperature and moisture are important for successful incubation of the eggs. In turtles and crocodiles, the temperature at which they are incubated determines the sex of the hatchlings. For most turtles a lower incubation temperature produces more male offspring, while higher temperatures produce more females; for crocodiles this pattern is reversed. The young hatch fully-developed, differing from their parents only in size and sometimes in colouring.

TURTLES AND TORTOISES

Turtles and tortoises (Order Testudines) possess a short body protected by a shell of bony plates, consisting of a carapace and a ventral **plastron**. In most cases, this bony shell is covered with horny plates, whose external pattern does not match the underlying bone; among the soft-shelled turtles (found in Brunei rivers), the bony shell is covered only by flesh and skin. The legs can be retracted into the shell, and the neck and head can often also be withdrawn.

Testudines have short but powerful legs. Tortoises have claws; aquatic species may have webbed feet or flippers. They have no teeth, but their sharp-edged jaws cut their food efficiently. Their diets are variable, including living prey and vegetation. They always lay their eggs on land, on beaches, river banks or gravel/sand bars.

Turtles are rare, possibly a result of past hunting. The Malayan softshell turtle (*Dogania subplana*), which occurs in Sungai Belalong, is generally found in the hill streams throughout South East Asia, hiding during the day under rocks and becoming active at night. Its massive head is thought to be adaptive

A Malayan flat-shelled turtle (*Notochelys platynota*), a freshwater species, commonly found in Brunei.

for crushing snail shells.

Another species recorded from Belalong is the Malayan flat-shelled turtle (*Notochelys platynota*) from the forest streams, which feeds on macrophytic vegetation.

One tortoise occurs in Borneo: the Asian brown tortoise (*Manouria emys*). Females build a leaf-litter nest, where over 50 small eggs may be laid. Nests are guarded for several days by the female following egg-laying.

CROCODILES

Crocodiles (Order Crocodilia) can exceed 10 m in length and possess a long snout, an elongate body and a powerful tail. They have powerful hind limbs and their body is covered with large bony plates and horny scales. Crocodiles are mostly tropical and subtropical, inhabiting rivers and lakes, estuaries and coastal seas. Females lay their eggs in pits excavated in a river bank or on the shore and usually guard the eggs and newly-hatched young. Crocodiles hunt living prey in and beside the water but also eat carrion.

Formerly abundant in the large rivers and estuaries of Brunei Darussalam, they have been heavily hunted and have been nearly exterminated in the country.

SNAKES AND LIZARDS

The remaining reptiles of Brunei

The Crested flying lizard (*Draco cristatellus*) with its gliding membrane partially expanded.

Darussalam belong to the Order Squamata, characterised by an elongate body, covered with a fine scaly skin. Their sense of smell is well-developed, relying on the forked tongue which collects samples of odours and is drawn in to pass over a depression in the palate containing olfactory receptors (known as the organ of Jacobson). Worldwide, there are about 3,000 living species, classified in two large suborders.

The first suborder comprises the lizards (Sauria). These mostly have well-developed fore and hind legs, but in some species the limbs are rudimentary or absent. Their ribs are movable permitting the flattening of the body. Extensions of the ribs form the gliding membranes of flying lizards, cicak kubing (*Draco* spp.).

Tail adaptations are also of interest. The gliding geckos of the genus *Ptychozoon* are thought to steer with their wide tail as they descend through the air. The powerful muscular tails of monitors, biawak (Family Varanidae)

> ## HOUSEHOLD FRIENDS
>
> Several species of amphibians and reptiles are commensals with humans, and therefore indicators of disturbed habitats. These include the Paddyfield frog (*Rana erythraea*), the Four-lined tree frog (*Polypedates leucomystax*) and the Asian house gecko (*Hemidactylus frenatus*). All have now been recorded from within the boundaries of the Belalong forest at KBFSC. The gecko established itself during the construction of the Centre buildings, and was probably transported with the timber. The other species appear to have arrived during the following year. The effects of these naturalised species on the local herpetofauna, if any, are at present unknown.

are highly effective weapons. Some lizards have a remarkable ability to cast off the end of the tail, a property known as **autotomy**. The tail does not snap between two vertebrae, but fractures across the weak central part of a vertebra. The lost tip of the tail regenerates, but never attains the original length, and its new scales differ in appearance from the old ones.

Lizards' sense of sight is well developed. The eyes usually have movable lids, but geckos and some skinks have fused lids, permanently closed but transparent. Lizards often show marked sexual dimorphism, males usually being more powerfully built and more brightly coloured than females.

Snakes (Serpentes) comprise the other suborder. All snakes have a long, limbless body, and a remarkable lightly-built skull in which the freely movable,

LIZARDS AT BELALONG

The water monitor (*Varanus salvator*) is the largest lizard at Belalong.

The Common tree skink (*Apterygodon vittatum*).

Seven lizard Families occur in Borneo. The earless monitors (Lanthonotidae) are rarest, known from Sarawak and not yet found in Brunei Darussalam. Two other Families, the glassworms (Anguidae) and the worm lizards (Dibamidae) each have a single representative in Borneo; neither has been found at Belalong. Others are lively members of the wildlife at KBFSC.

The monitor lizards (Varanidae) are largest and can be met anywhere from the river to the ridge tops; their lumbering run is surprisingly fast and they can climb trees at speed, using their long claws to get purchase. Skinks (Scincidae) are mostly shiny dark brown in colour, conical-headed with cylindrical bodies and long tails but short legs. Largely ground-dwelling, they are most often met scuttling away from sunny places, where they bask by day - the boardwalk at KBFSC is much frequented. By night they retreat into hiding. More brightly coloured are the Agamidae, which include the skinny long-legged, long-tailed Green crested lizard (*Bronchocela cristatellus*), whose colour can change from bright green to brown, and the brightly patterned flying lizards (*Draco* spp.).

Geckos are the most speciose among the lizards of the forest, with eight species recorded. These are also very vocal; the call of the Barking gecko (*Gekko smithii*) is commonly heard along river valleys. Three species of bent-toed geckos occur in the area: Inger's bent-toed gecko (*Gonydactylus ingeri*) is confined to the non-riparian forests, the Kinabalu bent-toed gecko (*Gonydactylus baluensis*) to the riparian ones, including the camp clearing, while Peters' bent-toed gecko (*Gonydactylus consobrinus*) is found in both these areas. The most unusual of these lizards must be the Horsfield's gliding gecko (*Ptychozoon horsfieldii*), which has flaps of skin on the sides of the body and broad webs between the fingers and toes. One that measured 60 mm in total body length, hatched out of an

Inger's bent-toed gecko
(*Gonydactylus ingeri*).

Kinabalu bent-toed gecko
(*Gonydactylus baluensis*).

Angle-headed lizard
(*Gonocephalus borneensis*).

Peters' bent-toed gecko
(*Gonydactylus consobrinus*).

egg 13.7 x 11.9 mm on 4 June, 1992. This egg was one of two found at a tree buttress, which may have been accidentally dislodged from their site of attachment on a high branch.

The Crested flying lizard (*Draco cristatellus*) from the riparian forests is one of three; the other two, the Six-lined flying lizard (*Draco quinquefasciatus*) and the Black-bearded flying Lizard (*Draco melanopogon*) are confined to the non-riparian forests. These lizards, like the gliding geckos, glide rather than fly with the aid of the expanded patagium on each side of the body, supported by extensions of the ribs. Flying lizards are specialised ant-eat-ers. They hunt their prey mainly on the trunks and larger branches of trees, climbing upwards by small darts and dashes, and gliding expertly, often for long distances, from tree to tree. Males are aggressively territorial, extending and lowering their brightly coloured throat flaps in display.

Five species of skinks have been recorded, including the arboreal Common tree skink (*Apterygodon vittatum*) and the aquatic Brooke's water skink (*Tropidophorus brookei*).

The most easily seen species is the Three-keeled ground skink (*Mabuya rudis*), commonly encountered basking and foraging on the walkways at KBFSC.

The Blue coral snake
(*Maticora bivirgata*).

Wagler's pit viper (*Tropidolaemus wagleri*).

The Flat-nosed pit viper (*Trimeresurus puniceus*) showing the triangular head covered with small scales and short prehensile tail.

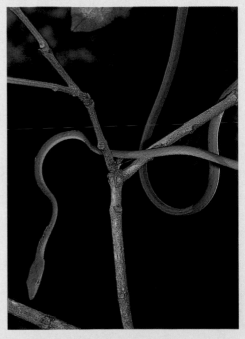

The Oriental whip-snake (*Ahaetulla prasina*).

The world's largest among non-venomous snakes (Reticulated python, *Python reticulatus*, total body length up to 10 m) and venomous snakes (King cobra, *Ophiophagus hannah*, to about 6 m) both occur. Perhaps most interesting of the snakes collected is the Sinister water snake (*Opisthotropis typica*); two specimens were taken at night from the same forest stream where they were probably hunting frogs. This species was hitherto recorded only from Mount Kinabalu in Sabah. Seven species, including the deadly Blue coral snake (*Maticora bivirgata*), have been found on the walkway of KBFSC. Of the 22 species of snakes recorded thus far 17 are harmless, most feeding on invertebrates and small vertebrates: a relatively large Litter skink was recovered from the stomach of an Annulated kukri snake (*Oligodon annulifer*); a Spotted water snake (*Enhydris punctata*) was seen fishing in the river; frog eggs were found in the stomach of a White-fronted water snake (*Amphiesma flavifrons*). The Blue coral snake feeds on other snakes; the enormous venom glands in this species extend to a third of its body length.

The Painted mock-viper
(*Psammodynastes pictus*).

The Striped bronze-backed tree snake
(*Dendrelaphis caudolineatus*).

rod-like bones are joined in the midline by an elastic, extensible ligament to enable the mouth to gape widely and swallow bulky prey. The teeth are long and sharp and may be connected to venom glands. The eyelids of all are fused and transparent, permanently closed over the eyes. When moulting, as soon as the epidermis has been detached, the snake loosens it by rubbing, and crawls out of it, so that the shed epidermis can often be found whole.

The snake's internal anatomy reflects the shape of its body and its habit of swallowing items of bulky food. The left lung is usually rudimentary, while the right is extremely long and expanded to form an air-sac. This comes into operation when the snake hisses, and also acts as an air reservoir during the prolonged process of swallowing food. In addition, the larynx lies well forward and during swallowing can be protruded to allow the intake of air. Most snakes lay eggs, but some species give birth to live young.

Among some species of lizards and snakes, the eggs are retained within the body of the female, and here the embryos undergo their entire development. They are then born at the instant when, or just before, they leave the egg. Sometimes (as in vipers) the female may give birth to several young and then produce eggs as well.

Most egg-laying reptiles leave their clutch unattended. In some, however, the female remains nearby (e.g. some geckos and cobras). The female python not only protects them, but also keeps

291

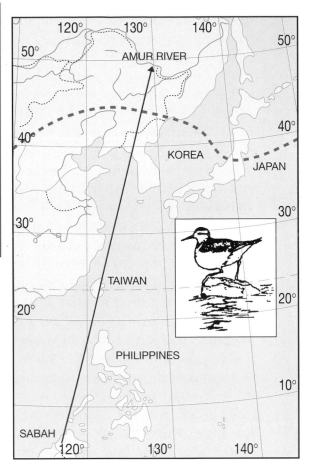

The movement of one Common sandpiper from Borneo to its northern breeding ground, shown by the place of ringing, in Sabah, and re-trapping on the China-Russian border. The dashed line shows the approximate southern limit of the breeding range. [Modified from H. E. McClure (1974. *Migration and survival of the birds of Asia*. USAMC, SEATO Medical Project, Bangkok. Fig 128)].

which provide external protection to the body, insulation, colour patterns important for functions as varied as threat and display or concealment and, of course, enable birds to fly. Their forelimbs have been modified for flight, while the hind limbs serve other purposes: perching, hopping, walking, swimming, grasping, digging, etc. They are toothless, but possess horny bills of many shapes and sizes. Birds are the most vocal vertebrates. Birds can maintain a constant, high internal body temperature. All lay large hard-shelled eggs, which are incubated by one or both sexes. The parents continue to care for their young hatchlings, often after they leave the nest, until they achieve independence. Birds occur almost worldwide, from the remotest oceans to high hills and dry deserts. Somewhat over 9,000 species are known, separated into many Orders and Families.

The power of flight gives birds great mobility. Many species take ad-

them warm by wrapping herself round the eggs. Female crocodiles watch over their eggs and some help the newly-hatched young to find their way out of the nest. Before hatching, the young make sounds to which the parent responds by scratching away the pile of earth covering the eggs. For a few days afterwards, the female guards her young.

BIRDS

Birds are distinguished from all other animals by the possession of feathers,

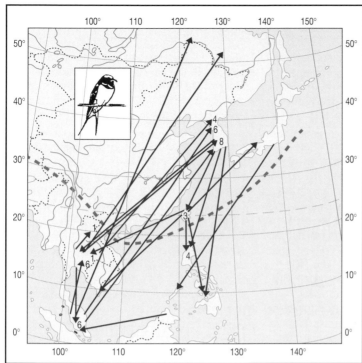

International movements of ringed Barn swallows. Figures indicated the numbers of recoveries in each case. The dashed line shows the approximate southern limit of the breeding range [Modified from H. E. McClure (1974. *Migration and survival of the birds of Asia.* USAMC, SEATO Medical Project, Bangkok. Fig 181)].

vantage of the seasonality of world climates by making long migratory journeys to distant breeding grounds which may be favourable for only a part of each year, but are rich in resources at that time (e.g. at high latitudes). The bird faunas of tropical countries are exceptionally species-rich and diverse, partly because they include large contingents of non-breeding migrants.

In Borneo, in a total bird fauna around 600 species, the proportion is 1:2, of migrants to known or presumed resident breeders. Populations of a few species with extended ranges consist of a mix of residents and migrants. As might be expected from the geographical position of Borneo, almost all migrants breed on the islands and mainland of continental Asia to the north. In

Brunei Darussalam, migrants are mostly birds of the shore, coastal and estuarine mudflats. One member of this community, the Common sandpiper (*Actitis hypoleucos*, Scolopacidae), follows river banks far inland and solitary birds can be seen alongside the Temburong at most times of year.

Other important migratory birds in Brunei Darussalam are those of in-

The Crested serpent eagle (*Spilornis cheela*) a raptor feeding below the forest canopy, the largest bird to be netted during 1991-92.

BIRDS OF BELALONG FOREST

The bird list of Brunei Darussalam, reasonably well known after years of cooperative work by professional and amateur ornithologists, amounts to 312 resident breeding species (of which 16 have non-breeding, migratory populations also), 108 regular migrants, plus 54 vagrants. The community of birds recorded in Belalong, up to the end of 1992, is 199 species, within 10-15% of the total expected. 25 are not forest dependent and a further 15 are also likely to be found outside forest. 128 species were found in the narrow fringe of riparian habitat in the river valley bottoms; 139 on slopes up to 460 m elevation and 121 above 460 m. The lower slope total may be most complete, since the main netting effort was concentrated in this habitat, at Pondok Bujat - where sufficient long-term retraps were recorded to confirm that a resident population was being sampled. No specifically montane birds have been seen on Bukit Belalong which is occupied by a lowland and submontane avifauna characteristic of hillside slopes. The Grey-breasted jungle flycatcher (*Rhinomyias umbratilis*, Muscicapidae), ordinarily a low altitude species, is found within a short distance of the summit.

Of the total, 20 species including the waterside forktails (*Enicurus*, Turdidae) are ground foragers, nine being exclusive to this habitat. 76 species are understorey birds (11 exclusive). 95 species were recorded frequenting the mid-levels of the forest (10 exclusive to this storey), and 75 species in the canopy (44 exclusive to this storey). Upslope from the riverbanks, species richness falls away more sharply in the understorey than in the canopy.

Conspicuous non-migratory lowland forest species expected but not encountered included the Malaysian eared nightjar (*Eurostopodus temminckii*), and several pheasants and partridges (Phasianidae). Cuckoos (Cuculidae) were well represented, particularly in January 1992, when D. R. Wells found the parasitic Indian cuckoo (*Cuculus micropterus*), Hodgson's hawk-cuckoo (*C. fugax*) and Banded bay cuckoo (*Cacomantis sonneratii*) all active on the East Ridge to well above Busiri, whereas the related Moustached hawk-cuckoo (*Cuculus vagans*) and Indonesian cuckoo (*Cacomantis sepulcralis*) were not heard much above Bujat. These ranges are likely to reflect the distribution of their hosts. There is a rich avifauna of bulbuls (Pycnonotidae), babblers (Timaliidae) and flycatchers (Muscicapidae). Most spectacular are the impressive numbers of hornbills (Bucerotidae), testimony to the protection afforded by Brunei gun law. Seven species are present: White-crowned (*Berenicornis comatus*), Bushy-crested (*Anorrhinus galeritus*), Wrinkled (*Rhyticeros corrugatus*), Wreathed (*R. undulatus*), Black (*Anthracoceros malayanus*), Rhinoceros (*Buceros rhinoceros*) and Helmeted hornbill (*Rhinoplax vigil*).

land open country, including aerial feeding insectivorous swifts (Apodidae) and swallows (Hirundinidae). By night the swallows roost gregariously, mostly in urban areas, including Bandar Seri Begawan where they line up along service wires and crowd into tree-tops. By day, they spread out to feed over all habitats, including the shore, river channels and the forest. During 1991/92 three migratory species were seen hunting flying insects borne on updrafts over Bukit Belalong: rare, solitary individuals of Red-rumped swallow (*Hirundo daurica*) and Asian house martin (*Delichon dasypus*), and abundant Barn swallows (*Hirundo rustica*), together with resident Pacific swallows (*Hirundo*

HORNBILLS

Hornbills are heard and seen throughout Belalong forest, which must now be one of, if not the best place to observe these magnificent birds. Numbers present are hard to assess. Plots of hornbills encountered during two timed walks in 1991/92 show that, even though they are so prominent, overall densities are low. The survival of viable populations in the Belalong catchment undoubtedly depends on the continuing integrity of the much larger area of adjoining forest in the whole Batu Apoi Reserve.

Rhinoceros hornbill (*Buceros rhinoceros*).

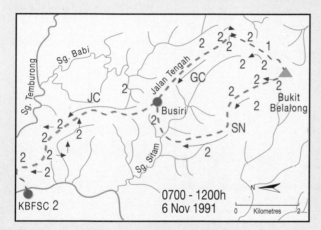

KBFSC 2

0700 - 1200h
6 Nov 1991

Hornbill Survey. On the morning of [6?] November, 1991, three observers walked the routes shown: two from Bukit Belalong to Busiri and one from Busiri to the northern end of Jalan Tengah. Rhinoceros hornbills were most numerous of all hornbills encountered: at least 47, all but one in pairs, as shown on the map (small arrows indicate direction of flight). With an estimated detection limit of *c.* 1km, the indicated minimum density of flying adults of this species was 3 birds per sq km.

tahitica). During the period of the SEATO MAPS international bird-ringing project (1963-71), in South East Asia and East Asia, over 280,000 Barn swallows were ringed and thousands subsequently recaptured and again released, or recovered as casualties, and many aspects of the migratory behaviour of this species in the region were investigated. It is evident that Brunei birds take part in complex patterns of movement, but most are likely to depart to northerly nesting sites during March-April and return, with the young of the year, during August to October.

Forest-dwelling migrants recorded in Belalong forest 1991-92, included the Siberian blue robin (*Erithacus cyane*, Turdidae), a conspicuous litter-feeding species. There was a noticeable influx in late October and November, when birds were seen throughout the forest at all elevations. Most apparently moved on; few were present in January and February of 1992. Other forest migrants were also scarce: total January contacts

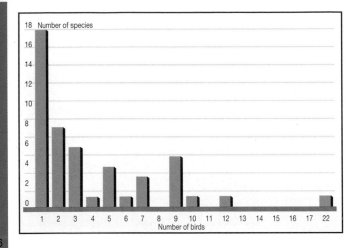

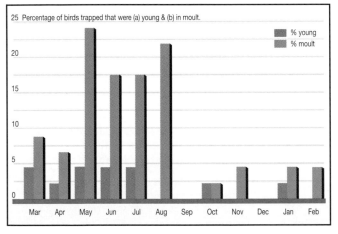

Statistics of understorey birds netted at Pondok Bujat 1991-92

by D. R. Wells (in 11 days) were two Siberian blue robins, two Arctic warblers (*Phylloscopus borealis*), one Asian brown flycatcher (*Muscicapa latirostris*) and one Crow-billed drongo (*Dicrurus annectans*); in February, a pair of migratory nightjars (*Caprimulgus indicus*), were seen hawking over forest below Bukit Belalong.

Migratory birds have to accumulate and store energy reserves to make the journey to and from the breeding grounds. Among migrants, many moult and renew their plumage on the breed-ing grounds, before the return journey. The swallows, however, moult slowly but continuously from their arrival back in South East Asia. Full adult breeding plumage is finally assumed in February - April and, thereafter, the birds accumulate body fat as an energy reserve for the long migratory journey. Barn swallows netted on the summit of Bukit Belalong in 1991/92, proved to be following this cycle, elucidated from studies elsewhere in the region.

The rainforest environment is partitioned by birds in many ways, especially in time, in space and by diet. Nocturnal species are few: the owls (Strigidae, Tytonidae), the frogmouths (Podargidae) and nightjars (Caprimulgidae), all predatory hunters of vertebrates or invertebrates. Most birds are diurnal, although their activity is not continuous but tends to peak early in the morning and again in the later afternoon. Within the forest profile, the activity zones of different species are more or less segregated into ground foragers or specialists of understorey, the mid-level zone of trunks, branches and shaded foliage, or the upper canopy. Bird densities overall, are not high in rainforests. During 1991/92 monthly mist netting at a site near Pondok Bujat provided a quantitative sample of the understorey bird fauna. The species frequency curve resembles that for forest trees in Plot AAU1 or that for moths (See Chapter 6), showing the predominance of rare species, each represented by a single catch, with only three species represented by 10 or more individuals. The principal diets are: fish and other aquatic animals; land vertebrates (with large invertebrates); fruit; nectar (often including arthropods). The group of nectarivores (notably Nectariniidae) have bills of varying lengths and curvature, apparently adapted to flower geometry. While taking nectar, their heads may get dusted with pollen but there is, as yet, no confirmed case of effective pollination of any forest plant in Borneo.

Apart from daily requirements for maintaining existence, once it is full-grown, the greatest physiological demands a bird must meet are in reproduction, (including for the female), production of the eggs over a short period, expenditure of time on incubation, and the gathering of extra food supplies for partner and for dependent young; and the periodic moult, involving a renewal of the flight feathers and body plumage. In most birds there is a post-juvenile moult and subsequently in adulthood one, sometimes two, annual moults. In a seasonal environment, it is clearly important for birds to time these energy-demanding activities to periods of enhanced productivity. During 1991-92, there were sufficient records of nesting or the appearance of young birds, to demonstrate an extended breeding season. This corresponded to expectation, from experience, more widely, in Brunei Darussalam and in Malaysian States at similar latitude. Twenty definite cases of breeding involving 16 species of bird were discovered. Egg-laying seemed to take place over an extended period with records from December to August.

Among netted birds of resident species, recently fledged juveniles were taken in all months of netting, except November, but formed a greater proportion of the catch in March - July. Some birds in moult were taken in every sample, but the proportion was highest in May - August (there was no catch in September 1991). Among the population of breeding residents as a whole, there is clearly a broad overlap between breeding and moult; there is no evi-

297

dence whether the processes can coincide in any individual but it seems likely, from the staggering of peaks, that breeding is followed by moult.

MAMMALS

A mammal (Class Mammalia) is clothed in hair and the female nourishes her young with milk secreted by specialised **mammary glands**. Most mammals

have four limbs, digits ending in claws, nails or hoofs, and a mouth armed with enamel-covered teeth, but there is enormous variation, encompassing the hairless whales of the deep ocean, the toothless pangolin, the winged bats and, of course, humankind. There are some 4,000 mammal species, worldwide, distributed from the polar ice to the tropical desert, the seas to the forests and the air above them.

In Borneo, 222 species of wild land mammals have been recorded (excluding sea mammals). The most diverse Orders are bats (Chiroptera) 93 species, rodents (Rodentia) with 61 and carnivores (Carnivora) with 26 species. A few mammal species are closely commensal

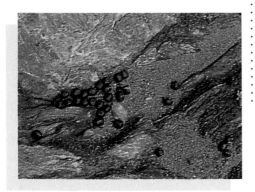

It is often easier to find their traces than to see large mammals themselves: droppings of Sambar deer (*Cervus unicolor*) on the bank of Sungai Engkiang.

Fish scales scattered on rock by the streamside betray the presence of otter in the Sungai Engkiang (January 1991).

The Bornean gibbon (*Hylobates muelleri*).

The tarsier (*Tarsius bancanus*), a small nocturnal primate.

The Yellow-throated marten (*Martes flavigula*) a small carnivore.

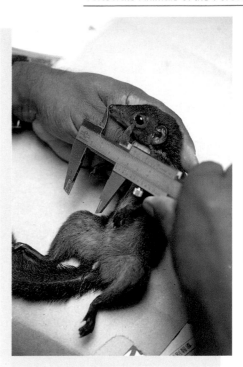

In the course of the small mammal survey, tree-shrews (*Tupaia*) were trapped, measured ...

...and released!

with people or their dwellings; several others are dependent on open habitat and cultivated land, sometimes as pests of crops; some, especially arboreal forms such as squirrels, inhabit tree plantations and the forest; but the largest proportion of mammal species is adapted to life in the forest. Within the forest, the resource is partitioned among the mammals in many ways.

Most mammals occupy limited home ranges and some are territorial, excluding others of the same species. Although some bats make long flights each day, from roost to feeding place, no Bornean species has adopted the long-distance migratory strategy of birds. The bearded pig of Borneo (*Sus barbatus*) is notorious for its mass move-

BATS AT BELALONG

Bats are important members of tropical ecosystems. Borneo has a rich bat fauna: 92 species, comprising 11% of the world total of 853 described species. In Brunei Darussalam, 46 species of bats have been recorded, 50% of those known in Borneo. During 1991-92, 32 species were recorded in Belalong forest, 11 fruit bats (Family Pteropodidae) and 21 insectivorous bats (Families Emballonuridae, Nycterididae, Rhinolophidae, Hipposideridae, Vespertilionidae and Molossidae). Most have been captured in forests in Sabah, suggesting homogeneity among forest bat faunas within northern Borneo. Several of the bats captured at Belalong are still poorly known. Of special interest is the White-winged pipistrelle (*Pipistrellus vordermanni*), previously known from only two specimens at two other localities, the Black-capped fruit bat (*Chironax melanocephalus*) and Least roundleaf bat (*Hipposideros sabanus*), each previously known in Borneo only from one

other locality, and Ridley's roundleaf bat (*Hipposideros ridleyi*) classified as an endangered species.

Two cave species have been recorded at Belalong, the Dusky fruit bat (*Penthetor lucasi*) and Cave nectar bat (*Eonycteris spelaea*), which probably roost under overhanging rocks. The Cave nectar bat pollinates durians and many other forest trees.

The Long-tongued nectar bat (*Macroglossus minimus*) is an important pollinator of bananas and mangrove trees. Some bats, such as *Cynopterus* species, fly with fruit to feeding roosts where they eat, dropping the seeds and hence acting as dispersal agents for the plants involved. The insectivorous bats are efficient predators of the large community of nocturnal flying insects; the hollow-faced bats (*Nycteris* spp.) are specialised gleaners, picking arthropod prey from foliage or other surfaces.

SMALL MAMMALS

Four rat species, Mueller's, Red spiny rat, Polynesian and Malaysian field rats, were trapped in riparian habitat but not Mixed Dipterocarp Forest. The species, the Long-tailed giant, Brown spiny, Whitehead's and Dark-tailed tree rat were trapped in both habitats. The treeshrew species, the Lesser, Slender, Large and Painted treeshrews, were trapped in dipterocarp forest, but only the last one also in the riparian forest site. Seven squirrels, the Plain pigmy squirrels, Giant, Prevost's, Low's, Plantain, Tufted ground and Horse-tailed squirrels, were seen (but only three trapped) in the dipterocarp forest areas; only the last two were not found in the riparian area.

Charles Francis mounted his harp trap in the forest.

GIBBONS AND MONKEYS

In Belalong forest the Bornean gibbons (*Hylobates muelleri*), Hose's langurs (*Presbytis hosei*) and Pig-tailed macaques (*Macaca nemestrina*) are common; Long-tailed macaques (*M. fascicularis*) are occasionally seen along the river. Although species diversity is low, abundance is high. Indeed, the density of Hose's langurs (6.0 groups per sq km) is the highest of any langur species known at any site in Borneo. The density of gibbons (5.3 groups per sq km) is also unusually high.

Hose's langurs (a species endemic to northern Borneo) live in larger groups than recorded elsewhere. The average number estimated per group is 11.0, and groups of at least 12 and 17 individuals have been seen (compared with an average of 6 in Sabah and Sarawak). The gibbons too, have unusual group structures. Normally monogamous, associating in groups of 4-5, comprising an adult male, adult female and their immature offspring, at Belalong, a high proportion of gibbon groups have more than one female. During a ten day period, 13 of 31 groups heard calling had more than one female (42%). One group had two apparently full-sized females and a third juvenile female. The two large females were obviously coordinating their calls with each other, a highly unusual phenomenon.

These uncommon social patterns may be due to the lack of hunting, to the distribution and size of food sources in Belalong forest or to some other, undiscovered factor.

301

In the survey of small ground mammals during 1991-92, rats were routinely trapped, marked and released.

The head and nose-leaf of the Trefoil horseshoe bat (*Rhinolophus trifoliatus*).

ments in response to irregular variations in food supplies. Other mammals occuring in Brunei Darussalam are permanently resident, and often territorial within traditional areas.

Most of the mammals have altitudinally restricted ranges, so that the montane community is distinct from that of the lowlands; a few species

Dark-tailed tree rat (*Niviventer cremoriventer*).

Small fruit bats (*Cynopterus* sp.) at roost under the shelter of a banana leaf, clinging to the mid-rib by the sharply recurved claws of their hind feet.

are confined to the upper zone of the highest mountains. Within the lowland community inhabiting Mixed Dipterocarp Forest temporal partitioning separates the diurnal forms from the nocturnal. Thus, among rodents (Order Rodentia), rats, mice and flying squirrels are nocturnal while the typical squirrels are diurnal. Among primates (Order Primates), the gibbons (*Hylobates muelleri*) and monkeys (Cercopithecidae) are diurnal but the smaller species, slow loris (*Nycticebus coucang*) and tarsier (*Tarsius bancanus*), are nocturnal. Tree shrews (*Tupaia*) are diurnal except the pentail (*Ptilocercus lowii*) which is nocturnal. Among carnivores, otters are active by day but most others by night. Ungulates, such as deer or pigs, generally live in sheltered concealment by day and emerge to forage at dusk. Bats are entirely nocturnal; their diurnal counterparts are birds, rather than other mammals.

Spatial partitioning separates both the diurnal and the nocturnal communities of mammals into vertical activity zones within the forest, further subdi-

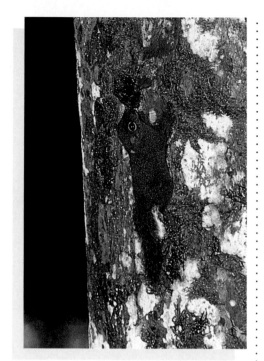

The Pygmy squirrel (*Exiliscirus exilis*) forages exclusively on tree trunks and large branches.

vided by dietic specialisations. Recognisable ecological zones are similar to those among birds: ground level, including water as a subzone; ground and understorey; middle zone, with tree trunks as special category; and the upper canopy. Otters, common at Belalong, are not confined to water but never move far from it. Only the ungulates are wholly tied to the ground. Bearded pigs derive much food from the soil itself and their workings can be found throughout Belalong forest, especially in patches of damp ground or river banks. They also depend heavily on fallen fruits and the long-distance mass movements, for which this species is notorious, appear to be in re-

sponse to sporadic mass fruiting of favoured food trees such as oil rich engkabang (*Dipterocarpus* species) or oaks and chestnuts (Fagaceae). Other ungulates, dependent on browsing and fallen fruit are the mouse-deer (*Tragulus* spp.), barking deer, kijang (*Muntiacus* spp.) and sambar, payau (*Cervus unicolor*).

Squirrels are **scansorial**, and members of this one, closely related taxonomic group provide an example of environmental partitioning, easily seen at Belalong. Species adapted to live on the ground and in the understorey include the insect-eating Shrew-faced squirrel (*Rhinosciurus laticaudatus*), which has an elongated muzzle and reduced teeth. The Pygmy squirrel (*Exilis exilisciurus*) exploits foods on tree-trunks, up and down which it moves in jerky darts and scurries; the Plantain squirrel (*Callosciurus notatus*) and Horse-tailed squirrel (*Sundasciurus hippurus*) frequent middle levels, and Prevost's squirrel (*Callosciurus prevostii*) and the Giant squirrel (*Ratufa affinis*), the canopy. All these species are **diurnal** (active by daylight). At nightfall the arboreal squirrels are replaced by the flying squirrels, while the rich fauna of rats (Muridae) can be considered as **nocturnal** counterparts of the ground-dwelling and understorey forms.

Many other mammals show arboreal adaptations. The grasping hands and feet of primates, such as the gibbons (*Hylobates* spp.) or macaques (*Macaca* spp.) and their forward facing eyes, giving binocular vision and hence

303

close judgement of distances, clearly fit them for a life in trees. Some arboreal rats, such as the pencil-tailed tree mice (*Chiropodomys*) show convergence, with their grasping feet and foreshortened muzzle.

Squirrels, too, have rounded muzzles, providing binocular vision, but their feet are non-grasping with sharp, recurved claws, while their long tails give them balance and equipoise in jumping from branch to branch. It is notable that those species of squirrels which have adopted a way of life on the ground, such as the Striped ground-squirrels (*Lariscus*), the Shrew-faced ground squirrel or the magnificent Tufted ground squirrel *(Rheithrosciurus macrotis)*, have elongated muzzles and tail hairs that fluff into cylindrical form, rather than the flattened pattern of tree squirrels or the tree-shrews (*Tupaia* spp.). The flight membranes of flying squirrels and the colugo (*Cynocephalus variegatus*) are extreme adaptations to arboreal life, enabling them to glide long distances between trees. In the dim light in which they are active, it is probably also a significant advantage to be able to leap from one branch towards an unseen objective, confident in the capability of manoevring in mid flight to select a landing point when it is close enough to be visible.

Several species of carnivore are arboreal; the most highly adapted is the binturong (*Arctictis binturong*), which possesses a prehensile tail, as does the scaly anteater or pangolin (*Manis javanica*).

VERTEBRATE BIODIVERSITY

The vertebrate community as a whole thus maintains diversity, in part by partitioning the environment spatially within the profile of the forest and temporally, by day and night. As we have seen, all Classes contain species specialised for existence in the upper canopy, or on branches and trunks, among the lower storey vegetation or on the ground.

The reptiles and amphibians of Brunei Darussalam also include burrowing species. Almost all frogs and toads are active by night, but the other terrestrial vertebrate groups follow either diurnal or nocturnal lifestyles; a few are **crepuscular** specialists of dawn and dusk. As we have noted, most birds are diurnal, excepting frogmouths, nightjars and owls and some swifts (Apodidae), which are crepuscular or nocturnal. The rich bat fauna seems to offer nocturnal counterparts to birds. Several genera of trees, including the durians and petai (*Parkia*), flower by night, producing blossom morphologically adapted to attract bats which serve as pollinators.

Among reptiles, the diurnal agamid lizards have their counterparts in the noctural geckos, although the scansorial adaptations of the latter place them in a different niche. Snakes are secretive by day, and half of them active only by night. Among these, too, behavioural differences provide for ecological separation, for instance, between mainly aquatic snakes, burrowing

PIG'S NESTS

The Bearded pig builds large, mound-like 'nests' on the ground. When due to give birth, a sow will select a dry area for the construction of the nest, often on a ridge top, within which the piglets are born. The nest offers shelter for the piglets during their first vulnerable hours or days, and the sow has been reported to defend her offspring by charging.

The nest itself is a large pile of leafy vegetation and saplings. One nest found on the West Ridge stood about 1 m high, and had a roughly circular base 2 m wide. It was made of 190 stems, consisting mainly of dicotyledonous saplings but also containing many stems of several species of gingers and palms. The stems were not interwoven but merely piled one on top of each other with the broken ends lying towards the outer edge of the nest. The broken end of the stems showed that the pig had gripped it in its jaws and had torn it off. Beneath the dome of vegetation was an oval depression in the bare ground, 17 cm deep and 62 cm across at its widest point. The hollow was covered with fine, dry, soft earth.

The stems varied in length from 80 to 320 cm, the longest with roots still attached. The height at which the stem had been bitten off varied from 20 to 74 cm above the ground, and their diameters at the point of breakage 0.5 - 1.9 cm. Within a radius of about 8 m virtually all saplings and herbaceous plants in that size range had been bitten off by the pig, leaving the area devoid of much of its ground, herb and shrub layer vegetation and broken stems were located up to 14 m from the nest. Nest construction by pigs must have a dramatic impact on forest dynamics by severely affecting sapling survival in the immediate area of the nest.

In adulthood, the Bearded pig *(Sus barbatus)* lightens in colour from dark to pale pinkish grey: this sow is stained by mud from wallowing.

305

snakes, ground-dwellers and climbers. All are predatory, but undoubtedly specialised for different prey; notable are the pit vipers (Elapidae) which possess organs to detect warmth, hence sensitive to the presence of mammalian prey. These are the top predators in the complex web of interactive adaptations.

Sungai Engkiang.

CHAPTER 13

FRESHWATERS

Freshwaters are an integral part of the rainforest ecosystem. Freshwaters contain a tiny fraction of the available water in the biosphere, yet are of great importance in the physical and chemical processes of the world and in the biological diversity they support. Also important are the ecological linkages of land and water in the forest and the exchange of resources between the terrestrial and aquatic environments, involving processes of physical and biological transfer. In Belalong forest, the two rivers, Belalong and Temburong, and their tributaries, are the dominant freshwaters, and our attention is focussed on them. Yet other, smaller water bodies are also biologically valuable to specialised communities. These include ephemeral rain pools or puddles and the reservoirs of water that collect in enclosed spaces, such as the holes and hollows in the trunks or limbs of trees, the nodal spaces of bamboo stems, the leaves or leaf axils of some epiphytes and the pitchers of pitcher

Riparian trees show specialised adaptations to their riverside habitat, such as these trailing adventitious roots.

plants (*Nepenthes*).

The role of water in shaping the land has been explained and the development of the Belalong catchment has been described (See Chapter 3). These flowing waters present a distinctive pattern of distribution of biological diversity involving the species that live within freshwater for all or part of their lifecycles.

Vascular plants have few species adapted to flowing waters. Green plant diversity is associated mainly with diatoms and other algae. There are also specialised aquatic fungi. As on land, the invertebrate fauna includes many undescribed species but, in this case, tropical biodiversity does not appear to exceed that found in temperate streams. All Classes of vertebrates include species whose ecology is dependent to a greater or lesser extent upon the freshwaters of the forest but, clearly, the fish dominate and are particularly diverse in tropical streams and rivers.

PHYSICAL CHARACTERISTICS

On the basis of stream gradient and current velocity, three zones can be recognised: upper, middle and lower. In the forest soil, percolating groundwater collects in natural drainage lines from which lighter particles of clay and even sand may be washed out. The smallest streams of the upper zone are those that spring from drainage lines at the head of the steep (i.e. > 30° slope) valleys. These are exceedingly variable in flow rate, springing into spate for short periods after rain. Those at higher elevations have been termed

Branches of the larger trees overhanging the river are covered with epiphytes.

'montane' streams.

Drainage lines and montane streams flow into permanent rocky streams of lesser (but still steep) gradient, cascading from pool to pool through a tunnel of vegetation closing over the water. The larger waters of the middle zone to which these streams are tributaries flow through Gallery Forest, dominated by ensurai (*Dipterocarpus oblongifolius*). The lower Belalong provides a typical example, with the big riparian trees arching over the river course, their boughs draped with epiphytes. Here pristine stretches survive in original grandeur and beauty.

As we have seen (See Chapter 3), in these streams and rivers, water levels and flow rates reflect the amount, timing and location of rainfall. Montane streams and small hill streams of the upper zone are particularly responsive to the vagaries of local precipitation. The run-off from a storm produces a raging torrent, but this rapidly subsides. Basal flow rate may be scarcely more than a trickle, and in dry weather reduced to a string of small pools or disappear altogether. Fluctuations are also pronounced in the lower reaches. Here, following storms, surface run-off produces a sharp rise in levels, but for short duration, followed by a rapid decline to normal.

In small streams, forest cover filters much of the incident light. In forested reaches, typically 2-15% of visible light reaches the water surface, with higher relative values in overcast conditions when diffuse radiation becomes more important than the direct component. The transparency of water

311

The tumbling, torrential waterfalls of small streams in Belalong forest are important aquatic habitats.

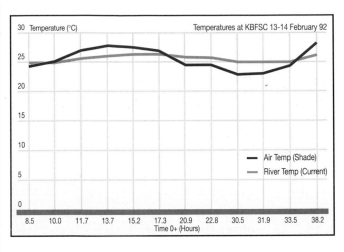

A plot of air and water temperatures of Sungai Belalong over two days at KBFSC from 0830 hours on 13 February 1992.

to light is critical for aquatic algae and other submerged plants. Attenuation increases with depth and is a function of turbidity. Rapid initial losses with depth are attributable to the diffuse nature of the incident light and the low reflectivity of the banks and bank vegetation. Even in clear water, at 40 cm below surface, intensity is reduced to about 60%. There is inevitably some erosion by storm run-off but any temporary rise in turbidity is moderate. In peak flooding, silt loads prevent light penetration beyond 5 cm.

The temperature regime of the water is more moderate than that of air, cooler by day and warmer by night. The dense shade of tree cover arching over forest streams lowers average temperatures and moderates diurnal variation. On hillsides at higher elevations, the waters are cooler, reflecting lower aver-

ANIONS AND CATIONS IN STREAMS

Chemical parameters (mean ± standard error) of rainwater and streams at Belalong:

	Rainwater	Streams
pH	5.56 ± 0.23	6.76 ± 0.31
Conductivity (µS/cm)	4.50 ± 1.10	24.70 ± 5.70
Na (mg/l)	0.07 ± 0.06	1.42 ± 0.31
K (mg/l)	0.20 ± 0.06	0.48 ± 0.33
Ca (mg/l)	0.29 ± 0.17	0.98 ± 0.43
Mg (mg/l)	0.03 ± 0.01	0.96 ± 0.21
Al		not detectable
Fe		not detectable
Cl^- (mg/l)	0.28 ± 0.04	0.33 ± 0.20
SO_4^- (mg/l)	0.26 ± 0.19	3.18 ± 1.12
NO_3^- (mg/l)	0.18 ± 0.04	0.38 ± 0.19
PO_4^- (mg/l)	< 0.04	< 0.04
HCO_3^- (mg/l)	–	< 0.09

The tributaries of Sungai Belalong are places of outstanding natural beauty.

age air temperatures.

The pH of a forest stream is largely controlled by the rock or soils over which it flows. Variations are attributable to factors including rainfall cycles and the production and consumption of carbon dioxide by aquatic organisms, affecting the bicarbonate buffering system found in most freshwaters. Rainwater is naturally acid but, typically, the streams of Belalong forest have a pH around neutrality.

Dissolved oxygen content is critical for the living organisms in the water. Oxygen tensions are highest in these fast-flowing, unpolluted forest streams and at Belalong can be expected to exceed 90% saturation. Under the prevailing high temperatures at lowland elevations, even fully saturated waters contain only a few mg of oxygen per litre, at concentrations in the range 7.0-8.0 mg O_2 per litre.

There is great variation in total dissolved carbon dioxide, even in fast-flowing forest streams. In all waters, there is a pronounced diurnal cycle, high in the early morning due to overnight respiration and diminishing during the hours of daylight as a consequence of uptake during photosynthesis by aquatic plants. The mean value for the streams in Belalong is about 3 mg per litre.

The concentrations of salts, conventionally measured as the sums of carbonate, halide and other strong acid anions, and sodium, potassium, magnesium and calcium cations, are characteristically low in forest streams and,

in many cases, the contribution from rain represents the most important input. High sulphate content at Belalong is due to leaching from the soil and decaying organic matter. The relative concentrations of cations ($Na^+ > Ca^{2+} > Mg^{2+} > K^+$) reflect soil chemistry. Low levels of calcium and magnesium are characteristic. Scarcity of dissolved calcium in the water has important consequences for the biota, affecting in particular animals that need large amounts, such as molluscs and crustaceans.

Iron and aluminium concentrations are normally very low, and often undetectable. Silica, on the other hand, is a major solute in freshwaters. Phosphate is very scarce, a feature attributable to low availability in the soils and efficient closed recycling in the forest vegetation. Levels of nitrogen are typically higher than phosphorus, with organic and ammonium-nitrogen dominating.

FRESHWATER PLANTS AND MICRO-ORGANISMS

MICRO-ORGANISMS

Under the conditions of low illumination, algae are not prominent although there is a diverse flora. In fast-flowing forest streams, attached algae predominate, encrusting rock surfaces, submerged roots and plant stems; planktonic forms are scarcer. Bacteria and fungi are also present in forest waters, and undoubtedly play important roles

THE RHEOPHYTIC PALM

The small rheophyte palm, *Pinanga tenella* var. *tenella*, branches basally by axillary buds and has thin stems up to 2 m in length. The leaves are simple, pinnate and finely divided; the inflorescence is simple, unbranched and pendulous, with a red rachis and rose pink bracts; fruits are ovoid, with a pointed tip, green when immature ripening to cream colour. In 1992, the distribution of this palm was surveyed along both banks of Sungai Belalong, for about 7 km, from its confluence with Sungai Temburong to about 1 km north of Sungai Engkiang. 1621 clumps were recorded along this stretch. There is a consistent increase in the occurence of the palm from the confluence up to Sungai Engkiang; numbers then decrease. The palm is confined to a 1-2 m wide zone along the margins of the river, within the flood line.

The palm does not grow well in open sunny positions but can tolerate some exposure to full sun. It thrives in places where there is some protection, as in dappled shade under forest overhangs. Many of the palms on rapid sections root deeply into rock crevices. In the slack stretches of the river, the palms trap silt around their roots and have a larger root mass but fewer stems than those growing on rocky ledges in fast flowing sections. It is unlikely that the river acts as a dispersal agent, but small mammals and birds may play a role in seed dispersal.

315

Pinanga tenella var. *tenella* is a rheophyte found in the rivers of Borneo, one of a small number of palm rheophytes.

The crystal clear water of Sungai Belalong, with trailing roots and sunken leaves.

Tectaria hosei, a common fern rheophyte in rocky gorges on Sungai Engkiang.

The aroid *Bucephalandra motleyana* growing with the rheophytic filmy fern *Trichomanes javanicum* on Sungai Baki.

Plants which are confined to the banks and beds of swift-flowing streams and rivers and which grow in the zone up to the level of flash floods are known as **rheophytes**. They are adapted to withstand the fast currents and submergence associated with the frequent floods from monsoon rains and tropical storms. A wide range of taxonomic groups are represented including ferns and flowering plants. Rheophytes are commoner in the tropics than in the temperate regions of the world, and in Borneo are particularly well-represented.

Many rheophytes have a characteristic morphology, with a strong root system and tough stems bearing narrow or finely dissected leaves - all features which may help prevent the plants from being swept away in fast currents. They occupy many different situations, from the steep rocky gorges of narrow streams to the gravel and sand bars of the larger rivers.

At Belalong there are no permanently submerged rheophytes (also known as **hydrophytes**) but a considerable number of terrestrial rheophytes occupy the banks of watercourses of all sizes. The ensurai is one of the most conspicuous of rheophytic trees, with massive leaning trunks supported by large buttresses towards the riverbank. The young saplings of ensurai have much narrower leaves than the adults, as expected of a rheophyte.

Muddy banks of the rivers support a wide range of rheophytes including the palm *Pinanga tenella* var. *tenella* (See p.119) and the attractive aroid, *Osmoxylon borneensis*, notable as a Borneo endemic and for its digitately compound leaves, unusual amongst rheophytes. The shrub *Myrmeconauclea strigosa* (Rubiaceae) with balls of cream flowers is found on lightly shaded mud banks; this is also an ant-plant (See p.168/169) having swollen internodes which are inhabited by small black ants.

The rheophytes *Osmoxylon borneensis* (foreground) and *Pinanga tenella* var. *tenella* on the bank of Sungai Belalong.

The rheophyte shrub *Myrmeconauclea strigosa* in flower on the banks of Sungai Belalong.

Myrmeconauclea strigosa in fruit beside the Sungai Belalong.

The swollen stems of *Myrmeconauclea strigosa*; a young inflorescence is in the centre.

Ferns too can be found in these habitats - *Pronephrium hosei* (Thelypteridaceae) in shady areas and the common *Tectaria angulata* (Dryopteridaceae) in more open sites. The fern *Dipteris lobbiana* (Dipteridaceae) is a conspicuous rheophyte of shale banks in fairly open conditions, together with *Pronephrium salicifolium* and *Mesophlebion oligodictyon* (Thelypteridaceae).

The smaller streams at Belalong are often confined in very narrow gorges with a closed canopy above. Ferns predominate on their banks, with several species of *Tectaria*, *Bolbitis* (Lomariopsidaceae) and *Trichomanes* (filmy ferns, Hymenophyllaceae) characteristic.

Under more open conditions, *Bucephalandra motleyana*, a small aroid (Araceae) with white flowers, can be found growing on the boulders of stream beds.

in the saprophytic breakdown of organic detritus. The aquatic fungi grow on submerged dead leaves and twigs in fast-flowing, unpolluted streams; some are local or tropical in range; others are cosmopolitan. Associated aquatic micro-consumers may be present in considerable numbers, but the role of minute heterotrophs in the trophic dynamics of forest freshwaters is little known. Those micro-organisms that inhabit the river or stream bed may cross the interface between these benthic deposits and the soils of the forest, especially in areas of seepage or outwelling from aquifers. To them, the water-filled pore spaces of soils provide a habitat in which they can thrive.

MACROPHYTES

The community structure of non-microscopic plants (commonly known as **macrophytes**) in freshwaters is much less complex than that of the terrestrial rainforest. For various reasons, true macrophytes are rare or absent in the Sungai Belalong and its tributary streams. As we have seen (Chapter 6), the rivers and streams are bordered by characteristic riparian trees. Shading causes a massive reduction in the visible light reaching the water surface and rapid attenuation at shallow depth. The low levels of light energy severely restrict the community of green aquatic plants. Submerged and floating macrophytes also have difficulty in rooting in the fast flowing waters.

Fallen fruit, leaves and other plant litter from the forest therefore represent the main organic input to the system and the chief source of food for many plant- or detritus-eating members of the aquatic fauna. The roots of riparian plants growing into the water form distinctive features in the bank and channel topography. Those of some, notably gapis, respond to submersion by branching into a luxuriant mass of rootlets. The dense mats so formed are of great importance as shelter and attachment sites for small aquatic organisms.

INVERTEBRATE ANIMALS

CRUSTACEANS

With the exception of woodlice (See Chapter 11), all crustaceans (Class Crustacea) are aquatic or dependent on water at some stage of their life history. They have a hard external protective body covering, composed largely of calcium carbonate, and many jointed appendages. In order to grow, this hard

---

MOLLUSCS

A single species of freshwater snails, (*Brotia* sp., Gastropoda), are found in only a few tributaries, such as Sungai Anak, Esu, Engkabang and Engkiang. Wherever they occur the abundance is low. Their rarity undoubtedly reflects the absence of calcareous rock and the consequent low concentration of calcium in these surface waters.

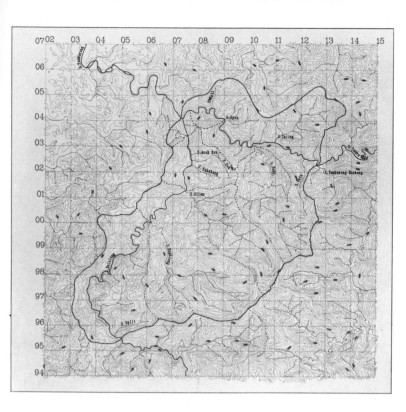

GIS map of the Belalong forest showing the major watercourses.

external skeleton has to be shed from time to time. They have a variable diet, frequently being carrion or detritus eaters. Many crabs emerge from the water to land and, in humid tropical environments, several species are terrestrial for much of their lives, relying on water only for moulting and breeding. The larger freshwater crustaceans are the crabs and prawns, both members of the Order Decapoda (meaning 'ten legs').

A majority of the 8,000 known species of crabs are marine, but several hundred species have colonised freshwater and terrestrial habitats. In South East Asia, including Borneo, true freshwater crabs belong to three superfamilies: Potamoidea, Gecarcinu-coidea and Grapsoidea. Unlike marine crabs, freshwater and terrestrial crabs have few large eggs which undergo direct or abbreviated development; free-

CRABS OF BELALONG

Four species of crabs, each belonging to a different genus, are known at Belalong. All were collected from streams, some very close to the source, with the exception of the land crabs (*Geosesarma*). Land crabs are effectively terrestrial, being found in the forest, all the way up to the ridges. They were often seen climbing plants up to about 3 m above the forest floor and at night are easily mistaken for spiders. All are new records for Brunei Darussalam. The species *Isolapotamon collinsi* has now been found for the first time outside Sarawak.

PRAWNS AND WATER QUALITY

Two species (*Atyopsis mollucensis* and *Caridina bruneiana*) of the primary fresh-water prawn family Atyidae occur in the Sungai Belalong. Only four other species have so far been located elsewhere in the freshwaters of Borneo - two in Brunei and two in Sarawak. In the estuarine areas however, six species were found within a relatively small area in Temburong. This raises the question: Why are primarily fresh-water taxa so poorly represented in the freshwaters of a geologically relatively-old landmass such as Borneo? It seems that water quality, particularly the low pH and poor buffering capacity, prevents success-ful colonisation by atyids. This is com-pounded by the fact that the lowland streams are inhabited by extremely efficient preda-tory fish.

Species of *Macrobrachium* tolerate relatively high salinity water. This genus is a member of the largely marine family Palaemonidae. Many so-called freshwater *Macrobrachium* species (such as udang galah, *Macrobrachium rosenbergii*) still mi-grate to the sea or estuarine areas to breed. At Belalong, an undescribed species of *Macrobrachium* is found mainly above wa-terfalls; it has few large eggs which un-dergo direct development. *Macrobrachium* sp. maintains its position in torrent condi-tions by adopting this reproductive strat-egy. Very few predatory aquatic organisms

A small udang galah (*Macrobrachium rosenbergii*); this species can grow to nearly 20 cm.

A new species of *Macrobrachium*, found only above waterfalls at Belalong.

are found in areas above waterfalls, and this, presumably, compensates selectively for low productivity.

swimming larvae are either absent or of very short duration.

The term 'prawn' is sometimes reserved for larger species while the smaller ones are known as 'shrimps', but there is no general agreement on which name applies to a particular size range, and only the first term is used here. There are two freshwater Families. Palaemonidae: generally larger with one

pair of claws (the second one) enlarged; in Borneo only the one genus *Macro-brachium* is truly freshwater; the others are brackish-water or marine. The Atyidae: generally less than 2 cm long, (often mistaken for juvenile *Macrobrachium*), distinguished by the tuft of brush-like 'hair' at the tips of the claws on the first two pairs of legs; two genera are known from Borneo, *Atyopsis*

A NEW SPECIES OF FRESHWATER PRAWN, *Caridina bruneiana*

Caridina bruneiana was the first record of the family Atyidae from Negara Brunei Darussalam (as well as from Borneo). The occurrence of atyid prawns here is not surprising considering the fact that they are found elsewhere all around Borneo (e.g. Peninsular Malaysia and Singapore, Sumatra, Java, Sulawesi and the Philippines). Their rather late discovery may be due to inadequate sampling in combination with identification problems. The distribution of atyid prawns seems to be restricted to less acidic waters, a type not common in Brunei Darussalam, where stream and river waters vary in pH range between 3 and 6. This may explain the rather restricted distribution of atyids within Brunei Darussalam. *C. bruneiana* was first collected at the confluence of the Belalong and the Temburong rivers on 16 May 1990. The stream characteristics (under flooded conditions) were as follows: width 10-30 m, depth 0.5-2.5 m, water velocity 3-150 cm per second, pH 6.3, sandstone and gravel substratum. More specimens were subsequently collected from further downstream in the Temburong near the Mini-Zoo at Batang Duri on 28 September 1990. The species has also been found in the lower reaches of the Sungai Apam and Sungai Esu. Stream characteristics here were similar to those at the confluence.

Egg-carrying female (above) and the smaller male of *Caridina bruneiana*, a shrimp first found at Belalong.

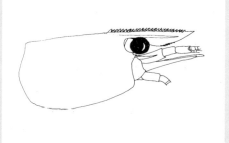

The head of *Caridina bruneiana*.

and *Caridina*.

INSECTS

Although the taxonomy of many groups of aquatic insects is not completely known, it is clear that the insect fauna of forest freshwaters are distinctive; few species also occur in open country. In Peninsular Malaysia, on the basis of adult distributions, different communities of forest stream dragonflies (Odonata) emphasise the ecological distinctness of upper, middle and lower level streams, the rivers and pools. Many insects are aquatic as larvae and terrestrial (or aerial) as adults. These therefore perform the role in the forest ecology of transferring resources from the water back to land. Insects inhabiting forest streams and rivers as larvae in-

321

clude dragonflies (Odonata), caddis flies (Trichoptera), mayflies (Ephemeroptera), and stoneflies (Plecoptera). Water beetles (Coleoptera) are mostly aquatic as larvae and as adults. Certain bugs (Hemiptera, Heteroptera), such as the water skaters and water striders, are tied to water but spend their lives exclusively on the water surface and can drown if they are immersed, while others, such as water boatmen, live mainly

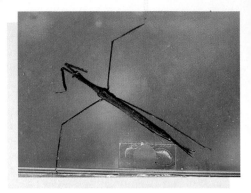

Water strider from Belalong.

WATER SKATERS AND WATER CRICKETS AT BELALONG

The very surface of the water itself is the habitat of the long-legged water skaters (Family Gerridae) and more compact water crickets (Veliidae). These are bugs, and possess piercing and sucking mouth parts by which they feed on body fluids from other small invertebrates which float on the water, either dead or living. In still waters, prey swimming just below the surface may also be captured; for a few species, mosquito larvae form a major component of the diet.

Water skaters

Among species occurring on Sungai Belalong or tributary streams near KBFSC, the following can be recognised: *Cylindrostethus scrutator*, a rather large skater (body length 12-15 mm), the body blackish in colour with a contrasting yellow stripe on each side of the fore-end, which forms groups in sheltered spots near the bank of Sungai Belalong. *Ventidius*, squat (about 3 mm long), recognisable by its colour, blackish with a central yellow mark on its back. *Ptilomera*, large (up to 20 mm), olive green or brownish, favouring shady places on the Belalong or quiet pools in tributary streams. *Rheumatogonus borneensis*, small (4-5 mm), and thin-bodied, frequenting moving water and looking

somewhat like a midge as it jumps horizontally up and downstream. *Metrocoris*, round-bodied (4-5 mm), pale yellow patterned with black lines and curves.

Water crickets

The riffle bugs, *Rhagovelia*, are small bodied (length 4 mm), blackish or orange tinged, which gather just downstream of riffles and disperse rapidly and irregularly over the rapid currents when disturbed. They are assisted in moving over the water surface by a fan of plumose hairs growing from a split in the last segment of each middle leg.

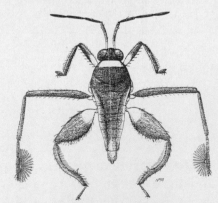

The riffle bug (*Rhagovelia papuensis*), showing the growth of plumose hairs on the last segment of the middle leg.

below the surface.

In rivers and streams, separate assemblages occupy different zones, characterised by features such as sandy bottoms, leaf drifts, root-bank complexes or stones in the current and sunshine. Predatory forms constitute a high proportion. For herbivores, most foods are of outside origin - notably, fallen leaf litter.

Larval mayflies are especially important in hill streams. Different species are specialised for distinctive modes of life and occupy exclusive habitats: for example, some are herbivores browsing on encrusting algae on stones; others are predators, others detritivores. On stream beds, some occur in clean unsilted situations and others among detritus or accumulations of submerged

BRACHYCERAN DIPTERA OF WATERCOURSES

One group of flies generally associated with standing or flowing water was the subject of a special study. The larvae of at least some of the species of the three families Dolichopodidae, Empididae and Rhagionidae are known to be aquatic in other parts of the world, and at Belalong the adults of some species were very restricted in distribution, being limited to patches of flowing or standing water.

The Dolichopodidae, with 50-60 species are the most abundant; these are small to minute (down to 1 mm long). They were frequent over exposed gravel and wet rock faces but scarce on fringing vegetation. Only a few metres from the watercourses, the stream-frequenting species were effectively absent. A few habitat preferences were obvious in some of the large dolichopodids. Several species were frequent on large stones and rocks close to the water's edge, and were the only ones occurring on the broad sunlit beaches of the larger streams and rivers. One large species was frequently found up to 20 m from the main rivers, occasionally near streams. These flies patrolled open surfaces,

such as large dead leaves, pieces of flat wood or cobbles, chasing away any large insects that landed on their plots and eating many of the smaller ones.

Fifteen species of Empididae were found; most of these are perhaps not truly aquatic as they were not strictly associated with water but a few minute species were collected from stones in riffles. It is to be expected that the larvae of such species are truly aquatic. Only five species of Rhagionidae were collected, of which only one was widespread.

Martin Drake set malaise traps over shallow watercourses.

A soldier fly, *Ptilocera quadridentata* (Stratiomyidae) from Belalong.

leaves. Mayflies are a major food of fish. The winged adults have vestigial mouthparts, do not feed and for their short lives subsist on stored reserves. The stoneflies by contrast have generalised chewing mouthparts, and corresponding unspecialised diets; they are abundant in hill streams, where they are important detritivores.

The bugs show a rich diversity. They frequent flowing and standing waters and nearly all are air-breathers. The water skaters and water crickets dart rapidly over the water surface supported by surface tension, each foot riding in a minute dimple. Many are gregarious and all are predatory. The water-boatmen (Corixidae) are powerful fliers, and will rapidly find and colonise puddles or other small waterbodies in the forest. Other bugs are found among roots and in detritus along stream banks.

Caddis-fly larvae are abundant in forest streams. Most caddis build tubes on which they rely for shelter; others make webs to ensnare their food. Tube building species are predominant in slower stretches of streams, while net-builders are commoner in the faster reaches. The latter are also found on the rock and boulder surfaces of waterfalls, cascades, runs and riffles.

Standing waters provide the larval habitat of some members of all insect groups. Distinct communities are found in pools or puddles in the forest. Certain dragonflies lay in puddles or other small, ephemeral bodies of water. Some damselflies are specialised to oviposit through small apertures, and are thus able to exploit the water that collects inside bamboo internodes or similar sites.

Larval flies (Diptera) are abundant and important components of the aquatic fauna, especially the mosquitoes, midges and black-flies.

Small bodies of rainwater collected in natural hollows in vegetation provide a habitat for larvae of several mosquitoes. The eggs of some species possess a degree of resistance to exposure and may be laid on the edge of a suitable container, to hatch later when the water level rises to submerge them. Forest mosquitoes are vertically stratified. Those that live high in the canopy exploit small water bodies in tree hollows. Others have been found as larvae in pockets of water held in leaf axils, contained in curled fallen leaves on the forest floor, in water collected on the leaves of ginger plants or in the pitchers of *Nepenthes*.

A selection of fishes (and a prawn) collected at Belalong.

VERTEBRATE ANIMALS

FISHES

There are some 22,500 described species of fish worldwide, and about 100 new species are discovered each year. Living fishes are divided into three Classes, the lampreys (Agnatha), the sharks and rays (Chondrichthyes) and bony fishes (Osteichthyes). Most freshwater fishes belong to the last group. An important ecological grouping among these fishes is based on tolerance to salt and, hence, capacity to live in the sea. Some fishes are tolerant of a wide range of salinities; these tend to inhabit estuaries, moving freely to sea or upriver. Others spend part of the life cycle in the marine environment, breeding there and moving to freshwaters for a period to feed and grow; others lay their eggs in freshwaters, where the young pass through early developmental stages. Cutting across taxonomic classification are others that normally live in freshwaters but can survive mild salinities, such as an important group (called the primary freshwater fishes) that are sensitive to even small concen-

Osteochilus, a member of the family Cyprinidae, dominant at Belalong.

FISHES AND POLLUTION

Fish tested under laboratory conditions exhibit high mortality and low metabolic rate at high suspended silt levels. As the silt level increases the surface area of the gills available for gaseous exchange decreases markedly, resulting in low respiratory rates and eventual death. High silt levels cause fish and prawns to migrate upstream or escape into side streams. Here, pressure is then increased on the space and resources available. Prolonged competitive pressure inevitably results in the extermination of less tolerant species. In Sungai Gombak, Peninsular Malaysia, 27 species of fish were recorded in 1969. In 1985 only 20 species were recorded while in 1990, despite repeated sampling, only 16 species were found. So, between 1969 and 1990, 11 species had disappeared, a reduction of 41% in fish diversity. This reduction was largely attributed to increased suspended silt loading in the Gombak resulting from logging activities and highway construction.

In the undisturbed Temburong drainage, the total suspended solids vary from 7.1 to 320 mg/l, but pronounced turbidity and high silt loads are episodic and of short duration. Evidently, the fish present in these waters can survive brief periods of adverse conditions.

ECOLOGICAL ZONATION

Species diversity of fish and prawns decreases upstream from the confluence of Sungai Belalong and Sungai Temburong while that of crabs increases. The main barrier to upstream colonisation of fish and prawns seems to be waterfalls. Of the 44 species of fish, 32 species (73%) were found only below waterfalls, 12 species (27% belonging to the Families Homalopteridae and Cobitidae) above and below and only 6 species (14%) were found exclusively above waterfalls.

In pools and slow flowing areas, *Nematabramis steindachneri* and *Rasbora argyrotaenia* were most abundant numerically while in faster flowing zones, *Paracrossochilus acerus* and *Gastromyzon* spp. were predominant.

The fish fauna of faster flowing stretches, including *Gastromyzon* species and *Paracrossochilus acerus*.

THE ENIGMATIC SUCKER FISHES

The sucker fishes, or gastromyzontins, are a very common sight in the faster flowing zones of the streams in the Belalong forest. They are dorso-ventrally flattened and their greatly enlarged pelvic fins are united to form large adhesive pads with which they cling on to rocks and maintain their position, even in the swiftest of currents. The mouth is located ventrally, well-suited for grazing on the cyanobacteria, diatoms and filamentous green algae growing on the rocks. So far 13 species belonging to four genera have been collected from the Temburong and Belalong watersheds, the highest concentration from Borneo.

The phylogeny of the gastromyzontins is still poorly known. Some authors have designated the Borneo gastromyzontins as the Family Gastromyzontidae. Others give it a subfamily status as Gastromyzoninae under either the Family Homalopteridae or Balitoridae. There are two main concentrations of the so-called gastromyzontins: China and Borneo. Some taxonomists have tried to integrate the Chinese and Bornean genera and species, but it is now believed that these two groups are not so closely related and probably do not even belong to the same subfamily. There is so little we know about these fascinating fish and some research effort into their biology would certainly be worthwhile.

A ventral view of *Gastromyzon* reveals the enlarged fins which form the sucker.

The sucker fish *Gastromyzon borneensis* in its natural habitat.

FISHES OF BELALONG

A total of 44 species of fish belonging to 10 Families and 28 genera were collected from the streams and rivers at Belalong. All but three are new records for Brunei Darussalam and 23 (52%) are endemic to Borneo. The new records extend the species known ranges of distribution. The Families Cyprinidae and Homalopteridae are predominant, with 13 species each. The prevalent genera are *Gastromyzon* and *Rasbora*.

With the exception of *Anguilla marmorata* and *Mystus baramensis* (which are known to be diadromous), all species of fish have strict freshwater distributions. At the species level, there is little overlap between these and the coastal fish fauna. Only *Rasbora*, *Puntius* and *Stigmatogobius* seem to have estuarine congeners. Within the study area, species distribution could not be related directly to water quality which was generally good.

Rasbora sp. (Family Cyprinidae), a member of the group of fishes found below waterfalls .

The torrent loach *Glaniopsis hanitschi*, found above waterfalls in montane streams.

trations of salt.

Fishes are also sensitive to other dissolved substances in water, especially to the concentration of dissolved oxygen. Other characteristics of water quality, including temperature, pH, sediment load and the presence of organic compounds may also be critical. Because of these ecological constraints, freshwater fish populations tend to become isolated within catchments. Present distributions can provide useful clues to past changes in the the course of river flow. Isolation within catchments also increases genetic and species diversity.

As other streams in South East Asia, those in Belalong forest are dominated by Cyprinoidea (3 Families, totalling 66% of the species) including the Families Cyprinidae and Homalopteridae comprising 13 species each. Only two of these species extend to the streams of the coast of Temburong District, where there is a predominance of other species of Cyprinidae and gobies (Gobidae).

Two distinct ecological groups of fish have been identified in the study area; those species confined almost exclusively to waters below waterfalls and those found mainly above. The latter group consists of species belonging to the torrent-loach Families (Homalopteridae and Cobitidae). It seems that

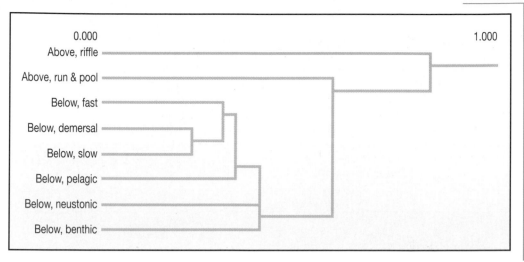

0.000   1.000

Above, riffle

Above, run & pool

Below, fast

Below, demersal

Below, slow

Below, pelagic

Below, neustonic

Below, benthic

Cladogram of fish fauna similarity in the different zones of the streams in Belalong.

the presence of waterfalls rather than altitude determines the separation of the two groups.

OTHER VERTEBRATES

Among other Classes of vertebrates at Belalong, the amphibians are most closely tied to freshwaters, as explained in Chapter 12. During the larval stage of their life cycle, the amphibians are members of aquatic ecosystems. Moving onto land as adults, they effectively transfer nutrients and other resources from the water to land. Among reptiles, soft-shelled turtles are obligatorily aquatic; several other reptile species are dependent on the resources of the streams and rivers to varying degrees and they, too, draw on aquatic resources for an otherwise terrestrial life. The transfer is even more marked among birds such as kingfishers (Alcedinidae) some of which are met mainly along river or stream courses, but which enter the water only when feeding on their aquatic prey, as do fish-eating raptors such as the fishing eagles at Belalong. Otters, the mammals most dependent on water, are not uncommon in these rivers.

These higher vertebrates that exploit the resources of the aquatic environment show a suite of convergent adaptations. The extension of a fold of skin between the digits, producing webbed feet, is an obvious aid when swimming in water and is found in all Classes. Among the warm blooded vertebrates, an effective waterproof and insulating layer is provided by the feathers of birds and the fur of mammals. To assist them to catch and hold slippery fish, the piscivorous snakes and the otters and other mammals have mouths armed with sharp teeth and, among birds, the margins of the bill of herons are minutely serrated.

Belalong sunshade.

CHAPTER 14

THE FOREST AND MAN

People have lived among these forests for millenia. The prehistory of Borneo reflects its geographical situation at the eastern margin of the Sunda shelf. As we have seen (Chapter 10), during glacial periods, low sea levels exposed this area as dry land providing connections with the Asian continent. Very early humans of the species *Homo erectus* were present in Java 500,000 - 1 million years ago and could have reached Borneo, although no fossils have been found to confirm this supposition. People of this early species made crude tools of stone and other hard materials, including bone; it is evident that they also had the use of fire.

Elsewhere across the continents of Africa, Europe and Asia, the discovery of artefacts and other cultural objects, and some skeletal remains, has demonstrated the existence of mankind of our present species (*Homo sapiens*) from about 200,000 BP. Further archaeological evidence, worldwide, also indicates that the final emergence of truly modern types occurred about 60,000 - 40,000 BP. During this phase, the Americas and Australia were settled and, as excavations at Niah cave, Sarawak, have shown, man was undoubtedly present in Borneo.

As far as physical traits can be judged by a few examples of their teeth and skulls, these early inhabitants of Borneo showed resemblances with the native Australians or present Melanesian races of New Guinea and the southwestern Pacific. In due course, they were succeeded by people of Mongoloid character, whose affinities lay in the region of southern China and whose progressive expansion finally reached out to Polynesia. These people, who have been called **Austronesians** and are the apparent ancestors of the modern inhabitants of interior Borneo, introduced domesticated fowls, dogs and pigs and, not later than 4,300 BP, the cultivation of crops including rice.

Their life style 2,000 years ago probably differed little from that of remote rural longhouses two generations back. Although sparse and scattered, their communities would have felled small tracts of forest each year for their farms, burnt the brush and timber, planted rice and vegetables and, after harvest, abandoned the land to the regrowth of weeds and secondary forest. In short, the practices of 'slash and burn' shifting cultivation must have been prevalent in Borneo at least as long as rice has been grown - for more

SHIFTING CULTIVATION ...

In the Temburong valley, the new season's clearing is burnt in the dry weather of August 1990.

Hill rice on the same spot, mid-season, December 1990.

May 1991, regenerating secondary growth has taken hold.

By August 1992, a closed canopy of regrowth and pioneer species has developed.

Today's cultivation on the banks of the Sungai Temburong; from the front, taro, manioc, maize, banana, and breadfruit.

The archaeological record in Borneo begins some 40,000 years ago, in the deposits in the west mouth of the huge Niah Cave, Sarawak. Here the inhabitants of those times discarded simple tools of flaked stone and of shaped bone, with the skeletal remains of their animal prey (pig being the most common at the earliest levels). One human skull from deep levels was dated to 38,000 years ago by the excavators, Tom and Barbara Harrisson. Full human skeletons have also been found at this site, the oldest dating back to 12,000 years ago. These have been identified as modern man (*Homo sapiens*), of Australomelanesian racial affinities.

In the Tingkayu Valley, Sabah, very fine bifacial tools of chert have been found at the place of their manufacture on the shore of a now vanished lake; these may be as old as 20,000 years. Nearby cave sites in the Baturong and Madai massifs have produced cruder (non-biface) stone tools of chert dating between about 18,000 and 8,000 years ago. The technical skill shown in the Tingkayu tools contrasts with the rather simple styles of those in the other sites, and it is possible that different peoples were involved.

There are rather few animals represented in the archaeological deposits at the very deepest (i.e. oldest) levels at Niah, but these did include an extinct, gigantic scaly anteater (*Manis palaeojavanica*). The presence of this mammal, and of a long-legged form of the two-horned rhinoceros (*Dicerorhinus sumatranus*) has been linked to the more open, wooded landscape thought to have prevailed at that time. After the earliest period, there is evidence of a gap in human frequentation at Niah cave, although bats still used it. We can conjecture that high sea levels, known to have occurred 35 - 30,000 years ago, cut off the limestone outcrop as a small island, just offshore. By the time their remains reappear, the people of Niah, Tingkayu and Baturong 18 - 12,000 years ago were evidently living inland. The animals they hunted were all of kinds still extant in rainforest habitats in South East Asia, although some - wild dog (*Cuon javanica*), tapir (*Tapirus indicus)* and Javan rhinoceros *(Rhinoceros sondaicus)* - no longer occur in Borneo. The people were, at some later time, able to expand their diet to include monkeys and other arboreal mammals. Their tools were made of flaked stone and of bone, which they ground into many shapes, including some that appear to be projectile tips.

About 4,500 years ago, as excavations show, populations of a new culture reached Borneo. Since all modern native languages of Borneo belong to the Austronesian grouping, we assume that these new arrivals were part of the expansion of these peoples who have spread from an original region in southern China, and now occupy all of island South East Asia and Oceania, with the exceptions of New Guinea and Australia.

The first presumed Austronesians in Borneo made polished stone (Neolithic) adzes, crude pottery and stone pounding tools which probably served to make clothing of beaten bark.

than 4,000 years. Of today's crops, they lacked those that originated in the Americas and which therefore cannot have been introduced locally before the 16th century AD: notably maize, manioc and the varied Solanaceae (including aubergine and chillies). They must have possessed an intimate knowledge of the resources of the forest, including the palms that provide harvestable quantities of starchy pith or edible shoots, as well as other plants

These Borneo people had domestic dogs, pigs and chickens, and grew a range of crops including rice, sugar cane, greater yam, taro, banana, breadfruit and coconut. It seems likely that they also possessed boats and were able to navigate the coasts and follow the rivers.

Neolithic artefacts dating between 4,500 and 2,000 years ago are known from Madai and Bukit Tengkorak in Sabah, and from the Niah Caves, Gua Sireh and Lubang Angin in Sarawak. In the Niah sites and at Lubang Angin, people used the caves for burial. Finds of stone tools elsewhere show that they were living in the surrounding lands, and they were certainly capable of making houses.

In Lubang Angin the dead were wrapped in barkcloth and placed in graves dug in the cave floor; at Niah many were placed in log coffins or wrapped in flattened sheets of bamboo, while a few were burnt, and their remains deposited in jars; there is thus evidence of social or cultural differences over the long time span involved. Associated with the burials as grave goods at Niah and Lubang Angin are distinctive large, incised and painted earthenwares and double-spouted flask-shaped vessels. At Gua Sireh rice grains are embedded in pottery dated to about 4,300 years ago.

In southeastern Sabah, in the rock shelter at Bukit Tengkorak, excavations have brought to light red-slipped pottery dating from about 3,000 years ago which resembles pottery found widely in the Philippines and eastern Indonesia, and also the Lapita pottery, made by the initial Austronesian settlers of Melanesia and western Polynesia. This pottery occurred at Bukit Tengkorak with shell beads and bracelets, an industry of agate drills for shell ornament manufacture made on superb prismatic blades, and small chips of obsidian from the Talasea source in the Lapita heartland zone of New Britain about 3,000 km to the east. The inhabitants of Bukit Tengkorak ate fish in profusion and evidently followed a mobile maritime lifestyle. They were perhaps related to the first Austronesian settlers in the Pacific, from whom sprang modern peoples such as the Micronesians, Polynesians and Fijians.

Some 2,000 years ago, metal objects (bronze and iron) were in use, and have been found at sites such as the Madai caves and Gua Sireh, together with glass and carnelian beads. The Madai, Baturong and Tapadong caves in Sabah have also yielded fine pottery dated to the first millennium AD, generally in association with jar burials. Very early woven textile, of vegetable fibre, has been found at Niah, in the form of cloth wrappings around an extended burial.

Also from about 2,000 years ago, contact with Indian civilisations and religions began to occur. Cultural influence is evident in the Sanskrit inscriptions of King Mulawarman found near Samarinda in East Kalimantan, dated to around 400 AD. During 1000-1500 AD enormous quantities of glazed ceramics were imported, from China and central Thailand. This trade, focused on coastal entrepot settlements (such as Kota Batu, Brunei) coincided with the expansion of the Malays from southeastern Sumatra. The advent of Islam to the coastal cultures of Borneo marked the transition from prehistory to true historic records, including the important Sila Sila of Brunei Darussalam.

337

yielding palatable leaves and fruits, and many further products of a useful nature. Most were possibly clothed in the beaten inner bark of trees such as terap (*Artocarpus*), although cloth woven from vegetable fibre was used for funereal wrapping in the Niah cave cemetery as early as 2,500 BP. They are likely to have stripped and woven rattans, pandans, ferns and other plants to provide garments, baskets, mats and personal adornments. Archaeological remains show that they were skilled artisans, making sharp tools from bone and stone before metals became available, and producing attractive ornaments of natural products, especially bone, animal teeth and mollusc shells.

These Austronesian people must have possessed seaworthy boats and been able to navigate the coastal waters of South East Asia. Archaeological remains testify to inter-island maritime transport or exchange of valued objects by 3,000 BP and by 2,000 BP, well established trading contacts with more distant civilisations and societies. Such links provided for cultural infusion and brought major world religions to the region, Buddhism was first, followed by Hinduism and then Islam.

In Brunei Darussalam, around 1405 AD, Sultan Muhammad (also known as Awang Alak Betatar) was the first ruler to embrace Islam, more or less simultaneously with his contemporary in Malacca. These emerging Malay sultanates were but two among many estuarine entrepots that were then thriving on the trade for rainforest produce. Documents show that goods traded during the Ming dynasty of the Chinese em-

pire, that is, before 1635 AD, included products, such as the edible nests of cave swiftlets (*Aerodramus*) or the casques of helmeted hornbills (*Rhinoplax vigil*), which originated beyond any territory under direct Chinese rule and could therefore only be acquired by import.

The maritime trade brought prosperity to those who controlled it, and in the 15th century Brunei Darussalam became established as a significant power around the coast of northern and northwestern Borneo.

Settlements were established at strategic river mouths to control this waterborne traffic. Inland peoples participated in the trade which provided them with objects of high value, (such as metal work, beads and ceramics), but largely retained their own social and cultural systems.

A longboat from Batang Duri heads up Sungai Belalong.

In cleared farmland on the true right bank of Sungai Temburong this clump of bamboo (*Gigantochloa*) has been left standing.

The first known contact with Europeans was the visit in 1521 AD of the small squadron of Portuguese ships, shortly after the death of their commander, Ferdinand Magellan. The writings of the official chronicler Antonio Pigafetta has provided an account of the contemporary splendour of Brunei Darussalam; and, incidentally, has posed the intriguing question of the

SOIL CHARCOAL

Although humid tropical rainforest is non-flammable under normal climatic conditions, it does become vulnerable to fire during prolonged drought. Charcoal is ubiquitous in the soils of the central Amazon basin and radiocarbon dating has established its coincidence with dry periods indicated by the pollen record. It is not yet clear whether hunting and agricultural activities of humans promoted the spread of forest fires during these regional droughts.

Although there are few published accounts of charcoal in Bornean soils, recent studies indicate that it is likely to be as frequent and abundant as in Amazonian soils. Soil charcoal has been found under dipterocarp forest in the upper Rajang basin and on the lower slopes of Gunong Mulu in Sarawak, at Andulau Forest Reserve and Kuala Belalong in Brunei, and throughout an extensive area in southeastern Sabah, as well as from peatswamp areas in East Kalimantan.

At the Kuala Belalong Field Studies Centre, soil charcoal dating from contemporary times to 10,000 years ago was found at sites along the east and west ridges and on the slopes leading up to them. The spread of charcoal ages mainly suggests scattered isolated fires, perhaps caused by lightning strikes. There is evidence, however, for a fire that affected the upper two-thirds of the west slope along the Ashton trail about 300 years ago. The nomadic agricultural Iban did not reach Brunei until early this century, and they claim not to have cultivated the area along Sungai Belalong. Their oral history, however, refers to orang tabun, possibly related to Murut, who may have occupied the area previously. Either group may have fired dead forest trees for 'entertainment' or to obtain charcoal, e.g. for parang making.

Whether forest fires were widespread or scattered, of natural or anthropogenic origin, their occurrence is of considerable ecological significance. They represent a form of repeated disturbance which contradicts the previously held notion of rainforest as a stable vegetation type persisting unchanged for tens or even hundreds of thousands of years.

Fire sweeps through Peatswamp Forest, destroying the community. Sporadic fires constitute one of the disturbance features at Belalong.

FISH AND FISHERMEN

Most species of fish and prawns are edible and a subsistence freshwater fishery exists in the Temburong area. Local freshwater fish seem to be preferred only by the longhouse communities; others prefer marine species. There also exists a small scale commercial fishery based on the giant freshwater prawn, udang galah (*Macrobrachium rosenbergii*). The impact of the fishery on the target species and aquatic community is not clear. There are claims by regular fishermen that stocks have decreased and certain species are now very seldom caught in the rivers. Such changes may be due to over-exploitation resulting from more efficient and intensive fishing methods. No major land-based activity which could endanger water quality exists in the Batu Apoi Forest Reserve, the upper catchment of both the Sungai Temburong and Belalong.

The exigencies of modern transport can affect topography and vegetation of hill summits.

MEDICINAL PLANTS AT BELALONG

One herbalist from each of three different indigenous communities (Kedayan, Murut, Iban) provided information on the vernacular names, therapeutic value and methods of prescription of plants in the Belalong forest.

Seventy-five plant species belonging to 38 families were used as remedies in contemporary folkloric tradition and domestic medicine. A wide range of health problems were treated with traditional remedies: 20 species to treat gastro-intestinal problems (stomachache, diarrhoea and gastritis), 15 species for skin problems (boils, scabies, herpes, cuts and bruises), 14 species for childhood ailments and 11 species for matters concerning the reproductive system (aphrodisiacs, contraceptives, childbirth and menstrual problems). Other ailments treated included leprosy, elephantiasis, toothache and jaundice.

Many different plant parts are used in traditional medicine, although roots are the most widely used organs. These are commonly prepared as a decoction or infusion, and used to treat illnesses of the reproductive and gastrointestinal systems. Leaves are often prepared as a poultice, and applied for skin problems (although almost any part of the plant may be so prepared and used). In most cases only a single plant organ is used, although another part of the same plant may also be considered suitable, but less efficacious. In some cases several plants are used in combination to prepare a single medicine.

Only five of the 75 species are used by more than one community, and of these five, there was not consensus on medicinal function. The five are shared by the Murut and Kedayan, with the Iban community having no remedies in common. Although the Murut informant identified more medicinal plants (45 species) than the Kedayan (29 species) and the Iban (6 species), this is perhaps a misleading indication of usage, as only one herbalist was available from each community. The difficulty in obtaining informants (all of whom were over 50 years old) suggests that knowledge of traditional medicine is rapidly being lost within Brunei Darussalam.

341

A Penan herbalist, Loya Kaling, collecting specimens.

Conseinium fenestratum: used by Kedayan as an antidote for poisons but by Murut to treat jaundice.

Dr Kamariah Abu Salim collecting medicinal plants, with a herbalist informant.

THE USE OF FOREST PRODUCTS BY THE PEOPLE OF BATANG DURI

The longhouse at Batang Duri consists of 17 bilek or family units, comprising 163 people at the time of survey (1990/91). It does not yet have piped water or mains electricity; water for drinking, washing and cooking is obtained from the river, and power from individual generators.

The longhouse was built in 1969, although the community has lived in the area for a much longer period; the former settlement was nearby, across the river. Many inhabitants are in temporary or permanent paid employment, usually in government service, construction work or the local gravel quarries. Many families have television sets and a range of other durable consumer goods. Much food is now purchased from shops in Bangar or Bandar Seri Begawan. Nevertheless subsistence farming, collecting forest products, fishing and hunting remain significant activities, although increasingly carried out on a part-time basis and by the older men and women. Most families grow rice; usually shifting cultivation of hill padi although some swamp padi is grown on alluvial land downriver.

Forest Products

In many cases products were only collected infrequently and there was general agreement that their use was not as significant as in the past. 54 different types of fruit were collected and consumed. These included succulent fruit such as durians (*Durio*), jackfruit (*Artocarpus integer*) and rambutan (*Nephelium*), and others used mainly for flavouring. Most of the fruit collected is for household use rather than sale. Even the oil from engkabang, the illipe nut (*Shorea macrophylla*) is only kept for domestic use for cooking, often stored in bamboo containers. 35 other species of plant were recorded as being consumed as food, including bamboo shoots and ferns. Nine types of edible fungus were named.

Species used mainly for flavouring include pandan (*Pandanus odoratus*) and cin-

namon (*Cinnamomum*). Plant leaves are also important for wrapping food, both in cooking and afterwards; ten species were recorded as being used for this purpose. Eighteen species of plants were mentioned as being collected for their medicinal properties. In some cases, the leaves, shoots or bark are crushed and applied to cuts and injuries; simpur, or buan in the Iban language, (*Dillenia beccariana*), senduduk or kemunting (*Melastoma malabathricum*) and mahang or mengkubong (*Macaranga gigantea*) are all used in this way. The leaves of other plants, such as kulipapar (*Vitex pubescens*) are boiled and extracts used for stomach disorders and diarrhoea. The extract from mambong (*Blumea*

An *Artocarpus* in fruit on the East Ridge at 350 m, February 1991.

Edible fruits of keranji madu (*Dialium indum*) in Belalong forest, February 1991.

Harvesting bamboo shoots.

Collecting the infloresence of wild banana for salad.

balsamifera) is used for skin diseases and engkuas or langkuas (*Languas galanga*) for curing discoloured patches of skin and round-worm. Other plants are used after childbirth, for eye infections, high blood pressure and waist pains. Tongkat Ali (*Eurycoma longifolia*) is used, as elsewhere in Borneo, as an aph-rodisiac, but it is also believed to be a cure for asthma.

The roots of tuba (*Derris elliptica*) and gadong (*Dioscorea hispida*) are sometimes used for fish poison, and the bark of pauh (*Diospyros*) and kasai (*Pometia pinnata*) was also said to be effective for this purpose.

The bark of petai or kupang (*Parkia* spp.) and limpanas puteh (*Goniothalamus tapis*) can be burnt to keep away mosquitoes and other insects, while the smoke from lukai (*Goniothalamus ridleyi*) is used to drive away bees while collecting honey. Limpanas puteh and mambong smoke is also supposed to keep off bad spirits.Other plants have more decorative or cosmetic functions. Langir (*Abarema* sp.) leaves are crushed to make shampoo; certain woods provide scents, the most valuable being gaharu (*Aquilaria*). Other leaves and flowers are used as decorations during ceremonies.

Altogether 38 species of plants were re-corded as providing materials for handicrafts. Mats, baskets, trays, hats and fish traps are made from rattans, bamboo, bark and leaves. Some plants have very specialist functions: gum from malau (*Agrostistachys lepostachya*) is used for fixing the blades of parangs into their handles; the stems of salak or ridan

(*Salacca affinis*), make excellent fishing rods; bark from *Eugenia* sp. is processed to make dye for preserving fishing nets; semambu (*Calamus scipionum*), one of the largest rattans, is suitable for making both furniture and spears. Ropes and fastenings are made from the fibres and bark of a variety of species.

Boat-building is an important activity at Batang Duri. The following trees are known to be especially suitable: bintangor (*Calophyllum*), kapur (*Dryobalanops*), meranti (*Shorea* spp.), nyatoh (Sapotaceae) and penarahan (Myristicaceae); gelam (*Melaleuca*) is used for caulking.

Although much of the Batang Duri longhouse itself has been constructed from purchased sawn timber, many households still cut their own timber for fencing, huts and rice barns. The hardest woods such as belian (*Eusideroxylon zwagleri*) and selangan batu (*Shorea* spp.) are used as posts. A total of 23 species of trees were recorded as being used for construction, fences or boats.

Fishing is still a common activity on the Temburong and Belalong rivers. Much fishing takes place near the longhouse but sometimes longer journeys are made upriver. Seventeen species of fish that are caught were listed.

Hunting now appears an occasional activity. Firearms were banned throughout Brunei in 1962. Traps and snares are often set near the longhouse; for expeditions further afield, spears, dogs and nets are

The buttress of ranggu (*Azadirachta excelsa*) on the West Ridge has been taken. The grain of this wood is highly decorative.

Boat-building at Batang Duri.

Great argus pheasant.

Sylvester Tan wears a parang sheath made of ranggu.

employed. Animals and birds killed most for food seem to be the Bearded pig (*Sus barbatus*), sambar deer (*Cervus unicolor*) and muntjak or barking deer (*Muntiacus muntjak*). Smaller animals hunted include squirrels, fruit bats, the pangolin (*Manis javanica*), Long-tailed macaque (*Macaca fascicularis*) and gibbons (*Hylobates muelleri*). Altogether 13 types of mammal were recorded as being hunted. In addition, freshwater turtles, monitor lizards and snakes are sometimes caught for food.

The only pantang (taboo) on killing or eating any species generally agreed upon was the sun bear (*Helarctos malayanus*), although some mentioned the moonrat (*Echinosorex gymnurus*) and clouded leopard (*Neofelis nebulosa*). The clouded leopard is protected under the Brunei Wildlife Protection Act (Chapter 102, *Laws of Brunei*), although this does not seem to deter the occasional hunting of other species on the protected list such as the slow loris (*Nycticebus coucang*) and the Great argus pheasant (*Argusianus argus*).

A Summary of the Use of Forest Products at Batang Duri

Uses	Number of Species
Fruit for food	54
Other foods from plants	35
Wrapping food	10
Traditional medicine	18
Handicrafts	38
Construction	23
Other uses	17

A gaharu tree (*Aquilaria*), the trunk scarred by parang marks testing it for the valuable black nodules.

The driver and prowman of the motorised longboat still depend on a pole cut from the forest to navigate through the rapids of the Sungai Belalong.

Batang Duri longhouse.

BRUNEI DURIANS IN THE MARKETS

Durian utak udang galah (*Durio graveolens*) are sold in Bandar Seri Begawan.

Durian sukang (*D. oxleyanus*) has very long slender spines.

The aril of durian simpur (*D. graveolens*) can vary from bright yellow to brilliant red.

Durian putih (*Durio zibethinus*): the familiar cultivated species; cream-coloured flowers, ramiflorous, bearing on the branches the large, elongated ellipsoid fruits which are heavily spiny. The aril varies in colour from cream to deep yellow and is richly fragrant. The taste varies. Selected clones from Malaysia or Thailand are generally sweet. Local selections have been identified, some of a quality surpassing that of the exotic clones.

Durian sukang (*D. oxleyanus*): a large forest tree; ramiflorous, with cream-coloured flowers; fruit small, spherical, with narrow, crowded spines; generally only four locules are filled, with up to three seeds per locule, the aril yellow, sweet and fragrant.

Durian simpur (*D. graveolens*): a large forest tree, with leaves 15 - 18 cm long; ramiflorous; flowers cream-coloured; fruit comparatively small, spherical, densely spiny, with one or two seeds per locule, often opening before falling to expose the aril which is bright yellow or intense red. *D. graveolens* is heterogeneous in several characters, including leaf shape, shade and intensity of coppery sheen, fruit size, fruit spine colour and aril colour. Fruit with yellow arils are named after the brilliant yellow flowers of simpur (*Dillenia*); those with red arils are aptly named durian utak udang galah in reference to the colour of the cooked brain of the giant prawn!

Durian pulu (*D. kutejensis*): a tall forest tree, with large leaves, 30 cm or more long;

The ripe yellow fruits of durian pulu (*D. kutejensis*) enclose seeds embedded in a deep yellow aril.

ramiflorous; flowers a rich red; fruit moderate sized, spherical or ovoid, with stout spines, turning from green to yellow when ripe; up to four or five seeds per locule. The aril is thick, usually deep yellow, dry yet creamy, with a mild fragrance appealing to those who find the durian odour too strong.

Durian kura-kura (*D. testudinarum*): a forest tree; cauliflorous, with white or pink flowers borne in thick clusters close to the base of the trunk. The fruits are weakly spiny, the aril creamy white to yellow, dull tasting or unpalatable to most people.

Durian maragang (*D. dulcis*): a large forest tree; ramiflorous, its fruit recognisable by their red colour when ripe, densely spiny, opening to five locules, each with one to three shiny black seeds, enclosed in a yellow aril, sweet but unpalatable, marred by a pungent resinous odour.

The fruits of durian kura-kura have rather blunt spines, a thin whitish aril and are generally judged unpalatable.

The fruits of durian kura-kura (*D. testudinarum*) are borne at the base of the trunk.

The fruits of durian maragang (*D. dulcis*) are a bright red when ripe.

origin of the elephants that were among the Sultan's entourage.

Increasing pressure from European markets encouraged the Portuguese to seek further contacts later in the 16th century. They were joined by Spanish, Dutch and British commercial and political interests, which progressively strengthened as time passed.

In the 19th century, Brunei influence was reduced by a succession of agreements transferring authority over parts of territory to Britain (Labuan), the Brookes (Sarawak) or the North Borneo Company (now Sabah). In 1888, a Protectorate Agreement was signed with the United Kingdom and in 1906 a British Resident was installed. Apart from the interval of the Japanese occupation (1942-1945), the administration continued under British Protection until 1984 when the government of His Majesty the Sultan and Yang Di-Pertuan resumed full sovereignty.

The Constitution of Brunei Darussalam recognises seven indigenous ethnic groups of the Malay race, the **puak jati** (Belait, Bisaya, Brunei, Dusun, Kedayan, Murut and Tutong). Until recently, these country people of the interior have pursued their lives in a traditional manner.

Development, particularly in the oil fields since 1929, has attracted an influx of many other people of different ethnic origins and nationalities. Important among these in rural Temburong District have been members of the Iban community.

The first Iban settlements were apparently established in the 1930s, but later immigration swelled the numbers. Today many of the occupants of the longhouse villages still have close relatives living across the Sarawak border in Limbang.

It was from these villages along the Bangar road, and particularly from the Batang Duri longhouse, that the 1991/92 Brunei Rainforest Project drew key field assistants. Batang Duri craftsmen built the longboats indispensible for transport up-river, and guides from Batang Duri helped to define the network of footpaths that give access to the forest itself.

For these and other rural people in Brunei Darussalam, the land and its products are seen as legitimate resources to sustain their lives, provide income and meet other needs. The state, too, has traditionally regarded land-based activities as appropriate economic uses, including forestry, agriculture, fisheries and mineral extraction.

The forests and forestry generally are administered under the Ministry of Industry and Primary Resources through the State Forest Department. According to national statistics, some 80% of the total land area is under forest cover, of which 60% is still primary forest. As part of a national resource survey, the Batu Apoi Forest Reserve was inventoried by consultants Anderson & Marsden (1984), and this work has been drawn upon in previous chapters. In 1991, as already noted, the Batu Apoi Forest Reserve was identified for National Park status.

A jambu (*Eugenia*) growing at Batang Duri.

Like its wild relatives, the jambu at Batang Duri flowers by night and sheds its blossoms in the morning.

Kuala Sungai Belalong, at its junction with Sungai Temburong.

CHAPTER 15

BELALONG: THE FUTURE

The co-ordinating theme for research during the 1991-92 joint University of Brunei Darussalam/Royal Geographical Society project was tropical diversity and its background. In these pages, we have brought together the contributions of participants, as a case study of a tropical humid evergreen environment: the Belalong forest.

WORLD BIODIVERSITY

The International Convention on Biological Diversity was opened for signature during the United Nations Conference on the Environment and Development (UNCED) at Rio de Janeiro, 5-14 June 1992. The Objectives of this Convention, declared in Article 1, are:

the conservation of biological diversity, the sustainable use of its components and the fair and equitable sharing of the benefits arising out of the utilisation of genetic resources, including appropriate access to genetic resources and by appropriate transfer of relevant technologies, taking into account all rights over those resources and technologies, and by appropriate funding.

Article 6 calls for the development of national strategies for the conservation and sustainable use of biological diversity or the adaptation for this purpose of existing strategies, plans for conservation and sustainable use of biological diversity into relevant sectoral or cross-sectoral policies. Article 8 con-

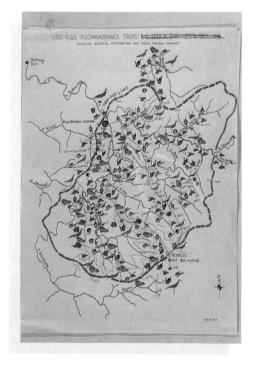

In 1990, preliminary exploration by Samhan Nyawa, assisted by guides from Batang Duri, established the principal routes and provided initial sight records of members of the larger terrestrial fauna.

Solar energy powers the rainforest ecosystem.

tains 13 clauses, covering *in situ* conservation, including the establishment of various protected areas in a sympathetic manner.

With overwhelming support from the international community, it can be expected that the terms of this Convention will provide worldwide guidance during the next decade. Yet, conserving world biodiversity requires actions that will go beyond the Convention itself. There are already other, existing international instruments that are important to the conservation of biological diversity, such as the Ramsar Convention (wetlands) and the World Heritage Convention, and other measures for the protection of the environment against pollution.

Strongly linked with UNCED was the 4th World Congress on National Parks and Protected Areas, held at Caracas, 10-20 February 1992. This Congress issued a Declaration recognising that nature has intrinsic worth, and warrants respect regardless of its usefulness to humanity; that the future of human societies depends upon people living in peace among themselves, and in harmony with nature; that development depends on the maintenance and productivity of life on Earth; that this

---

BENEFITS EXPECTED FROM THE ULU TEMBURONG NATIONAL PARK

1. Preservation of biodiversity, species and ecosystems
2. Preservation of ecological processes
3. Watershed protection
4. Scientific research
5. Recreation and tourism
6. Environmental education
7. Consumption benefits: forest products
8. Non-consumptive benefits: aesthetic, spiritual
9. Local employment and income

Not all the benefits listed are compatible. This poses problems for park management. One solution could be a system of zoning which restricts certain uses to particular areas. This is already planned with proposals for research in the Kuala Belalong Field Studies Centre area and recreation and tourism concentrating on the navigable, middle reaches of the Sungai Temburong, leaving much of the south of the park preserved as a wilderness area. Consumption benefits, such as the use of the area for collecting forest products, hunting and fishing, appear to be least compatible with other uses. Present levels of hunting and collecting appears to have a limited impact on park flora and fauna, other than riverine fish and high value products, such as gaharu wood. Nevertheless, there are dangers that with improved access, the construction of a road and tracks and more outsiders visiting the area, there could be greater pressure on its resources. There appears to be a need for management rules governing the collection of forest products, hunting and fishing. These rules could possibly contain certain exemptions for the people with traditional claims.

The legal basis for management is complicated by the fact that there is not yet any specific national parks legislation. The use of existing legislation appears to have been ineffective in the past. The restrictions on hunting and collecting in forest reserves contained in Section 19 of the Forest Act do not appear to have been rigidly enforced. The schedule of protected animals in the Wildlife Protection Act seems inadequate and, again, this legislation is rarely enforced and little known in rural areas. There is a need for it to be updated and provision made for both the protection of flora and fauna for national park establishment and its management.

---

natural wealth is being eroded at an unprecedented rate, because of the rapid growth in human numbers, the uneven and often excessive consumption of natural resources, mistaken and socially harmful styles of development, global pollution and defective economic regimes, so that the future of humanity is now threatened; and that this threat will not be averted until these problems have been redressed, the economies of many countries strengthened, and poverty conquered through processes of sustainable development.

The Caracas Declaration includes a closely argued justification of the value of national parks and protected areas, and closes with nine specific recommendations for national action to consolidate and enlarge well-managed protected areas. In particular, governments are urged:

• To ensure that the environmental and economic benefits which protected areas provide are fully recognised in national development strategies and national accounting systems.

A school party visits the Field Studies Centre.

The national flag of Brunei Darussalam is raised at Kuala Belalong Field Studies Centre.

• To ensure that effective international, national, regional and local administrative, legal, accounting and financial mechanisms for supporting protected areas are established as a matter of priority and regularly reviewed.

• To strengthen environmental education, and to provide training that will improve professionalism in the management of protected areas.

• To foster publicly funded scientific research and monitoring that will improve the planning and management of protected areas and to use such areas as sites for studies that will improve understanding of the environment.

In Brunei Darussalam, critical steps have already been taken. The Batu Apoi Forest Reserve was designated a protected area many years ago. A further resolute commitment was taken when, in his speech welcoming World Forestry Day 1991, the Minister of Industry and Primary Resources announced plans to establish a National Park to include the main southern block of Batu Apoi Forest Reserve (48,854 ha). For Brunei this represents an enormous area of pristine rainforest habitat, amounting to almost 10% of the national land surface, dedicated to permanent protection and longterm conservation management. It is clear that development of the National Park and

Aerial view of the field station.

the Kuala Belalong Field Studies Centre will progress hand in hand with mutual benefits. This double action will ensure the conservation and sustainable management of a biodiversity resource of global importance.

INTERNATIONAL RESEARCH OPPORTUNITIES

The University has introduced an imaginative scheme for Annual Research Fellows. The first appointees became involved in the Project and made valuable contributions. It is the hope that this scheme will be extended as part of a programme to continue research into the tropical rainforest environment.

EXPERIENCE FOR SCHOOLS

Universiti Brunei Darussalam and the Brunei Ministry of Education have firm plans for the future use of the KBFSC by schools. In Brunei Darussalam, as much as any country nowadays, increasing urbanisation and social development mean that, more and more, there is a need to ensure that the education curriculum gives opportunities for students to have direct experience of the natural environment of their own countryside and to be guided to a knowledge of the science of its ecology and conservation. Already, the new generation of this modern country begins to benefit from the rainforest experience.

GLOSSARY

(M.) = Malay language terms

A

abdomen: hind part of the body, excluding the tail.

acrisol: a class of weathered, iron-rich acidic soils, commonly developed on silicious rocks throughout the tropics.

akar: (M.) liane

alates: the reproductive caste of termites, with wings.

alpha (α) diversity: species composition at a particular place and time.

anion: ion bearing a negative charge.

argillic: soil horizon with high clay content.

aril: fleshy part of a fruit surrounding a seed.

Austronesian: a people who spread throughout the islands of South East Asia around 4000 BP.

autotomy: ability to cast off part of the body, usually the tail.

autotroph: organism which obtains nutrition from simple inorganic substances.

B

BP: dates "Before Present", by convention before 1950 AD.

Beccarian bodies: food bodies produced on some plant leaves.

beta (β) diversity: species composition of samples at different times or places.

binomial: name consisting of two words.

biodiversity: variability among living organisms.

biotic: living components (of an ecosystem).

bole: stem of a tree.

bukit: (M.) hill

C

cannibalism: (animal) preying on members of its own species.

canopy: upper layer formed by the crowns of forest trees.

carapace: upper bony shell of Testudines.

caste: (of insects) functional form among social insects, especially termites.

caterpillar: larva of moths or butterflies.

cation: ion bearing a positive charge.

cauliflorous: bearing flowers and fruit on the trunk.

cellulose: form of carbohydrate; the main structural component of plant tissue.

cephalothorax: combined head and thorax; (of spiders) the anterior part of the body.

chlorophyll: green pigment by which plants capture light energy from the sun to enable photosynthesis.

clay: soil comprising particles less than 0.002 mm diameter.

climax: (of vegetation) the final, equilibrium stage of succession.

commensalism: relationship between organisms of different species where one may be beneficiary, but the other is not harmed.

community: association of species forming an ecosystem.

conidium: form of spore produced by certain fungi.

convection: upward movement of a warm fluid or gas.

crepuscular: active at dawn and dusk.

crustose: encrusting.

culm: main stem above ground of certain plants, especially Poaceae.

D

dbh: diameter (of a tree stem) conventionally measured at 130 cm above ground or immediately above buttresses, if present.

DNA: deoxyribonucleic acid.

deciduous: periodically leafless.

decomposer: organism which breaks down dead matter.

detritus: fragmentary waste material.

diadromous: (of fish) living both in the sea and freshwaters.

distichous: in two ranks.

diurnal: pertaining to the day or daylight period.

domatia: small chambers or groups of hairs on leaves, used as nesting sites for ants.

E

ecdysis: (of arthropods) periodic shedding of the hard outer skeleton.

ecosystem: identifiable environmental component; the combination of living things with their non-living habitat.

ectomycorrhiza: form of symbiotic root fungus.

ectoparasite: parasite living outside its host's body.

edaphic: influenced by the soil.

elytra: hardened forewings of certain insects (Coleoptera).

emergent: (of forest trees) tall trees whose crowns emerge above the canopy.

endemic: confined to a defined geographical area.

endomycorrhiza: form of symbiotic root fungus.

endoparasite: parasite which lives within its host's body.

enzyme: natural catalyst produced by living organisms.

epidermis: outer layer of the skin of animals.

epigeal: ground-based.

epiphyte: plant that grows on another but not parasitically.

eukaryote: organism characterised by cells in which the genetic material is contained within a nucleus.

evapotranspiration: combined effect of evaporation and transpiration.

F

foliose: leaf-like.

food-chain: succession of nutrition transfers, starting with plant-eating primary consumers.

food web: complex food-chain, in which different species prey and are preyed upon by others.

forest formation: functional classification of tree communities.

fructification: production of fruits or fruit-bodies.

fruticose: tufted.

G

gall: (of figs) infertile floret or fig.

gamete: haploid sexual cell.

gametophyte: plant that produces gametes.

geocarpic: (of figs) fruiting underground.

glossa: tubular 'tongue' of a bee.

H

heath: low vegetation, dominated by woody shrubs and shrublets.

hemiparasite: parasitic plant which possesses a stem and green leaves.

herbs: non-woody, soft-stemmed plants. The herb layer of the forest is the lowest.

heterogeneity: variety or mix of characters.

heterotroph: organism dependent for its nourishment on the ingestion of complex organic compounds.

hierarchic: stratified arrangement, in which 'higher' groups contain related sets of 'lower' groups.

horizon: (of soils) layer recognisable in a soil

profile.

host: organism on which another, e.g. parasite, is dependent.

hydrophyte: plant of the water's edge, permanently submerged.

hyperparasite: parasite of parasites.

hyphae: fine thread-like tissue of fungi.

I

imago: final instar of insects that undergo metamorphosis.

immobilisation: fixing of substances, in a form not available for chemical activity.

indusium: (of ferns) flap of tissue which protects individual sori of ferns.

inquiline: living in the nest of another organism.

instar: (of insects) life stage, with distinct body form.

Inter Tropical Convergence Zone (ITCZ): geographical area of meeting of low-level winds blowing towards the equator.

invertebrate: animal which lacks an internal jointed bony skeleton; not a vertebrate.

ion: electrically charged atom or group of atoms.

isotope: one or more varieties of an element, differing in atomic weight.

K

kampong: (M.) village.

kerangas: (M.) heath forest growing on leached, acidic free-draining soil.

kuala: (M.) river junction, river mouth.

L

landform: shape of the surface of the earth; topography.

larva (pl. larvae): distinctive juvenile growth stage.

leaching: removal of constituents of soil in solution in water.

leaf-exchanger: functional group of perennial plants in which leaf growth is intermittent and falling old leaves are simultaneously replaced by new growth.

liane: large woody climber, rooted in the soil and usually reaching the canopy.

locule: cavity in a fruit.

lower plants: non-vascular groups, including bryophytes and green algae.

M

macrophyte: non-microscopic green plants.

macropores: (in soil) large channels.

Malesia: botanical region comprising Malaysia, Brunei Darussalam, Indonesia, the Philippines and Papua New Guinea.

mammary glands: specialised glands of mammals which secrete milk.

mangal: forest formation associated with coastal muddy soils; mangrove community.

mantle: (of molluscs) protective covering around the body; (of the earth) zone below the crust.

marsupium: pouch-like enclosure of the female's body, within which the young are held.

mast flowering: synchronised mass flowering.

metamorphosis: (of insects) radical restructuring of the body, undergone between instars.

meteorological equator: zone where the sun is overhead at noon.

microlepidoptera: informal classification, the 'little' moths.

Mixed Dipterocarp Forest: forest dominated by trees of the Family Dipterocarpaceae.

mobilisation: release of substances, e.g. by decomposer organisms.

monopodial: (of plants) with a single growing tip.

morphospecies: recognisable set of organisms, apparently members of one species.

mutualism: relationship whereby participating organisms derive benefit.

mycelium: hyphal network of a fungus.

mycobiont: fungal partner of a symbiotic association.

mycorrhiza: non-parasitic association of fungal hyphae with roots.

myrmecophyte: plants which have a close association with ants.

N

nasus: snout of nasutiform termites, through which a toxic chemical can be ejected.

niche: functional position of a species within an ecosystem.

nocturnal: of the night; active during periods of darkness.

non-pioneer: (of forest trees) species forming the climax community.

nucleotides: proteins which constitute DNA.

nucleus: part of a eukaryotic cell, surrounded by a double membrane, which contains the genetic material.

O

orthic acrisols: prevalent soil type of Belalong forest.

ovipositor: egg-laying organ of a female.

P

parasite: organism which derives benefit from another organism, the host, which is harmed.

parent material: (of soils) rock from which soils develop.

pathogenic: causing disease or injury.

peatswamp: low-lying and poorly drained land in which undecomposed litter accumulates as peat.

pedicel: narrow waist dividing two parts of the body.

photobiont: autotrophic partner of a lichen.

phytobiont: plant partner of a mycorrhizal association.

pioneer: (of forest trees) species which germi-
nate in open conditions or gaps but do not form part of the climax community.

plankton: organisms suspended freely in water.

plastron: ventral bony shell of Testudines.

plectrum: (of Orthoptera) scraping organ which produces noises.

primary consumer: first in the series of consumers in a food chain; a plant-eating organism.

prokaryotes: Bacteria; organisms in which the genetic material is not contained within a nucleus.

prothorax: (of insects) fore-part of the thorax.

protist: unicellular eukaryotes which may combine characters of plants and animals.

pupa: (of insects) third instar, generally non-mobile within a protective covering.

R

rachis: axis of a compound leaf.

radula: feeding apparatus of a snail.

rainforest: subject matter of this book; see Chapter 1.

ramiflorous: plants that bear flowers on branches.

rheophyte: plants adapted to withstand the effects of flowing water.

rhizoid: filaments possessed by some lower plants to attach them to the substrate.

rhizome: subterranean plant stem, from which aerial shoots grow.

rhizomorph: thick, root-like strands of fungus mycelium.

riffle: shallow, fast-flowing section of a river.

riparian: pertaining to the river bank.

S

sand: soil whose particle size exceeds 0.02 mm.

saprophagous: (of animals) feeding on dead remains of other organisms.

saprophyte: living on dead remains of other organisms.

scansorial: adapted for a climbing mode of life.

secondary consumer: member of a food chain feeding on primary consumers.

sedimentary: (of rocks) laid down in or by the action of water.

seed bank: supply of dormant seeds in the soil.

shrub: multi-stemmed woody plant, generally not exceeding 10 m height.

silt: soil with particles between 0.002 - 0.02 mm in diameter.

soil profile: vertical section through soil from the surface layer down to the parent rock, exposing the different horizons.

solute: dissolved substance.

sorus (pl. sori): (of ferns) cluster of sporangia.

species: recognisable set of organisms with shared resemblances, reproductively, morphologically or geographically isolated from other such sets.

specific leaf area: (of leaves) area expressed as square centimetres per gramme.

spinneret: (of spiders) silk-producing organ.

sporangium (pl. sporangia): organ producing spores.

spore: non-motile and asexual reproductive cell.

sporophyte: plant that produces spores.

strangler: (of figs) plant which begins as an epiphyte on a host tree attached by roots which can extend until the host trunk becomes enclosed.

strata: (forest classification) categories which represent different stages of forest development.

style: part of the flower designed to receive pollen.

subcanopy: (forest) vegetation layer below the canopy.

symbiont: member of a symbiosis.

symbiosis: living together of organisms of two (or more) species to the benefit of at least one and the significant detriment of none.

synusia (pl. synusiae): functional grouping of plants of similar life form.

T

tadpole: larva of an amphibian (anuran or urodele).

taxonomy: activity of identification, scientific description and formal naming of organisms.

tepal: sepal or petal in flowers in which these are indistinguishable.

tertiary consumer: member of a food chain that feed off secondary consumers.

thorax: mid-part of the body; (of insects) the part which bears legs and wings.

tree: long-lived vascular plant which increases in size and stem thickness by the growth of woody tissue, and can achieve large stature.

tymbal: (of cicadas) noise-producing organ.

U

understorey: (of forest) layer consisting of small trees and shrubs, immediately above the herb layer.

urostyle: sword-shaped fused caudal vertebrae of anurans.

V

vascular: pertaining to tissue through which fluids move; (of plants) those groups possessing such tissue, ferns and flowering plants.

vector: organism which transmits a pathogen from one host to the next without itself being infected.

vernacular name: common name in any language or dialect.

vertebrate: animal possessing an internal jointed backbone.

Z

zygote: diploid cell formed by the union of two gametes.

GENERAL INDEX

A

Aarhus University, 103, 149, 155, 199
abdomen, 231, 264
Acari, 262, 265, 266, 269
acrisols, 53, 104
agama, 285
agamid lizards, 285, 288, 304
agarics, 183, 186
Agnatha, 325
akar katup-katup, 162
akar seburek, 162, 164
alan, 92, 94, 96
  Bunga, 92
alates, 237, 240
Alcedinidae, 329
algae, 169, 170, 314
  blue-green, 234
  green, 170, 327
alluvial forest, 98, 100
alpha diversity, 76, 104
altitudinal zonation, 213, 218
aluminium, 52, 314
Amblypygi, 262
ammonium, 182, 215
Amphibia, 277, 304, 329
Anacardiaceae, 196
Anak Esu, Sungai, 318
anchorage, 52, 213
Andalau Forest Reserve, 109
Anguidae, 288
Anisoptera, 231, 232, 233
Annelida, 225, 226
ant-plants, 168
anteater
  gigantic scaly, 336
  scaly, 304
antennae, 231, 258, 262
ants, 168, 169, 182, 240, 244-246, 248, 266-269
  giant, 181, 245, 250
Anura, 277
api-api, 92, 94, 95
aping, 116, 119, 227
Apoda, 277
Apodidae, 304
Araceae, 115, 149, 157, 158, 317

Arachnida, 230
Araneae, 262, 264, 267, 269
Araneidae, 264
arboreal, 236
Arecaceae, 116, 169
argillic, 56
aril, 135, 346
aroids, 115, 149, 157, 159, 166, 169, 253, 315, 317
arthropods, 223, 230, 262, 266
Asclepiadaceae, 169
ascomycetes, 182, 183, 188
Ascomycotina, 181, 183-186
Ashton, Peter, 102, 106, 109
Aspleniaceae, 151
Atyidae, 320, 321
aubergine, 336
auricles, 154
Australia, 171
Australomelanesian, 336
Austronesian, 333, 336-338
autotomy, 287
autotrophs, 84, 86
Awang Alak Betatar, 338

B

babblers, 294
bacteria, 73, 76, 87, 174, 208, 223, 314
bakau, 92, 94
Balanophoraceae, 175
Balitoridae, 327
bamboo, 69, 121, 122, 309, 324, 337, 339, 342
Bambusoideae, 121
banana, 153, 154, 202, 302, 335, 337
Bandar Seri Begawan, 6, 7, 21
Bangar, 9, 97, 98
bark, 130, 131, 133, 135, 188, 223, 249, 254, 343
barkcloth, 337
basidiomycetes, 182, 183, 188
Basidiomycotina, 183, 186, 187
baskets, 337
Bataguridae, 285
Batang Duri, 9, 10, 97, 321,

338, 342, 343, 344, 345, 348, 349, 353
bats, 135, 239, 240, 298, 299, 300, 302, 304
  Black-capped fruit, 300
  cave nectar, 300
  fruit, 153, 344
  hollow-faced, 300
  Dusky fruit, 300
  Least roundleaf, 300
  Long-tongued nectar, 300
  Trefoil horseshoe, 301
  whiskered, 158
Beach Forest, 91, 92
beads, 338
Beccarian bodies, 246
bedrock, 44
bees, 128, 132, 172, 248, 249, 268, 269
  giant, 133, 250
  long-tongued, 251
  stingless 250, 251
beetles, 131, 172, 231, 252, 266-269, 273
  ambrosia, 182, 254
  atlas, 254
  bark, 254
  clerid, 253
  darkling, 253
  ground, 253
  jewel, 253
  leaf, 253
  longhorn, 253
  ptiliid, 253
  rove, 253
  scarab, 253
  three-horned atlas, 252
  violin, 74
  water, 322
begonia, 149, 159, 161
belian, 343
berangan, 266
berus, 94
biawak, 287
bilberries, 140, 141
bilek, 342
binomial, 69
bintangor, 343

364

binturong, 304
bioassay, 217
biodiversity, 67, 78, 353, 355
biomass, 267
birah, 158
bird's nest fern, 166, 167
birds, 78, 277, 292, 293, 304
birdwing, Rajah Brooke's, 70, 71
biru, 116, 118
black-flies, 324
Blattodea, 269
blues and hairstreaks, 260
boas, 285
boat-building, 344
bog-moss, 148
Boidae, 285
bole, 189
Bombacaceae, 133
bone, 338
bony fishes, 325
branches, 122
breadfruit, 335, 337
Brunei Bay, 9
bryophytes, 111, 148, 150, 214, 234
buan, 342
Bucerotidae, 294
bugs, 231, 243, 248, 268, 269, 322, 324
  green lantern, 72
Bukit Belalong, 10, 20, 24, 26, 27, 38, 82, 101, 105, 106, 107, 109, 111, 118, 119, 122, 143, 148, 150, 153, 173, 188, 214, 215, 219, 227, 265, 294
bulbuls, 294
Buprestidae, 253
Burmanniaceae, 174
burning, 211
Burseraceae, 196
butterflies, 75, 78, 239, 258, 260, 262, 269
  Skippers, 260
  swallowtail, 77, 260
  whites and yellows, 260
buttress, 109, 131, 207, 212
buttresswood, 131

C

caddis flies, 269, 322, 324
calcium, 52, 314
Calopterigidae, 232
camel's foot, 162
cannibalism, 243

canopy, 60, 123, 125, 138, 165, 196, 197, 202, 204, 210, 214
Caprimulgidae, 297
Carabidae, 253
carapace, 286
carbohydrate, 86
carbon dioxide, 86, 314
carbon, 87
carbonate, 87, 314
cardamon, 157
carnivores, 84, 298
carotene, 170
carpenter bee, 250
carrion, 286
caterpillar, 262
  fern-feeding (Geometridae), 224
cations, 52, 314
cauliflorous, 135
cave swiftlets, 338
celery pine, 110
cellulose, 203, 237
centipedes, 229, 230, 267
cephalothorax, 264
Cerambycidae, 253
ceramics, 338
Cercopithecidae, 302
charcoal, 339
chestnuts, 266, 303
chickens, 337
chillies, 336
Chilopoda, 229, 230, 267
Chiroptera, 298
Chlorocyphidae, 232
Chlorophyceae, 170
chlorophyll, 84, 85, 147, 170, 179, 203
Chondrichthyes, 325
Chrysomelidae, 253
cicada, 238, 239, 240, 244, 268
cicak kubing, 287
cinnamon, 342
civets, 153, 250
  Malay, 240
class, 70
classification, 70
clay, 53, 105
climate, 22, 23
climax, 201, 204
climax species, 205
climbers, 115, 121, 136, 147, 153, 162, 163
club-mosses, 148, 152, 153
Cobitidae, 326
cobras, 285

King, 290
coconut, 120, 337
Coleoptera, 80, 231, 247, 252, 267-269, 322
Collembola, 266, 269
Colubridae, 285
colugo, 304
commensalism, 85, 225
cones, 152, 164
conifer, 214
conservation, 353
consumers, 86
convection, 17, 18
Corixidae, 324
crabs, 319
  land, 319
cranberries, 140
crepuscular, 304
crickets, 238, 239, 242, 269
  mole, 238
  water, 322, 324
crocodile, 284, 286, 292
crust, 32
Crustacea, 230, 318
crustose, 188
cryptic colouration, 242
Cryptostigmata, 267
cuckoo, 294
  Banded bay, 294
  Hodgson's hawk, 294
  Indian, 294
  Indonesian, 294
  Moustached hawk, 294
culm, 122
Curculionidae, 253
cyanobacteria, 73, 170, 327
Cyatheaceae, 150, 151
cynipid, 247
Cyperaceae, 149, 154
Cyprinidae, 325, 328

D

DNA, 68
damar, 127
damselflies, 231, 233, 324
Darwin, Charles, 79
day-length, 22
Decapoda, 319
deciduous, 216
decomposer, 86, 208, 225
decomposition, 50, 52, 211, 265
dedalu, 85
deer, 302
  barking, 303, 344

sambar, 298, 303, 344
Dermaptera, 269
detritivores, 267
detritus, 169, 266, 318, 319, 324
diadromous, 328
diatoms, 310, 327
Dibamidae, 288
dicotyledon, 123, 159, 182
Diopsidae, 254, 255
Diplopoda, 230, 267
Diplura, 267
diplurid, 265
Diptera, 231, 254, 257, 269, 324
dipterocarp, 101, 103, 105, 107-111, 115, 123, 128, 129, 135, 182, 187, 202, 208, 210, 213, 217, 233, 253, 266
Dipterocarpaceae, 102, 123, 128, 182, 196, 214
discomycetes, 183, 185
diurnal, 302, 303
diversity, 106, 149, 223, 277, 353
division, 70
dog, 333, 336, 337
Dolichopodidae, 323
domatia, 168
dormancy, 218
dragonflies, 72, 75, 231, 233, 269, 321, 324
drainage, 34, 38
drift fences, 280
drip tips, 204
drongo, crow-billed, 296
drought, 215
Dryobalanops, 202
Dryopteridaceae, 153, 317
Drypetes, 202
durian, 133, 135, 217, 268, 342
Durio
  kura-kura, 347
  maragang, 347
  pulu, 134, 135, 346
  putih, 346
  simpur, 346
  sukang, 346
  utak udang galah, 346

E
eagle
  crested serpent, 293
  fishing, 329

earthenwares, 337
earthworms, 267
earwigs, 269
East Ridge, 100, 150, 157, 198, 199, 261
Ebenaceae, 196
ecdysis, 224, 231, 262
ecosystem, 79, 83, 87, 208, 209, 265, 309
ectomycorrhizae, 182
ectoparasites, 85
Elapidae, 285
elephants, 348
elytra, 252
Emballonuridae, 300
emergent, 197, 198
Empididae, 323
endemic, 123
endomycorrhizae, 182
endoparasites, 85
engkabang, 218, 303, 318, 342
Engkiang, Sungai, 10, 44, 46, 318
engkuas, 343
Ensifera, 239
ensurai, 92, 97, 98, 127, 218, 311
enzymes, 84, 181
Epallagidae, 232
Ephemeroptera, 231, 269, 322
epidermis, 284, 291
epigeal, 236
epiphylls, 170
epiphytes, 111, 115, 121, 136, 141, 143, 147, 151, 153, 157, 159, 166, 169, 170, 198, 309
equator, 18
equilibrium, 106
Equisetaceae, 152
Ericaceae, 140, 187
erosion, 32, 57, 58, 60, 61
Esu, Sungai, 318
Eucarya, 73
eugenia, 135
eukaryotes, 75
Euphaeidae, 232
Euphorbiaceae, 196, 202
evaporation, 218
evapotranspiration, 27
excretion, 225
eyestalks, 254, 257

F
Fagaceae, 214, 303
false-scorpions, 262

Family, 70
fan palms, 118
fats, 84
faun, Bornean, 260
feathers, 265, 292
ferns, 111, 147, 150, 153, 167, 169, 224, 317, 337
  filmy, 152, 153, 200, 315, 317
  stag's horn, 166
  tree, 150, 151
fig, 115, 136, 137, 138
  strangler, 139
  wasps, 136, 138, 248
fish, 11, 297, 325, 326, 328, 340
flatworms, 225
flies, 172, 175, 231, 254, 269, 323, 324
  horse, 254
  soldier, 257, 324
flycatchers, 294
  Asian brown, 296
  Grey-breasted jungle, 294
foam, 244
fogging, 266, 268, 271, 273
foliose, 188
food chain, 86, 225
food web, 86, 253
Forest Department, 7, 348
forest formations, 91
forest strata, 273
forewings, 231
forktails, 294
formation, 33
Formicidae, 248, 267, 269
fowls, 333
frogmouths, 297
frogs, 240, 278, 279
  Black-spotted rock, 281
  Blyth's, 281, 283, 284
  Bornean horned, 281, 284
  Cricket litter, 280
  Four-lined tree, 287
  Kuhl's creek, 281
  Large-eyed litter, 280
  Paddyfield, 287
  Poisonous rock, 281
  Red-sided sticky, 284
  Saffron-bellied, 284
  Smooth guardian, 281, 284
  Tree-hole, 283
fronds, 151, 157
fruit bodies, 179, 180
fruits, 208, 210

365

fruticose, 188
Fulgoridae, 243
fungal, 252
fungus, 68, 71, 84, 170, 174, 179, 181, 183, 223, 237, 245, 248, 253, 266, 310, 318, 342
  bracket, 181, 186
  cup, 183
  gill, 183
  horse-hair, 188
  lady's veil, 185
fur, 265

G

GIS, 8, 11, 319
gadong, 343
gaharu, 343, 345
gall-flowers, 136, 138
Gallery Forest, 97
gametophyte, 148, 149, 150
gap, 200, 201
gapis, 92, 99, 100, 318
Gasteracanthinae, 264
Gastropoda, 230, 318
Gause, 84, 206
Gecarinucoidea, 319
geckos, 285, 304
  Asian house, 287
  Barking, 288
  Gliding, 287
  Horsfield's gliding, 288
  Inger's bent-toed, 288, 289
  Kinabalu bent-toed, 288, 289
  Peters' bent-toed, 285, 288, 289
gelam, 343
genetic code, 67
Geometridae, 80, 224
Gerridae, 322
Gesneriaceae, 115, 149, 159
gibbons, 138, 303, 344
  Bornean, 298, 301
ginger, 155, 156, 157, 159
glacial period, 195
glassworms, 288
Global Positioning System, 8
glossa, 249
gnetum, 162
gobies, 328
Gombak, 208, 326
Grammitidaceae, 152
Grapsoidea, 319
grass, 116, 121, 154
grasshoppers, 242
  long-horned, 239

Gryllidae, 239

H

halide, 314
harp trap, 300
Harpagophoridae, 228
harvestmen, 262
Heath Forests, 100
heaths, 140, 187
hemi-parasites, 85
Hemiptera, 77, 231, 243, 268, 269, 322
herbivores, 84, 247, 323
herbs, 84, 115, 141, 147, 149, 197, 214
herons, 329
Hesperiidae, 260
heterogeneity, 273
heteropodid, 263, 265
Heteroptera, 231, 322
Heteropteryginae, 239, 242
heterotrophs, 84, 223, 318
hill rice, 217
hillslope profile, 42
Hipposideridae, 300
Hirudidae, 226
hirudin, 230
Homalopteridae, 326, 327, 328
Homoptera, 247
honeybees, 128, 250
  giant, 249, 250, 252
  Malesian 250-252
honeydew, 244, 248
hornbill, 138, 294, 295
  Helmeted, 294, 338
  Rhinoceros, 295
  White-crowned, 294
  Wreathed, 294
  Wrinkled, 294
horsetails, 152
host, 85, 137, 180, 244
humidity, 25
hydrology, 51
hydrophytes, 316
Hymenophyllaceae, 152, 153, 317
Hymenoptera, 231, 248, 268, 269
hyperparasite, 138, 248
hyphae, 180

I

Iban, 339, 341, 348
ice-cap, 193
illipe nut, 342

immobilisation, 208
indusium, 151
infiltration, 57
infiltrometer, 59
insects, 218, 225, 230, 231, 321
Inter Tropical Convergence Zone, 21
invertebrate, 223, 297
ions, 86
iron, 314
iron oxides, 55
Isopoda, 227, 230, 267, 269
Isoptera, 233, 267
isotopes, 169
Ixodiodea, 265

J

jackfruit, 342
Jalan Tengah, 109, 198
jambu, 135, 349
jarum-jarum, 142, 143
Java, 195, 333
Java Sea, 195
Jengka, 103, 104
jongkong, 92

K

Kalimantan, 5, 337, 339
kaolinite, 51, 52
kapur, 130, 271, 273, 343
  bukit, 108
  paji, 107, 108, 169, 170, 204
kasai, 97, 99, 209
katup-katup, 164
katydids, 238, 239
kayu kelat, 135
Kedayan, 341
kedondong, 127
kelam padang, 141
kelapa sawit, 120
kelulut, 250
kempas, 108, 133, 217, 218
kemunting, 342
kerangas, 93, 101, 110, 168, 187
keranji madu, 342
kerapah, 93
keruing merah, 93
kijang, 303
Kinabalu, Gunung, 153, 193, 195, 291
Kingdom, 70
kingfishers, 329
Kuala Belait, 7

366

Kuala Belalong, 24, 26
Kuala Belalong Field Studies Centre (KBFSC), 7, 10-12
Kuala Temburong Macang, 10
kulipapar, 342
kumus, 108, 196, 198
kupang, 343

L

lacewings, 269
Lambir National Park, 162
lampreys, 325
landform, 31
landslides, 39-41, 52, 106, 201
langir, 343
langkap, 99, 100, 116
langkuas, 343
langur, Hose's, 301
Lanthonotidae, 288
larva, 244
Lauraceae, 110
Laurel, 110, 111
leaching, 51, 208
leaf insects, 239
leaf-exchangers, 216
leaf-loss, 216
leeches, 226, 230
Leguminosae, 133, 162, 182
leopard, clouded, 344
Lepidoptera, 81, 231, 239, 247, 258, 262, 269
Lesong, Bukit, 38
lianas, 162
lice, bark, 269
lichens, 85, 86, 169-171, 181, 188, 189, 234
light, 196, 311, 318
lightning, 24
Liliaceae, 174
Limbang, 7
limpanas puteh, 343
linggadai, 94
Lithini, 224
litterfall, 214
liverworts, 111, 147-149, 170
lizards, 240, 284, 285
  Angle-headed, 289
  Black-bearded flying, 289
  Crested flying, 287, 289
  Earless monitors, 288
  flying, 287, 288
  Green-crested, 276, 288
  monitor, 285, 287, 288, 344
  Six-lined flying, 289
  Water monitor, 288

Worm, 288
loach, 328
locule, 135, 346, 347
Lomariopsidaceae, 317
Lonchodinae, 240
longboat, 345
longhouse, 342
luba, 118
lukai, 343
luminescence, 189
Lycaenidae, 259, 260
Lycopodiaceae, 152
Lycosidae, 265

M

macaque, 303
  Long-tailed, 301, 344
  Pig-tailed, 301
macrophytes, 318
macropores, 51
Macrotermitidae, 234, 237
Madagascar, 171
Magellan, Ferdinand, 339
magnesium, 52, 314
mahang, 202, 207, 248, 342
maize, 335, 336
Malacca, 338
malaise trap, 271, 273
malaria, 254
malau, 343
Malesia, 129
mambong, 342, 343
mammals, 78, 277, 298, 329
mammary glands, 298
Mangal Forest, 92, 93, 95, 120, 259, 277
manioc, 335, 336
mantis, 242, 269
  orchid, 243
Mantispidae, 257
mantle, 32, 230
Marantaceae, 149
marsupium, 230
marten, Yellow-throated, 299
martin, Asian house, 294
mass flowering, 217
mats, 337
mayflies, 269, 322, 324
meanders, 38
medicine, traditional, 341
megachilids, 250
Megascolecidae, 267
Melastomataceae, 141, 143
Meligan Formation, 33, 34
Meliponinae, 127, 250

mempening, 211
mengaris, 107, 108, 133, 216-218, 250
mengkubong, 342
meranti, 92, 110, 125, 127, 129, 196, 211, 235, 343
  binatuh, 108
  majau, 107, 108
  melantai, 108
  menalit, 108
  paya, 108
  sarang punai, 93, 107, 108
mersawa, 218
Mesostigmata, 267
metal work, 338
metamorphosis, 231
Metastigmata, 265
micro-organisms, 75, 210, 237, 254, 265, 266, 314, 318
Microhylidae, 283
microlepidoptera, 247, 258, 259, 270
midges, 254, 324
migrants, 293, 295
millipedes, 228, 230
  pill, 228
mimic, 264
minerals, 169
mistletoes, 85
mites, 230, 262, 265-267, 269
mobilisation, 208
Mollusca, 230
Molossidae, 300
monkeys, 302
  leaf, 138
monocotyledons, 116, 159
monopodial, 115
montane forest, 109-111, 214
moonrat, 344
Moraceae, 136
mordellids, 253
morphospecies, 227, 264
mosquitoes, 173, 254, 268, 269, 324
moss, 74, 111, 147, 148, 149, 167, 170
moths, 81, 172, 224, 239, 258, 259, 262, 268, 270, 297
  death's head hawk, 239
  geometrid, 224
  hawk, 239
mouse, 302
moult, 297
mouse-deer, 138, 303
mudur, 119

mudur belukar, 120
Mulu, Gunung, 77, 153
muntjak, 344
Muridae, 303
Murut, 339, 341
Musaceae, 202
Muscicapidae, 294
mushrooms, 179
mutualism, 85, 172
mycelium, 179, 180, 182, 189
mycobiont, 131, 182, 187, 188
mycorrhizae, 106, 131, 182, 183, 208
mycorrhizal symbiosis, 125, 181
mycotroph, 174
myrcophytes, 169
Myriapoda, 267, 269
Myristicaceae, 196, 343
myrmecophytes, 168
Myrtaceae, 131, 135, 182, 196, 214

N
nasus, 236
Nasutitermitinae, 234, 236
nawab, Common, 258
Necrosciinae, 242
nectar, 249
Nectaries, 173
Nectariniidae, 297
Nematoda, 225, 266, 267
nemesu, 108
Nepenthaceae, 171
Neuroptera, 231, 257, 269
New Caledonia, 171
nibung, 92, 93, 94, 119
niche, 84, 86, 304
nightjar, 297
  Malaysian eared, 294
  migratory, 296
nipah, 92, 94, 95, 97, 120
nipis kulit, 143
nitrate, 215
nitrate ions, 87
nitrogen, 53, 56, 84, 86, 87, 171, 182, 208, 210, 215
nocturnal, 302, 303
non-pioneer, 201, 203
nucleotide, 68, 71
nucleus, 75
nutrients, 60, 61, 84, 86, 87, 105, 106, 171, 173, 181, 182, 207-209, 216, 219, 246, 265
nutrition, 84

nyatoh, 108, 343
Nycterididae, 300
nyireh, 92, 94
Nymphalidae, 247, 258, 260

O
Oak-Laurel Forest, 110, 111
oak, 111, 211, 303
Odonata, 231, 232, 269, 321
omnivores, 85
Oonopidae, 265
Opiliones, 262, 269
orchids, 116, 149, 167, 169, 174, 187, 188
Order, 70
organ of Jacobson, 287
Orthoptera, 231, 239, 242, 247, 269
Osteichthyes, 325
otter, 298, 329
owl, 297
oxygen, 84, 314, 328

P
padi bukit, 217
Pagon, Gunung, 175
Palaemonidae, 320
palm, 116, 118, 316
  Betel, 120
  Fishtail, 116, 120
  Oil, 120
  Sago, 118, 120
  Sealing wax, 120
  Sugar, 119
pandan, 98, 120, 121, 337, 342
pangolin, 240, 298, 304, 344
pantu, 118
Papilionidae, 77, 259, 260
parang, 339, 343
parasites, 85, 147, 175, 180, 181, 248, 265
parasitism, 225
partridges, 294
pauh, 343
payau, 303
peat, 195
peatswamp, 92, 94, 96, 168, 340
pedada, 92, 94
pedicel, 264, 265
pelawan, 102, 131, 235
pelong, 266
Penan, 118, 341
penarahan, 343
Peninsular Malaysia, 77

pentail, 302
perah, 196, 209, 216
perfume, 172
perius-perius, 97
petai, 216, 304, 343
Phasianidae, 294
Phasmida, 82, 231, 239, 240, 242, 269
pheasants, 294
  great argus, 344
phosphate, 314
phosphorus, 53, 56, 84, 86, 171, 314
photobiont, 188
photosynthesis, 87, 202, 203
phytobiont, 182, 187
Pieridae, 259, 260
pigs, 138, 302, 333, 336, 337
  bearded, 299, 305, 344
pinang, 119, 120
pinang laka, 114, 120
pioneer, 201, 205, 206
pipistrelle, White-winged, 300
pisang, 153
pitcher plant, 107, 111, 168, 170-172, 324
pitfall trap, 280
planarian, 226
plastron, 286
Plate Tectonics, 32
Platyhelminthes, 225
Platypodidae, 254
Plecoptera, 322
plectrum, 239
plots, 196, 198, 199
Poaceae, 121, 154
Podargidae, 297
pollen, 249
pollination, 297
pollinators, 175, 225
pollution, 188, 326
Polygalaceae, 174
Polynesian, 300
Polypodiaceae, 151-153
Pondok Bujat, 198, 294, 297
ponerine, 245
pools, 47
porcupines, 138
Potamoidea, 319
potassium, 52, 84, 314
prawns, 319, 320, 326, 340
predators, 229, 248, 267, 305
prey, 173
Primates, 302
profile, 194, 196, 198, 200,

368

207
prokaryotes, 73, 75
proteins, 84
prothorax, 243
Protists, 73
protozoa, 225
Pseudophyllinae, 239
Pseudophylline, 243
Psocoptera, 269
pteridophytes, 77, 150
puak jati, 348
Pulai, 92
pupa, 231, 262
putat, 97
Pycnonotidae, 294
Pyraloidea, 259, 270
pyrenomycetes, 185
python, 285, 291
  reticulated, 290

R
rachis, 165
radiation, 17, 20, 203
radula, 230
Rafflesiaceae, 175
rain, 23-25, 27, 87, 196, 210
rainfall, 19, 20, 21, 23, 56
rainstorm, 87, 218
rainwater, 312
Rajah Brooke, 71
rambutan, 342
ramiflorous, 134, 135
Ramin, 92
ranggu, 344
rasau, 97, 98
rat, 153, 300, 302, 303
  Brown spiny, 300
  dark-tailed tree, 300, 302
  Long-tailed giant, 300
  Mueller's, 300
  Red spiny, 300
  Malaysian field, 300
  Whitehead's, 300
rattan, 118, 119, 164, 165, 168, 337
  fishtail, 166
rays, 325
Red harlequin, 261
regeneration, 200
relative humidity, 196
rengas, 196, 210
reptile, 277, 284, 304, 329
resak, 93, 196
resins, 249
respiration, 202

Retak Bukit, 38, 175
Rhagionidae, 323
rheophyte, 119, 153, 168, 315, 316
rhinoceros, 294
  Javan, 336
  two-horned, 336
Rhinolophidae, 300
rhizoids, 148
rhizome, 122, 155, 156
rhizomorph, 180, 188
rhododendrons, 140
  Straits, 69, 141
rice, 333, 337, 342
ridan, 343
Ridley's roundleaf bat, 300
riffles, 47
ring-shake, 133
Riparian Forest, 92, 97
roaches, 269
robin, Siberian blue, 295
rodents, 298, 302
root mat, 57
roots, 57, 126, 148, 169, 207, 211, 213
rotan
  dahan, 166
  semut, 166
roundworms, 225, 226
ru laut, 91, 92
Rubiaceae, 142, 159, 169, 316
runoff, 60

S
Sabah, 5, 32, 122, 161, 259, 291, 300, 336, 337, 348
salak, 118, 119, 227, 343
salinity, 93
Salticidae, 263, 264
sandflies, 254
sandpiper, Common, 292, 293
sandstone, 32, 33, 43, 45
Sapotaceae, 108, 110, 343
saprophyte, 84-86, 147, 174, 180, 187
Sarawak, 5, 77, 91, 103, 104, 122, 161, 162, 233, 266, 267, 319, 320, 333, 336, 337, 339, 348
Sauria, 285, 287
scales, 265
scansorial, 303
Scarabaeidae, 253
scent, 123
Scincidae, 285, 288

Scolopacidae, 293
Scolytidae, 131, 254
scolytids, 253
scorpions, 262
  Pseudoscorpiones, 262, 269
  whip, 262
  wind, 262
Scorpiones, 262
scramblers, 153
screwpine, 97, 120
scrub typhus, 265
sealing wax, 114
seasonality, 189, 213
sedaman mahang, 202
sedges, 149, 154, 155
sediment, 45
seed, 225
seed bank, 205
seed predation, 218
seedlings, 131, 187, 201, 202, 203, 205
seepages, 257
Selaginellaceae, 152
selangan
  batu, 196, 343
  batu padi, 108
  batu tulang ikan, 108
  merah bukit, 108
  pelanduk, 107
selunsor, 131
semambu, 343
sempili, 110
Senduduk, 141
senduduk, 342
Seria, 7
Serpentes, 285, 287
Setap, 33, 161
shales, 43, 45, 51, 55
sharks, 325
shell, 230
shifting cultivation, 211
shoot growth, 216
shrimps, 320
shrubs, 84, 115, 140, 197
sial menahun, 143
silica, 51
silk, 264
silverfish, 269
simpur, 71, 97, 342, 346
  gajah, 70
skink, 285, 288
  Blue-bellied litter, 285
  Brooke's water, 289
  Common tree, 288, 289
  Three-keeled ground, 289

369

370

slow loris, 302, 344
snail, 230, 318
snakes, 240, 284, 329, 344
  Annulated kukri, 291
  Blue coral, 291
  coral, 290, 285
  Oriental whip, 290
  Sinister water, 290
  Spotted water, 291
  Striped bronze-backed tree, 291
  White-fronted water, 291
sodium, 52, 314
soil, 51, 186, 187, 208-211, 217, 266
Solanaceae, 336
somboi-somboi, 171
sori, 151
South China Sea, 32, 195
spathe, 158
species, 71, 204
spermatophytes, 77
Sphingidae, 239
spider, 186, 230, 262, 264-267, 269
  bird-eating, 265
  corrinid, 264
  huntsman, 263, 265
  jumping, 263, 264
  orb-web spinning, 263, 264
  spiny, 263
  wolf, 265
spiderhunters, 153
  Little, 158
spines, 118, 121, 164
spinnerets, 264
sporangium, 148, 149, 150-152
spores, 148-150, 180, 189
sporophyte, 148-150
springtails, 266, 267, 269
Squamata, 285
squirrel, 153, 240, 299, 304, 344
  flying, 302-304
  Plain pigmy, 300
  Giant, 138, 300, 303
  Horse-tailed, 300
  Low's, 300
  Plantain, 303
  Prevost's, 300, 303
  Pygmy, 303
  Shrew-faced ground, 303, 304
  Tufted ground, 300, 304

Striped ground, 304
stalk-eyed fly, 255
Staphylinidae, 253
stemflow, 56
stick insects, 240, 269
stilt roots, 98, 121
stipules, 209, 246
stomatal conductances, 203
stoneflies, 322
stones, 188, 338
storm, 23, 25, 63, 311, 312
stranglers, 115, 136, 140, 147
strata, 107, 108
Stratiomyidae, 257, 324
streams, 223
Strigidae, 297
subcanopy, 197
sucker, 327
suction, 63
sugar cane, 337
sulphate, 314
sulphur, 87
Sumatra, 175, 195, 250, 321, 337
sun bear, 240, 250, 344
Sunda region, 102
Sunda Shelf, 195, 333
sunflecks, 202, 206
Sungai
  Anak Esu, 318
  Apam, 321
  Bulir, 9
  Engkiang, 10, 34, 35, 37, 39, 41, 44, 46, 298, 308, 315, 318
  Esu, 34, 44, 318, 321
  Sitam, 34-36
sunlight, 218
swallow
  Red-rumped, 294
  Barn, 293-296
  Pacific, 294
swifts, 304
symbiont, 85, 86
symbiosis, 85, 169, 182, 187, 188, 225, 237, 244, 249
Symphyla, 267
synusia, 115, 147

T
Tabanidae, 254
tapir, 336
taro, 335, 337
tarsier, 299, 302
taxonomy, 69, 183

Temburong, 7, 9, 161
temperature, 22, 23, 196, 215, 216, 312, 328
tendril, 165, 171
Tenebrionidae, 253
tensiometer, 59, 62
tepal, 159
Tephritidae, 254, 256
terap, 205, 337
Terentang, 92, 94
termites, 77, 182, 188, 231, 233, 236, 237, 240, 267
  processional, 181, 234
  soldiers, 236
Testudines, 285, 286
Tetrablemmidae, 265
Tetragnathidae, 264
Tettigoniidae, 239, 243
Thelypteridaceae, 150, 152, 153, 317
Theraphosidae, 263, 265
Theridiidae, 264
thorax, 231
thrips, 129, 269
thunder, 24
Thyrididae, 247
Thysanoptera, 129, 269
Thysanura, 269
ticks, 262, 265
Timaliidae, 294
timber, 107
toads, 278, 279
  Giant river, 280, 283
  Long-fingered slender, 280
toadstools, 179
tolong, 93, 110
Tongkat Ali, 343
tortoises, 284
  Asian brown, 286
traps, 271, 273
tree, 84, 115
treefall, 104
treeshrew
  Lesser, 299, 300, 304
  Slender, 300
  large and painted, 300
  pencil-tailed, 304
Trichoptera, 231, 269, 322
Trionychidae, 285
Triuridaceae, 174
Tropic of Cancer, 18
Tropic of Capricorn, 18
truffles, 183
tualang, 108, 133
tuba, 343

Tudal, Bukit, 38
Turbellaria, 225
Turdidae, 294, 295
turmeric, 157
turtles, 284, 344
  Malayan flat-shelled, 286
  Malayan softshell, 286
  hardshell, 285
  sea, 285
  soft-shelled, 285, 329
Tutong, 6
tymbals, 239
Tytonidae, 297

U
ubah, 97, 135, 235
udang galah, 320, 340
ultisols, 53, 104, 105
umbut, 119
undergrowth, 155
understorey, 197
urat mata, 108
Uropygi, 262

V
Varanidae, 285, 287, 288
vascular plants, 148, 310
vector, 223, 254, 265
Veliidae, 322
vertebrates, 223, 277
Vespertilionidae, 300
vipers, 285, 291
  Flat-nosed pit, 290
  Painted mock, 291
  pit, 285, 305
  Wagler's pit, 290
virus, 223, 244
Vittariaceae, 151

W
Wallace, Alfred R., 79
warblers, Arctic, 296
wasps, 247, 248, 268, 269
water boatmen, 322, 324
water skaters, 322, 324
water strider, 322
waterfalls, 320, 328
wax, 244, 249
weather, 17, 18
webs, 264
weevils, 253
West Ridge, 58, 125, 149, 175,
  196, 199, 261, 305
wind, 20, 21, 22, 24, 26, 104,
  123

woodlice, 227, 230, 267, 269,
  318
Woodsiaceae, 153, 199

Y
yam, 337
yeasts, 183

Z
Zingiberaceae, 149, 155, 156
zodariids, 265
Zygoptera, 231, 232
zygote, 149, 150

SPECIES & GENUS INDEX

A

Abarema, 343
Acacus, 242
 sarawacus, 240
Acherontia lachesis, 239
Acrosorus, 152
Actinacantha globulata, 264
Actitis hypoleucos, 293
Aeschynanthus, 115
 vinaceus, 159
Agathis, 93
 dammara, 110
Agrostistachys lepostachya, 343
Ahaetulla prasina, 290
Alocasia, 24, 158
Alpinia glabra, 155, 156
Alstonia, 92
Amanita princeps, 182
Amegilla, 250, 251
Amorphophallus, 157
Amphiesma flavifrons, 291
Amydrium medium, 158
Anarchoides lyratus, 82
Anguilla marmorata, 328
Anisoptera, 123, 129
 grossivenia, 93
Ansonia longidigita, 280
Anthene, 259
Anthracoceros malayanus, 294
Aphyllorchis, 174
Apis
 andreniformis, 250
 cerana, 250
 dorsata, 128, 132, 249, 250
 koschevnikovi, 250, 251, 252
Aporosa lunata, 202
Appias, 259
Apterygodon vittatum, 288, 289
Aquilaria, 343, 345
Arachnothera, 153
 longirostra, 159
Arctictis binturong, 304
Areca, 119
 minuta, 119
 catechu, 120
Arenga, 119, 227
 borneensis, 119

distincta, 119
undulatifolia, 99, 100, 116,
 117, 119
Argusianus argus, 344
Argyrodes, 264
Aristolochia, 77
Artocarpus, 205, 337
 integer, 342
Asplenium, 166
 nidus, 167
 tenerum, 151
Atyopsis mollucensis, 320
Avicennia, 92, 94, 95
Azadirachta excelsa, 344

B

Barringtonia, 97
Bauhinia, 162, 164
Begonia, 159, 161, 199
 baramensis, 160, 161
Berenicornis comatus, 294
Bipalium, 225
Blastophaga, 136
Blumea balsamifera, 342
Boesenbergia
 belalongensis, 157
 orbiculata, 156
Bolbitis, 317
Borassodendron borneense, 118
brachycladum, 122
Bronchocela cristatellus, 276,
 288
Brotia, 318
Bruguiera, 94
Bucephalandra motleyana, 315,
 317
Buceros rhinoceros, 294, 295
Bufo
 asper, 283
 juxtasper, 280
Bulbitermes, 237
Burbidgea, 156
 stenantha, 157
Burmannia, 174

C

Cacomantis

sepulcralis, 294
sonneratii, 294
Calamus
 flabellatus, 165
 marginatus, 165
 pogonacanthus, 165
 scipionum, 343
 sordidus, 165
Callosciurus
 notatus, 303
 prevostii, 303
Calophyllum, 343
Caloptilia, baringi, 81
Campnosperma, 92
Camponotus, 181
 gigas, 245, 250
Carausius, 242
 everetti, 241
Caridina bruneiana, 320, 321
Caryota, 116, 119
 mitis, 120
Castalius, 259
Castanopsis, 266
Casuarina equisetifolia, 91, 92
Caudacaecilia nigroflava, 279
Cepora, 259
Ceratobolus concolor, 165
Cervus unicolor, 298, 303, 344
Chalcosoma, 252, 254
Chaperina fusca, 284
Charaxes durnfordi, 261
Chironax melanocephalus, 300
Chiropodomys, 304
Chondrichthyes, 325
Cinnamomum, 342
Cocos nucifera, 120
Conseinium fenestratum, 341
Cookeina tricholoma, 185
Cordyceps, 181
Cotylelobium, 123, 129
 lanceolatum, 93
Cratoxylon, 235
Ctenopteris alata, 152
Cuculus
 fugax, 294
 micropterus, 294
 vagans, 294

Cuon javanica, 336
Cyathea, 66, *150*
Cyclophorus, 226
Cyclosa, 264
Cylindrostethus scrutator, 322
Cynocephalus variegatus, 304
Cynopterus, 153, 300, 302
Cyrtandra, 159
Cyrtodiopsis
  quinqueguttata, 255
  whitei, 255
Cyrtostachys renda, 114, 120
Cystorchis variegata, 149

D

Dacrydium beccarii, 110
Dactylocladus, 92
Daemonorops
  periacantha, 165
  oxycarpa, 165
Dares, 242
  validispinus, 241
Delichon dasypus, 294
Dendrelaphis caudolineatus, 291
Dendrobium cinnabarinum, 188
Derris elliptica, 343
Diacamma intricatum, 245
Dialium indum, 342
Dicerorhinus sumatranus, 336
Dicrurus annectans, 296
Dicuspiditermes nemorosus, 235, 236
Didymocarpus amaenus, 159
Dillenia, 97, *346*
  beccariana, 342
Dinochloa, 123
  trichogona, 122
Dioscorea hispida, 343
Diplazium, 200
  cordifolium, 199
  crenatoserratum, 199
Dipteris lobbiana, 317
Dipterocarpus, 123, 129, 196, 210, 214, 303
  oblongifolius, 92, *97*, 98, *127*, 311
  verrucosus, 93
Dischidia, 169
  rafflesiana, 169
Dogania subplana, 286
Draco
  cristatellus, 287, 289
  melanopogon, 289
  quinquefasciatus, 289

Dryobalanops, 123, 129, 130, 210, 214, 343
  aromatica, 93
  beccarii, 108, 273
  lanceolata, 93, *107*, 108, 169, 202, 204
Drypetes, 202
Dundubia, 244
Durio, 133, 342
  dulcis, 347
  excelsus, 135
  graveolens, 346
  kutejensis, 346, 347
  oxleyanus, 346
  testudinarum, 347
Dysphania fenestra, 80

E

Echinosorex gymnurus, 344
Elaeis guineensis, 120
Elaeocarpus, 97
Elateriospermum tapos, 196, 209
Enhydris punctata, 291
Enicurus, 294
Entomopteryx amputata, 224
Eonycteris spelaea, 300
Epipremnum falcifolium, 157, 158, 253
Epirixanthes pallida, 174
Erica, 140
Erithacus cyane, 295
Etlingera, 155
  brevilabris, 156
  fimbribracteata, 156
  muluensis, 157
Eugeissona utilis, 118
Eugenia, 97, *135*, 235, 349
Eumorphus marginatus, 80
Euphaea subcostalis, 233
Euphaeidae, 232
Eurema, 259, 261
Eurostopodus temminckii, 294
Eurycoma longifolia, 343
Eurydiopsis argentifera, 255
Eusideroxylon zwagleri, 343
Exilis exilisciurus, 303

F

Faunis, 261
  stomphax, 260
Ficus, 115, 136
Flos morphina, 261
Freycinetia, 121

G

Gasteracantha arcuata, 263, 264
Gastromyzon, 326, 328
  borneensis, 327
Geosesarma, 319
Gibellula pulchra, 186
Glaniopsis hanitschi, 328
Glanycus tricolor, 81
Gluta laxiflora, 196
Gnetum, 164
Goniothalamus, 343
  ridleyi, 343
  tapis, 343
Gonocephalus
  borneensis, 289
Gonostylus, 92
Gonydactylus
  baluensis, 288, 289
  consobrinus, 285, 288, 289
  ingeri, 288, 289
Graphium evemon, 259
Gryllotalpa, 238
Guepinia spathularia, 184

H

Haaniella, 242
  echinata, 239
Haemadipsa, 226
Hedychium, 156
Helarctos malayanus, 344
Hemidactylus frenatus, 287
Hipposideros
  ridleyi, 300
  sabanus, 300
Hirundo
  daurica, 294
  rustica, 294
  tahitica, 294
Homo
  erectus, 333
  sapiens, 333, 336
Hopea, 123, 129
Hoploclonia, 242
  cuspidata, 241
Hospitalitermes, 78, *181*, 234, 235
Hydnophytum, 168, 169
Hylobates, 303
  muelleri, 298, 301, 302, 344
Hymenochaete villosa, 186
Hymenophyllum lobii, 152

373

I

Isolapotamon collinsi, 319
Ixias pyrene, 259
Ixora, 142

K

Kalophrynus pleurostigma, 284
Koompassia, 132, 218
  excelsa, 107, 108, 133, 250
  malaccensis, 108, 133
Korthalsia, 165, 166, 168

L

Lacessititermes, 235
Languas galanga, 343
Lariscus, 304
Lecanorhis multiflora, 174
Lemmaphyllum, 152
Lentaria surculus, 184
Lentinus
  connatus, 179, 187
  squarrosulus, 180
Lepidotrigona, 250
Lepiota pulverulenta, 182
Leptobrachium montanum, 280
Leptosia nina, 260, 261
Leucobryum bowringii, 74
Leucocoprinus caepistipes, 179
Licuala, 116, 118, 169
Lithocarpus, 110, 211
Lonchodes harmani, 242
Longipeditermes, 236
Loranthus, 85
Lycopodium, 148

M

Mabuya rudis, 289
Macaca, 303
  fascicularis, 344
  nemestrina, 301
Macaranga, 168, 199, 202, 206,
  208, 216, 248
  ëtheadenia, 209
  beccariana, 207, 209, 246, 247
  gigantea, 342
  hosei, 209, 246
  hullettii, 209
  kingii, 209
  trachyphylla, 202, 206, 209,
  246, 247
  thypoleuca, 209
  winkleri, 246
Macrobrachium rosenbergii, 320,
  340

Macroglossus minimus, 300
Manis
  javanica, 304, 344
  palaeojavanica, 336
Manouria emys, 286
Mapania monostachya, 155
Marasmius, 189
Martes flavigula, 299
Masteria, 265
Maticora bivirgata, 290, 291
Medinilla, 143
Megophrys nasuta, 281, 284
Melaleuca, 343
Melastoma malabathricum,
  141, 342
Memecylon, 143
Merremia, 163
Mesophlebion oligodictyon, 152,
  317
Metaphrynella sundana, 283
Metroxylon sagu, 120
Microcerotermes dubius, 235,
  236
Moca auxobathra, 81
Mormolyce phyllodes, 74, 254
Muntiacus, 303
  muntjak, 344
Musa, 202
  campestris, 153, 154
  "flavida", 153
  muluensis, 154
  textilis, 154
Muscicapa latirostris, 296
Myotis muricola, 158
Myrmarachne, 264
Myrmecodia, 169
Myrmeconauclea, 168
  strigosa, 316, 317
Mystus baramensis, 328

N

Nacaduba, 259
Nematabramis steindachneri,
  326
Nemophora secisella, 81
Neofelis nebulosa, 344
Nepenthes, 111, 168, 310, 324
  ampullaria, 172
  gracilis, 171
  hirsuta, 107, 173
  lowii, 111
  rafflesiana, 172
  reinwardtiana, 170
  stenophylla, 111

Nephelium, 342
Nephila, 263
  pilipes, 264
Nephilengys malabarensis, 264
Nephrolepis hirsutula, 224
Nesobia mjobergi, 280
Neurobasis chinensis, 232
Niviventer cremoriventer, 302
Notochelys platynota, 286
Nycteris, 300
Nycticebus coucang, 302, 344
Nyctixalus pictus, 282
Nypa, 92, 94

O

Octomeles, 92
Odontoponera transversa, 245
Odontotermes, 236
Oligodon annulifer, 291
Omphalina, 68
Oncosperma, 92, *93*, 94
  horridum, 119
Oniscomorpha, 228
Ophiophagus hannah, 290
Ophiorrhabda quartaria, 81
Opisthotropis typica, 290
Orsima ichneumon, 264
Oryza sativa, 217
Osmoxylon borneensis, 316
Osteichthyes, 325
Osteochilus, 325

P

Paccius, 264
Pachycentria, 143
Paculla, 265
Pandanus, 97, *120*
  odoratus, 342
Paracrossochilus acerus, 326
Paralaxita telesia, 261
Parashorea, 123, 129
  macrophylla, 202
  smythiesii, 108
Pariotrigona pendleburi, 250
Parkia, 216, 304, 343
Peltonotus malayensis, 253
Pentaspadon motleyi, 266
Penthetor lucasi, 300
Petrosavia, 174
  stellaris, 150
Phallus indusiatus, 185
Pharnacia saggita, 242
Philautus, 282
Phormingochilus, 265

Phylloscopus borealis, 296
Pinanga
  tenella, 119, 315, 316
  veitchii, 119
Pipistrellus vordermanni, 300
Plagiostachys strobilifera, 156
Platycerium, 151, 166
Plectocomiopsis, 165
Podocarpus, 214
  motleyi, 214
  neriifolius, 110
Polypedates leucomystax, 282, 287
Polyura athamas, 258
Pometia, 209
  pinnata, 97, 99, 343
Portia fimbriata, 264
Presbistus fulvipennis, 242
Presbytis hosei, 301
Pronephrium
  hosei, 150, 317
  salicifolium, 317
Prosotas, 259
Psammodynaste pictus, 291
Psilogramma menephron, 239
Pternandra, 143
Ptilocera quadridentata, 324
Ptilocercus lowii, 302
Ptilomera, 322
Ptychozoon horsfieldii, 288
Puntius, 328
Pyrops sultan, 72
Python reticulatus, 290

Q
Quercus
  percoriacea, 111

R
Rafflesia, 85
  arnoldii, 175
  pricei, 175
Rana
  blythi, 281, 284
  erythraea, 287
  hosei, 281
  kuhli, 281
  palavanensis, 281, 284
Rasbora, 328
  argyrotaenia, 326
Ratufa affinis, 303
Rhacophorus
  kajau, 282, 283
  nigropalmatus, 282

  pardalis, 283
Rhagovelia papuensis, 322
Rheithrosciurus macrotis, 304
Rheumatogonus borneensis, 322
Rhinoceros sondaicus, 336
Rhinocypha, 232
  aurofulgens, 232
  biseriata, 232
Rhinolophus trifoliatus, 301
Rhinomyias umbratilis, 294
Rhinoplax vigil, 294
Rhinosciurus laticaudatus, 303
Rhizanthes, 85, 173
  lowii, 173, 174, 175
Rhizophora, 92, 94, 259
Rhododendron, 111
  javanicum, 140
  longiflorum, 140
  malayanum, 140
Rhyticeros
  corrugatus, 294
  undulatus, 294
Rigidoporus lineatus, 181
Rigiolepis, 141

S
Salacca, 118, 119, 227
  affinis, 343
Saraca, 92, 99, 100
Schizostachyum, 121, 122
  latifolium, 122
Sciaphila, 174
Scolopendra, 229
Scutigera, 229
Shorea, 92, *123*, 125, 127, 129, 210, 211, 218, 235, 343
  albida, 92, *96*
  argentifolia, 108
  coriacea, 93, *110*
  falciferoides, 202
  ferruginea, 108
  flaviflora, 108
  flemmichii, 93
  johorensis, 266
  laevis, 108, 196, 198
  leprosula, 202
  leptoclados, 107, 108
  macrophylla, 266, 342
  macroptera, 108
  obscura, 108
  parvifolia, 93, 107, 108, 196
  pauciflora, 108
  platyclados, 108

  superba, 108
Sieboldius japponicus, 233
Sonerila, 143
Sonneratia, 92, *94*
Sphagnum, 148
Sphenomorphus cyanolaemus, 285
Sphyracephala, 255
Spilornis cheela, 293
Staurois natator, 281
Stigmatogobius, 328
Strobilomyces, 187
Sundasciurus hippurus, 303
Sus barbatus, 299, 305, 344
Syncratomorpha euthetodes, 81

T
Tanaecia, 247
Tapirus indicus, 336
Tarsius bancanus, 299, 302
Tectaria
  angulata, 317
  hosei, 315
Teleopsis
  belalongensis, 252, 255
  pallifacies, 255
Termitomyces, 188, 237
Tetrastigma, 175
Themara hirtipes, 256
Thliptocerus, 224
Thyropygus, 228
Tragulus, 303
Trentepholia, 170
Trichoglottis, 167
Trichomanes, 317
  javanicum, 315
  singaporeanum, 200
Trigona
  (Heterotrigona) thoracica, 250
  (Heterotrigona) collina, 251
  (Heterotrigona) fuscobalteata, 250
  (Homotrigona) fimbriata, 250
  apicalis, 250
  collina, 250
  haematoptera, 250
  hobbyi, 250
  melanocephala, 250
Trimeresurus puniceus, 290
Tristania, 102, 131, 235
Trithemis aurora, 72
Tropidia, 174
Tropidolaemus wagleri, 290
Tropidophorus brookei, 289

375

Tupaia, 299, 302
Tympanophyllum, 239

U
Upuna, 123

V
Vaccinium, 111, 140
  kemulense, 141
Varanus salvator, 288
Vatica, 123, 129
  odorata, 196
Ventidius, 322
Vestalis, 232
Vitex pubescens, 342
Volvariella terastia, 186

X
Xylaria
  fockei, 185
  ianthino-velutina, 184
Xylocarpus, 92, 94
Xylocopa myops, 250

376

ACKNOWLEDGEMENTS

377

This book is but one product of the fruitful cooperation between Universiti Brunei Darussalam and the Royal Geographical Society. The story began for us personally in August 1988 when, together with Dr Wong Khoon Meng (then Forest Botanist at the Brunei State Forest Department), Dr Clive Mann (then a schoolmaster at M.M.P.S.B.S. Sekolah Sains) and Flora Hardy, we made our first trip by longboat up the Temburong river, from Kampong Batang Duri to Kuala Belalong. All else followed in due course.

The preparatory groundwork for the Rainforest Project 1991-92 was overseen by the Universiti Brunei Darussalam Committee, inspired by its Chairman, YM Dato Seri Laila Jasa Dr Hj Ahmad Hj Jumaat, Deputy Minister of Education, with the participation of Prof Datuk Hj Sharom Ahmat (Permanent Academic Advisor), Datin Hjh Azizah PADP Hj Abdullah (Deputy Vice-Chancellor), Aw Hj Mirhassan PDL Dato Hj Abu Bakar (Registrar), Aw Janin Erih (Bursar) and Mr Adrian L Williams (Dean, Faculty of Science) from UBD, and Pg Hj Hashim Pg Hj Mohd Jadid (Muzium Brunei), Dato Zakaria bin Dato Paduka Hj Noordin and Pg Othman bin Pg Hj Omar (JKR), Aw Hussin Ahmad (Public Affairs Manager, Brunei Shell Bhd) and Dr Morni bin Othman (Director of Forestry).

The counterpart Royal Geographical Society Committee was assisted by Aw Damit Ibrahim (Education Attaché, Brunei Darussalam High Commission, London), Dr Neil Chalmers and Mr John Peake (Natural History Museum), Dr Stephen Cox and Mr Len Mole (Royal Society of London), Prof. Ghillean Prance and Mr Leonard Forman (Royal Botanic Gardens, Kew), Mr Ron Kemp (Overseas Development Administration), Dr Bernard Tinker and Dr Mike Morris (NERC), Mr Nicholas Robertson (Shell International), Miss Helena Sharpe (British Council) and Prof. William Chaloner, with support from FM Sir John Chapple, Lord Chorley, Prof. Grenville Lucas, Mr David Hall, Dr John Hemming and Mr Nigel de Winser (all RGS).

Scientific proposals were scrutinised and approved by a UBD Scientific Committee, chaired by Aw Hj Mohd Yassin Ampuan Salleh, with the participation of Dr Webber E Booth, Dr Kamariah Abu Salim, the Earl of Cranbrook, Dr David Edwards, Dr Marina Wong, Dr Goh Kim Chuan and Datin Hjh Norsiah Hj Md Daud.

On behalf of UBD, Dr David Edwards took overall responsibility for the conduct of the 1991-92 expedition phase, assisted by Dr Kamariah Abu Salim; for the RGS, Lord Cranbrook was formally designated the leader, but the main tasks of local management fell on the redoubtable shoulders of Ms Catriona Prebble. Aw Samhan Nyawa was appointed to the key post of KBFSC Supervisor. Samhan conducted a most valuable initial survey of the allocated study area in the Belalong forest, including the marking of principal trails. He was subsequently responsible for overall administration in the field, and was ably assisted by Ms Amanda Simpson, a qualified nursing sister. The level of morale for two years owed much to the good spirits and culinary skills of the two ladies recruited from Java by Hj Abidin Hj Kula to be KBFSC cooks, Sdri Yulistiana and Wartinah.

Colleagues who contributed to the scientific programme and, in many cases, also to this book: Mr Ian Abercrombie; Aw Ashri Hj Ahmad; Dr Alan Andersen; Dr George Argent; Hj Bakar Hj Metamit; Dr Henrik Balslev; Dr Martin Barker; Professor Roger Beaver; Dr Peter Becker; Dr Elizabeth Bennett; Dr Webber Booth; Mr Phil Bragg; Mr David Buck; Mr Peter Burgess; Professor Dietrich Burkhardt; Dr Joe Charles; Dr Satish Choy; Mr Mark Cook; Dr Indraneil Das; Dr Nick Davies; Dr Martin Drake; Dr John Dransfield; Dr Soejatmi Dransfield; Mr Alan Dykes; Dr Peter Eaton; Mrs Jen Elkin; Dr Graham Elmes; Dr Charles Francis; Mr Freddy Gathorne-Hardy; Dr Goh Kim Chuan; the late Dr Carlo Hansen; Dr David Jones; Dr Kam Tin Seong; Dr Kamariah Abu Salim; Dr Chris Kofron; Ms Ruth Levy; Dr Philip McGowan; Dk Mahani Pg Momin; Dr Clive Mann; Mr Nick Mawdsley; Jason, Lord Medway; Mr David Mitchell; Mr Tom Mitchell; Dr Ingrid de la Motte; Mr Mark Mulligan; Dy Munah Hj Yahya; Dr Ivan Nielsen; Mr Conrad Ožóg; Mr Colin Pendry; Mr Axel Dalberg Poulsen; Dr John Proctor; Aw Abdul Rahman Hj Marsal; Hj Ramlee Hj Shadan; Dr Christopher Reading; Dr Gaden Robinson; Dr Sheila Ross; Dr David Roubik; Dy Sarimah Abu Bakar; Mr Gavin Smith; Mr Rowland Snazell; Mr Brian Spooner; Ms Mary Stockdale; Dr Nigel Stork; Mr Sylvester Tan; Professor John Thornes; Dr David Wells; Mr Peter Wilkie; Ms Yanina Willcox; Mr John Wills. We are indebted for their support, and their company in the field.

Completely indispensable to much of the scientific programme, especially when paths were traced, plots were surveyed, collections made and experimental systems put in place, were the field assistants, mostly from the villages of Batang Duri and Sumbiling Lama in the lower Temburong valley, but also from elsewhere in Brunei Darussalam, from Malaysia and, more widely, from other countries: Jali Amba; Limang Amba; Gawing Anggat; Kuni Anggat; Nyua Anggat; Simpurai Anggat; TK Timbang Bawa; Baya Busu; Wilson Denggat; Maxine Elkin; Rupert Hanbury-Tenison; Draman Jamban; Stewart Elly Jamban; Anthony Jenggak; Masing Kasi; Isah Laju; Impin Lasa; Ariffin Lasa; Osman Linggi; Mujah Ngambat; Samsudin Panyu;

378

Ramlah Sapong; Shahminan bin Awok; Mrs Judith Stockdale; Entaring Timbang; Inggul Timbang; Marcus Welsh; Lord Nicholas Windsor.

We were joined for a time by the artists, Ms Fionnuala Boyd & Mr Leslie Evans, whose great canvases now commemorate the Project on the walls of the Universiti Brunei Darussalam, the Royal Geographical Society premises in London, and worldwide in the hands of others fortunate enough to buy their art. One fine example of their work serves as the dust jacket of the hard cover edition of this book.

These pages also testify to the skills of the photographers specially invited to take part: Mr Chris Caldicott; Mr Paul Harris; Dr Brian Rogers.

Some preliminary accounts of our activities, serving good public relations, were written for the Press and specialist journals by: Mr Tor Eigeland; Ms Debbie Macklin; Ms Susan Raven.

A successful children's programme was produced by Royal Geographical Society Films Ltd for BBC Children's Television, directed by Pete Brown and shot by his team of Frank Battersby, Val Corbett, Trevor Gosling, Tony Miller and Gilly Sykes, involving guests from the UK and from Brunei Darussalam: Severine Bernasconi, Kieran Hebden and Tom Hewlett, with Paul Sitau, Raffais Juned and Rosalina Hj Johrai.

The base secretariat at RGS was run, with great dedication, by Mrs Venetia Simonds.

On behalf of all involved we acknowledge the generous support of our Sponsors and other benefactors, without whose wholehearted commitment, nothing would have been possible: foremost, Brunei Shell Bhd and other Corporate Patrons, Royal Brunei Airlines, the Baring Foundation, Daiwa-Dicam, GreenCard Trust, Hongkong Bank, Morgan Grenfell and Nomura-NIMCO.

Other key donors and generous collabora-

tors, in UK and in Brunei Darussalam, included: British Council; Dulverton Trust; Esmee Fairbairn Charitable Trust; Inchcape Charitable Trust Fund; Leverhulme Trust; Lok Wan Tho Memorial Foundation; Lloyds Bank Charitable Trust; Natural Environment Research Council; Natural History Museum; Peat Marwick McLintock; Royal Botanic Gardens, Edinburgh; Royal Botanic Gardens, Kew; Standard Chartered Bank; Vosper Thornycroft; Winston Churchill Memorial Trust. Also Alexander & Alexander UK Ltd; AEC Airconditioning & Engineering (Sdn) Bhd; Ampuan Salleh Boat Company; British Institute of Management; Brunei Hotel; Centre for British Teachers (Brunei); Champion Motors (Brunei) Sdn Bhd; John S Cohen Foundation; Edinburgh Trust; Fuji Photo Film (UK) Ltd; Grand Avenue Primary School; Godinton Charitable Trust; Golden Bottle Trust; Walter Guinness Charitable Trust; J H Communications Development; Meyer International plc; Ohio Express; Philip Harris' equipment; Lord Rootes Charity; Mrs Shillingford's carol singers; A R Taylor Charitable Trust; Teamwork Sdn Bhd (Taylor Woodrow) and Timber Trade Federation.

379

We are also particularly grateful for the personal support of YB Pehin Orang Kaya Laila Wijaya Dato Seri Setia Awang Hj Abdul Aziz Begawan Pehin Udana Khatib Dato Seri Paduka Awang Hj Umar, Minister of Education, and Dato Paduka Hj Abdul Razak Hj Mohammad, Permanent Secretary; Dato Hj Abu Bakar Hj Apong, Vice-Chancellor, Universiti Brunei Darussalam; YB Pehin Orang Kaya Setia Pahlawan Dato Seri Setia Hj Abdul Rahman Dato Setia Hj Mohammad Taib, Minister of Industry & Primary Resources; YB Pengiran Dato Seri Paduka Dr Hj Ismail Pengiran Hj Damit, Minister of Development; Dato Paduka Awg Hj Yunos Mohd Noh, Surveyor-General; YDM Pehin Dato Indera Setia Dato Paduka Seri Hj

Sulaiman Hj Damit, Major-General & Chief of Armed Forces; Dato Hj Abdul Rahman, Permanent Secretary, Ministry of Defence; Aw Hj Alidin Hj Othman, Director, Radio Televisyen Brunei and Hj Metussin bin Omar, Director, Muzium Brunei. We received much valued assistance from the Brunei High Commissioner in London at the time, HE Pengiran Dato Paduka Mustapha Pengiran Metassan, and successive UK High Commissioners in Bandar Seri Begawan, HE Mr Roger Westbrook and HE Mr Adrian Sindall, and British Council Representatives, Mr John Dobson and Mr John Semple, and the local officer, Ms Susan Mathews. We forged valued links with Aw Hj Aliakbar Hj Abu Bakar, District Officer, Temburong and Dr Tho Po Da, Chief Medical Officer, Bangar Hospital. At Royal Brunei Airlines we were greatly helped by Pengiran Dato Paduka Haji Tengah, Managing Director, Mr Doug Kelly and Ms Sandra McGough and at Hongkong Bank, particularly by Mr Tim Henderson. British Armed Forces provided assistance in the field: our thanks to Lt Col Christopher Lavender and 2nd Battalion, King Edward's Own Goorkha Rifles; 67 Gurkha Field Squadron, the Queen's Gurkha Engineers; Training Team Brunei, and Lt Col David Scotson.

380

In Memoriam

Dr Carlo Hansen

The Herbarium, University of Copenhagen

A forest botanist of great knowledge and enthusiasm, member of the Brunei Rainforest Project 1991-92.

TEXT CREDITS

George Argent — Heaths — 140-141

Bananas at the Field Studies Centre — 153-154

Henrik Balslev — West Ridge Plot — 196
(with Ivan Nielsen &
Axel Dalberg Poulsen)

Martin Barker — Variations in Leaf Physiology and Morphology within a Single Tree — 204

Roger A Beaver — Bark and Ambrosia Beetles — 254

Peter F Becker — Soil Charcoal — 339

Peter S Bellwood (with — Human Prehistory — 336-337
Earl of Cranbrook)

Elizabeth L Bennett — Gibbons and monkeys — 301

Webber E Booth — Epiphylls — 170

Leaf Dynamics of Gap and Understorey Seedlings — 202-203

Philip E Bragg — Insect noises: Phasmida — 239

Figure: male & female stick insects — 241

Stick Insects at Belalong — 242

Dietrich Burkhardt — Stalk-eyed Flies at Belalong — 255
(with I de la Motte)

Tephritid Flies — 256

Joe K Charles — Small Mammals — 300

Satish C Choy — Anions and Cations in the Stream — 312

Molluscs — 318

Crabs of Belalong — 319

Prawns and Water Quality — 320

A New Species of Freshwater Prawn — 321

Fishes and Pollution — 326

Ecological Zonation — 326

The Enigmatic Sucker Fishes — 327

Fishes of Belalong — 328

Figure: Fish fauna similarity — 329

Fish and Fishermen — 340

Mark A Cook — Fern-feeding — 224

Earl of Cranbrook — *New leaf growth, flowering and fruiting at Ulu Gombak, Peninsular Malaysia* — 208

Figure: Hornbills — 295

	Figure: Birds netted at Pondok Bujat	296
	Figure: Air & water temperatures	312
(with Peter S Bellwood)	Human Prehistory	336-337
Indraneil Das	Amphibian Studies	279
	Amphibian Diversity	283
	Tree Frogs	282
	Reptile Diversity at Belalong	285
	Turtles and Tortoises	285-286
	Household Friends	287
	Lizards at Belalong	288-289
	Snakes in Belalong Forest	290-291
Martin Drake	Diptera and Water	257
	Brachyceran Diptera of Watercourses	323
John Dransfield	Palms of Belalong Forest	118-119
Soejatmi Dransfield	Bamboos of Belalong	122
Alan P Dykes	Figure: Winds blowing across Borneo	18
	Figure: Average monthly rainfall	19
	Automatic Weather Stations	20
	The Climate of Belalong	23
	Air Temperature	23
	Figures: Monthly & hourly rainfall	23
	Figure: Monthly temperatures	24
	Rainstorm patterns	24
	Figures: Daily rainfall	25
	Relative Humidity	25
	Winds at Belalong	26
	Figures: Hourly climate changes	26
	Evapotranspiration	27
	Figures: Temperature & rainfall variation	219
Peter P Eaton	The Use of Forest Products by the People of Batang Duri	342-344
	Benefits Expected from the Ulu Temburong National Park	355
David S Edwards	Ferns at Belalong	153
	Ant Plants	168-169
	Flowering Plant Parasites	175
	Rheophytes	316-317
Charles M Francis (with Chris F Kofron)	Bats at Belalong	300

Freddy Gathorne-Hardy	Processional Termites	234-235
David T Jones	Termites at Belalong	236
	Pigs' Nests	305
Kamariah Abu Salim	Medicinal Plants at Belalong	341
Chris J Kofron	Bats at Belalong	300
(with Charles M Francis)		
Ruth Levy	Ants at Belalong	245
	Diacamma	245
A Q Malik	*Figure: Daylength at Bandar Seri Begawan*	21
Clive F Mann	Birds of Belalong Forest	294
Nick Mawdsley	Beetles of Belalong	253
	Investigating Beta diversity	273
Jason, Lord Medway	Woodlice (Isopoda) of Belalong Forest	227
Tom C Mitchell	Species Richness in Tropical Forests	205
	Species Richness – Studies on *Macaranga*	206
Jonathan Moran	Prey of Pitcher Plants	172
D Neil Morgan	Experience for Schools	357
Ingrid de la motte	Stalk-eyed Flies at Belalong	255
(with D Burkhardt)		
	Tephritid Flies	256
Mark Mulligan	Sediment Patterns in a Confined Channel	46-47
(with Y Willcox)		
Ivan Nielsen	West Ridge Plot	196
(with Henrik Balslev &		
Axel Dalberg Poulsen)		
Nico Nieser	Water Skaters and Water Crickets at Belalong	322
Samhan bin Nyawa	*Figure: Sketch Map of Belalong Forest*	353
Albert G Orr	Dragonflies & Damselflies of Belalong	232
	Butterflies of Belalong	260-261
(with Penroose Saleha	Macaranga and Ants	246-247
& Yong Nget Yung)		
Colin A Pendry	Altitudinal Zonation	214-215
Axel Dalberg Poulsen	*Figure: Plot AAUI species distribution*	101
	Figure: Plot AAUI species frequency	101
	Ground Herbs	149
	Gingers	155-157
	Araceae	157-158
	Gesneriaceae	159
	Saprophytes	174

383

(with Henrik Balslev & Ivan Nielsen)	West Ridge Plot	196
	Figure: Plot AAUI	197
	Figures: Species distributions in Plot AAUI	199
Klaus Riede	Insect Noises: Orthoptera	238-239
Gaden S Robinson	Alpha Diversity	76
	Insects Noises: Lepidoptera	239
	Moths at Belalong	259
	Beta Diversity: Moths	270
Sheila M Ross	Nutrient Cycling	208
David Roubik	*Figure: Pollen brush on bee's leg*	248
	Bees at Belalong	250-251
Penroose Saleha (with Albert G Orr & Yong Nget Yung)	*Macaranga* and Ants	246-247
Martin Sands	Begonias in Brunei	159-162
Haji Serudin Tinggal	Brunei Durians in the Markets	346-347
Gavin C Smith	The Rheophytic Palm	315
Rowland Snazell	Spiders of Belalong Forest	264-265
Brain M Spooner	Fungi of Brunei Darussalam	183
Mary C Stockdale	Rattans	165
Peter Wilkie	Soils Bioassay	217
Yanina Willcox (with Mark Mulligan)	Sediment Patterns in a Confined Channel	46-47
John T Wills	Geographical Information System	8-9
	Figure: GIS map of forest types	105
	Figure: GIS map of water courses	319
Yong Nget Yung (with Albert G Orr & Penroose Saleha)	Macaranga and Ants	246-247

384

PHOTO CREDITS

Gaden S Robinson: 81 (top, centre, bottom left & top, centre, bottom right)
Brian M Spooner: 68

Chapter 6
Webber E Booth: 107, 109, 110
Dietrich Burkhardt/Ingrid de la Motte: 95 (top), 99 (top)
Chris Caldicott: 88/89, 99 (bottom), 103
Earl of Cranbrook: 91, 92, 94, 96 (left), 97, 98 (top right & bottom left & right), 99
    (centre), 104
John Dransfield: 95 (bottom)
David S Edwards: 90, 96 (right), 98 (top left)
Paul Harris: 98 (top left), 100 (left & right), 102 (top)
Clive Jermy: 111
Samhan Nyawa: 106
Brian Rogers: 102 (bottom)

Chapter 7
Philip E Bragg: 143 (top)
Dietrich Burkhardt/Ingrid de la Motte: 135
Chris Caldicott: 112/113, 128, 130, 132, 137
Earl of Cranbrook: 114, 116 (bottom left & top, right), 120 (top), 121 (top left & right),
    123, 124, 125 (top right & bottom, left & right), 127 (top), 128, 131 (top, bottom right),
    138 (left & right), 139 (bottom left & right), 141 (right)
Martin Drake: 120 (bottom)
John Dransfield: 118 (top & bottom), 119 (bottom), 121 (bottom), 122 (left & right), 140
David S Edwards: 139 (top left & right)
Paul Harris: 115, 116 (bottom right), 117, 126, 142
Nick Mawdsley: 125 (top left)
Samhan Nyawa: 119 (top), 127 (bottom)
Axel Dalberg Poulsen: 143 (bottom)
Catriona Prebble: 131 (bottom left), 141 (left)
Haji Serudin Tinggal: 133, 134 (top, centre, bottom)

Chapter 8
Webber E Booth: 170 (bottom left), 175 (top & bottom)
Chris Caldicott: 166 (bottom left)
Earl of Cranbrook: 144/145, 151 (right), 154 (top left & right), 155 (top right), 164
    (bottom left & centre, right), 166 (top left & bottom right), 167 (top, bottom left), 171
    (left & right)
Martin Drake: 162
John Dransfield: 150 (left), 160 (top, right), 165 (right)
David S Edwards: 148 (top left & right), 150 (top, bottom right), 151 (left), 152 (top, left
    & right), 168 (top & bottom), 169 (bottom left & right), 170 (top right)
Paul Harris: 146, 155 (bottom), 163 (bottom right), 164 (top left & top, bottom right),
    167 (bottom right), 173 (top left & right)

Nick Mawdsley: 163 (top right), 165 (left)

Jason, Lord Medway: 163 (top left), 169 (top right)

Jonathan Moran: 172 (left & right)

Samhan Nyawa: 147 (left & right), 148 (bottom), 152 (bottom), 154 (bottom), 170 (bottom right), 173 (centre & bottom right), 174 (top left & right)

Albert G Orr: 158 (top left & right)

Axel Dalberg Poulsen: 149, 155 (top left), 156 (top, bottom left & top, bottom right), 157 (top, centre, bottom left & bottom right), 158 (bottom left), 159 (top & bottom), 161, 174 (centre left & right & bottom)

Catriona Prebble: 163 (bottom left)

Brian Rogers: 167 (top right)

Martin Sands: 160 (top, bottom left & bottom right)

Chapter 9

Chris Caldicott: 180 (bottom), 182 (right), 185 (bottom)

Joe K Charles: 189

Earl of Cranbrook: 180 (top), 184 (top), 186 (top), 187 (bottom)

John Dransfield: 183

Paul Harris: 178, 188

Brian M Spooner: 176/177, 179, 181 (top & bottom), 182 (left), 184 (centre & bottom), 185 (top centre), 186 (bottom centre), 187 (top)

Chapter 10

Webber E Booth: 201 (bottom), 202 (bottom left & right), 203 (bottom left & right)

Chris Caldicott: 190/191, 192, 196 (top), 200, 207 (top right), 213

Earl of Cranbrook: 196 (bottom), 201 (top), 207 (bottom left), 209 (top & bottom), 210 (top left & right), 211 (top)

Martin Drake: 205, 212

John Dransfield: 211 (bottom), 214 (top)

Paul Harris: 203 (centre right), 216, 217

Samhan Nyawa: 203 (top right), 204

Albert G Orr: 206, 207 (top left)

Colin A Pendry: 214 (bottom), 215 (top & bottom)

Axel Dalberg Poulsen: 198, 199 (top & bottom left)

Catriona Prebble: 193

Brian Rogers: 202 (top left)

Sheila M Ross: 207 (bottom right), 208 (top right)

Training Team Brunei: 210 (bottom)

Chapter 11

Philip E Bragg: 229 (bottom), 240, 241 (left & right)

Dietrich Burkhardt/Ingrid de la Motte: 222, 228 (centre), 242 (bottom), 252 (bottom), 255 (left & right), 256 (left & right), 263 (top right)

Joe K Charles: 229 (top), 272

Mark Cook: 224 (top centre & bottom left & right)

Earl of Cranbrook: 222, 226 (bottom), 242 (top), 244 (bottom right), 245 (top), 253

Martin Drake: 257 (bottom)

David S Edwards: 243 (top)

Paul Harris: 243 (bottom), 245 (bottom), 257 (top), 271 (bottom)

David T Jones: 220/221, 225, 235 (top, centre &bottom), 237, 244 (top right), 263 (top left)

Robert G Kemp: 233 (top & bottom)

Nick Mawdsley: 268, 271 (top)

Jason, Lord Medway: 227 (top, bottom left & top, bottom right), 251 (top right)

Samhan Nyawa: 226 (top), 228 (top), 249, 252 (top)

Albert G Orr: 246 (top left & right, bottom), 247 (left & right), 258, 259, 260 (top & bottom), 261 (top center & bottom left & right)

Axel Dalberg Poulsen: 232 (top & bottom)

Chris J Reading: 263 (center left)

Klaus Riede: 238

Brian Rogers: 245 (center)

David Roubik: 251 (top left & bottom left & right)

Rowland Snazell: 263 (center left)

Brian M Spooner: 228 (bottom), 244 (left), 263 (bottom left)

Chapter 12

Dietrich Burkhardt/Ingrid de la Motte: 302 (bottom)

Chris Caldicott: 286

Joe K Charles: 290 (top right), 293, 303

Indraneil Das: 274/275, 279, 280 (top left & bottom left), 281 (centre left, bottom left), 282 (top left & right & bottom left), 287, 288 (left & right), 289 (top left & right & bottom left & right), 290 (top left & bottom right), 291 (top & bottom), 298 (right), 299 (bottom left), 305

Paul Harris: 276, 299 (top right), 301 (left), 302 (top)

Robin Hanbury-Tenison: 299 (top left)

Debbie Macklin: 300

Clive F Mann: 295 (top)

Samhan Nyawa: 298 (top & bottom left), 301 (right)

Chris J Reading: 280 (center left & top, bottom right), 281 (left, top/center & right, top/center), 282 (bottom right), 283 (top left & right & bottom)

Brian Rogers: 290 (bottom left)

Chapter 13

Peter Burgess: 322, 325 (bottom), 327 (top), 328 (bottom)

Chris Caldicott: 306/307, 308, 310, 311, 313, 315 (top left)

Satish C Choy: 320 (top & bottom), 321 (left), 328 (top)

Earl of Cranbrook: 316 (right)

Indraneil Das: 327 (bottom)

Martin Drake: 323

John Dransfield: 316 (left)

David S Edwards: 315 (bottom left & right), 317 (top & bottom), 325 (top)
Paul Harris: 309
Roger Key: 324
Samhan Nyawa: 326
Gavin C Smith: 315 (top right)

Chapter 14
Peter F Becker: 340 (top)
Chris Caldicott: 338
Earl of Cranbrook: 335 (bottom), 339, 345 (bottom), 346 (left)
David S Edwards: 338 (top)
Paul Harris: 332, 334 (bottom), 341 (bottom right), 344 (bottom right)
Kamariah Abu Salim: 341 (bottom left & centre)
Clive F Mann: 344 (bottom left)
Nigel de Winser: 334 (top), 344 (top right), 345 (top right)
Samhan Nyawa: 330/331, 334 (centre), 342 (top & bottom), 343 (left & right), 345 (top left)
Catriona Prebble: 344 (top left), 349 (top & bottom)
Brian Rogers: 340 (bottom)
Haji Serudin Tinggal: 346 (top & bottom right), 347 (top, centre, bottom left & right)

Chapter 15
Chris Caldicott: 350/351, 352
Earl of Cranbrook: 356 (right)
Paul Harris: 354
D Neil Morgan: 356 (left)
Training Team Brunei: 357

Acknowledgements
Chris Caldicott: 363, 366

389

NOTES

NOTES

NOTES

NOTES

NOTES

NOTES